elementary
school
mathematics
methods and
materials

alex b. crowder, jr.
Texas Tech University

olive boone wheeler
St. Edwards University

CALVIN T. RYAN LIBRARY
KEARNEY STATE COLLEGE
KEARNEY, NEBRASKA

WM. C. BROWN COMPANY PUBLISHERS
Dubuque, Iowa

MATHEMATICS AND SCIENCE

Consulting Editor
Laury Harding
Ohio State University

Printed in the United States of America

This Book Is Dedicated to:

Buddy
Susie
DeNisa
Paul
Claire

CONTENTS

Unit 3—ENRICHMENT ACTIVITIES AND SUPPLEMENTARY INFORMATION

PREFACE

This book is written for teachers of elementary school mathematics and for those who are preparing to become teachers. The authors of this book are engaged in a program of teacher education and in their work have as part of their responsibility the interpretation of mathematical ideas and concepts to students who will teach elementary school children.

We have not found a textbook which is written simply enough so that students can read it and understand the learning situations described. Therefore, we have attempted to write in such a way in this text that teachers will understand some of the things they can do to stimulate and guide the learning activities of children. We have tried to describe what the child needs to learn, methods that will help him become more and more independent in learning, and the materials needed to set up a good learning situation. No attempt has been made to furnish the total mathematical knowledge needed by the teacher, however, since there are many excellent books available which were written for this purpose. Rather, mathematical content has been used as a vehicle for teaching the methods of teaching this same content to children.

Both authors have had much experience in teaching mathematics in grades one through twelve. They have both had public school experience in working with in-service teachers and experience in teaching students in a teacher education program. Both have observed that it is often difficult to teach concepts in such a way that the basic principles carry over to material to be taught in higher grades. One of the purposes of this book, therefore, is to help teachers and prospective teachers to understand the principles and processes of elementary school mathematics so that they, in turn, will be able to help children in elementary school gain a very real understanding of mathematics. An effort has been made to combine the findings of child development study and educational psychology and to apply them to one phase of the school curriculum, elementary school mathematics.

This book, then, is designed to help teachers when they are teaching new concepts and new ways of mathematical thinking. It is chiefly intended for use in education classes in methods of teaching. Mathematical content is included, but only as a means of discussing the teaching of that content to children. Very careful attention has been given to the purposes behind materials and methods of teaching and organization for teaching.

The material included in this book has been used with students in college classes for seven semesters. The students have made oral and written criticisms and the authors have used these observations to rewrite material to make it easier to understand.

The authors have attempted to maintain a common sense point of view throughout the book. Both are convinced that children can learn a great deal more mathematics than is taught in traditional programs if there is good teaching and if appropriate, concrete materials are provided. Learning is much more than memorization; understanding must be established, and memorization will come with use. The child must know and employ the correct process; the correct process will lead to correct answers. The emphasis should be upon the child's becoming independent in quantitative thinking. Mathematics becomes a way of life to the child who learns that he can be successful in problem-solving.

So large a body of experimental work has bearing upon the approach we have taken that it has been impossible to document many aspects as adequately as we would like to have done. If the material seems incomplete or naive to some, we can only reply that the book is a result of honest effort over a period of several years. It is offered with the hope that teachers will find security and success in its pages and that children will find joy in the study of mathematics as teachers organize the material with a structure that is understandable to the child.

UNIT ONE
INTRODUCTION

CHAPTER 1

THE NEWER MATHEMATICS

As man has progressed in the exploration of his universe, new demands have been made upon his mathematical systems, and man has created new mathematical concepts and processes in response to these demands. Unfortunately, some of the programs have been labeled "new mathematics" or "modern mathematics." This has been true for more than a century, though many teachers think of these terms as having been applied only to programs developed in the last few years. While some teachers and many parents are frightened by changes in terminology, and by other phases of expanding programs, it has been possible to make such changes as educators have learned more about children and about effective learning processes, and it has been necessary to make these changes because technology has demanded increasingly mature concepts and theories.

Many people believe that so-called modern mathematics had its beginnings in 1957 with the launching of Sputnik by the Russians. As a matter of fact, much of it was created during the latter part of the nineteenth century, with the content of elementary school mathematics taken from higher mathematics and simplified for the elementary school child. Because of an improvement in teaching methods and strategies, a child today is able to learn more mathematics than under older programs. He learns at his own pace and is able to develop a good foundation upon which to develop success in mathematics. Some children learn faster than others and should not be held back by slower learners; on the other hand, the slower child does not thrive if he is pushed to keep up with faster learners.

Because educators have come to understand more about the structure of content and the presentation of simple concepts early in a child's school life, the teacher no longer tries to teach a concept to a high degree of mastery when it is first introduced. Through spaced practice and the reintroduction of a topic, a child gradually gains a depth of understanding which is not possible at first, and as a

3

concept is used in a higher grade, a child is able to meet the new with a familiar way of thinking about an idea or concept. An example of this can be found in the study of geometry. Today a child is taught to identify many geometric forms at an early age. His manner of thinking changes from year to year as the material is presented at a slightly higher conceptual level from grade to grade.

No mathematics program can be successful unless teachers consider many factors relating to the child, how he learns, and the importance of a classroom environment that allows him to maintain his equilibrium and self-concept. Children are sturdy and resilient; they will work hard to fulfill expectations in school, provided they do not have to try to learn under unremitting pressure. They must be able to know that their best efforts are accepted and that they are held in high esteem by their peers and teachers. Under constant criticism and pressure, children cannot maintain their own best effort, much less become creative and imaginative. In order to be able to succeed, children periodically need to have a resting place, often called a plateau of learning. During these pauses the child takes stock of himself, basks for a moment in the glow of past successes, and then turns to a new task.

Teachers are also under pressure. They are told daily how poor schools are today, and even the best of them has a tendency to judge his teaching by the accomplishments of the slowest learners in his class. If parents and other members of the community would recognize the value of a little praise for and a great deal of faith in teachers, schools would improve since teachers, on the whole, want to do a good job.

The best teacher of mathematics:

1. feels that he is competent
2. feels that he has the respect of his pupils
3. feels that he has the respect of the community
4. feels that he is free to plan content and methods to meet the needs of his pupils
5. knows that he can take the time that pupils need to develop a concept

The successful child:

1. feels that he is competent
2. feels that he is accepted by his peers and his teacher
3. feels that his best effort will be accepted by his teacher
4. knows that his teacher will plan work that will give him success
5. knows that each day's work will be a challenge

Children can learn more mathematics than they did under traditional programs, and this can be accomplished with less pressure upon children and with less frustration to teachers, but if this learning is to take place, the curriculum must be examined closely to ensure that it is free of unnecessary subject matter. Time must be taken in the early grades to make sure that children learn how to learn, how to be independent in problem-solving, and how to see relationships between processes. Subject matter must be taught in a sequence that will facilitate understanding and cut down on retroactive inhibition (that is new learning which interferes with what has been previously learned). Methods must be both clear and flexible: clear enough that each child develops understanding, and flexible enough that each child can develop his own way of working and succeeding.

The lockstep of more traditional programs is frustrating to the slow and fast alike: on the one hand, the slow child cannot keep up; on the other, proposed problem situations are not problems to the fast learner: he already knows the answers. When competitive situations are eliminated, each child is free to move toward a development of an understanding of the deductive axiomatic nature of mathematics. Some may reach this goal before leaving elementary school; others will have developed a strong foundation for this understanding; all will know the thrill of experimentation with materials and the excitement of discovery.

Mathematics programs for the elementary school have much in common with science programs that are being developed. As teachers participate in workshops and classes in both areas, they will make less and less distinction between mathematics and science and will teach mathematics *as* science.

Experimental studies have revealed that many children already know a majority of the mathematics usually taught in the first grade when they enter school and that children can learn a great deal more mathematics than educators have previously thought they could. Better organization of the content and improved methods of teaching have resulted in children developing greater insights and, also, the necessity for less *un*learning as they progress through the grades.

Change has been slow, however. Some of the mathematical ideas of such men as Bertrand Russell are only now beginning to be accepted, sixty years and more after they were first put forward. In the early part of this century, the program of mathematics in the elementary schools was based upon the skills that educators assumed adults would need in business and industry. More than three-fourths of the time of the child was spent in computation and the memorization of facts, with little thought for the use of concepts in problem-solving.

In the early 1940s a change began to take place in the teaching of elementary school mathematics. Great progress had been made both in the study of how learning takes place and in the study of the developmental characteristics of children. Curriculum builders began to recognize that the expanding field of mathematics could be studied better if an articulated structure could be devised so that programs at every level would be based upon certain mathematical principles. They reasoned that two things would be necessary if children were to develop a sound mathematical foundation: first, the programs must be built upon mathematical principles with no deviations, and second, the program must be adapted to the abilities of the developing child.

Curriculum builders and authors of textbooks began to develop programs called *meaningful arithmetic*. It soon became clear that new programs and traditional methods of teaching were not compatible; memorization and drill did not develop the understandings necessary.

The extensive work of Jean Piaget influenced researchers in their experimental programs. Through a study of his writings, educators came to understand much about how a child develops concepts. Piaget traces the child through the preoperational stage, the operational stage, and the formal stage of conceptualization. During the years usually spent in the elementary school, the average child is in the stage of concrete operations in relation to concept formation. Teachers have begun to understand these stages of development of the child and to translate them into methods of teaching mathematics, particularly as the idea of stages relates to the use of models in teaching.

Jerome Bruner influenced contemporary curriculum reform by his insistence upon the understanding of the structure of the subject under consideration and that subject matter should be distributed for teaching over a number of years. His ideas were reinforced by other psychologists who recognized that spaced learning is beneficial and that subject matter studied over a period of years is learned with deeper insights at each new approach to concepts.

Characteristics of Newer Programs

Here are some of the distinguishing characteristics of the newer programs:

1. The entity of mathematics is emphasized and is illustrated by the ideas and patterns that occur and reoccur in all branches of elementary school mathematics.
2. Provision is made for continuity in a program.

3. A change of emphasis in subject matter and the elimination of many topics are characteristic. Children are introduced to topics which have the potential of usefulness both in future mathematics programs and in problem-solving over a long period of time. Although children solve problems from the social environment, these topics are adjuncts to the program, not its main features.

4. Topics are introduced into the program earlier. Care must be taken in selecting these topics and in teaching them in such a way that children will understand the concept and appreciate its use.

5. Many concepts such as set nomenclature, nonmetric geometry and the use of bases other than ten have been included in more recent programs.

6. Precision of the statement of ideas is emphasized. Children are encouraged to talk about problems, ideas and solutions. In this way they develop maturity in the operation and explanations of ideas.

7. The use of number sentences has been encouraged. There is some danger today in the overuse of written symbols in the mathematical sentence.

8. The use of structured concrete materials such as cubes, rods, number lines, and other appropriate models in teaching concepts and processes is probably one of the most important changes in the newer programs.

This book, then, is designed to help teachers when they are teaching new concepts and new ways of mathematical thinking. It is chiefly intended for use in education classes in methods of teaching. Mathematical content is included, but only as a means of discussing the teaching of that content to children. Very careful attention has been given to the purposes behind materials and methods of teaching and organization for teaching.

Related References

Bloom, Benjamin S. *Taxonomy of Educational Objectives.* New York: Longmans Green Co., 1956.

Bruner, Jerome S. *The Process of Education.* Cambridge, Mass.: Harvard University Press, 1961.

Copeland, Richard W. *How Children Learn Mathematics.* London: Macmillan-Collier, 1970.

Dienes, Z.P. "The Growth of Mathematical Concepts through Experiences," *Educational Research,* November, 1959.

Dienes, Z.P. *Mathematics in the Primary School.* London: Macmillan Co., Ltd., 1964.

Gattengo, C.A. *Teachers' Introduction to the Cuisenaire Rods.* New York: Cuisenaire Company of America, Inc., 1960.

Hawley, Newton and Suppes, Patrick. *Geometry for Primary Grades.* San Francisco: Holden-Day Inc., 1961.

National Council of Teachers of Mathematics. *An Analysis of New Mathematics Programs.* Washington D.C.: The Council, 1963.

Page, David. *University of Illinois Arithmetic Project.* Urbana: University of Illinois Press, 1961.

Piaget, Jean. *The Child's Concept of Number.* London: (International Library of Psychology, Philosophy, and Scientific Method), Routledge and Paul, 1952.

———. *The Psychology of Intelligence.* Patterson N.J.: Littlefield, Adams & Co., 1960.

Rogers, Vincent R., ed., *Teaching in the British Primary School.* London: Collier-Macmillan Ltd., 1970.

Stern, Catherine. *Children Discover Arithmetic.* New York: Harper and Brothers, 1949.

U.I.C.S.M. Project Staff. *Arithmetic Project, University of Illinois.* Urbana, Ill.: University of Illinois Press, 1963.

CHAPTER 2

CLASSROOM MANAGEMENT AND MATERIALS

Classroom Management

The teacher who attempts to manage a classroom alone is neglecting the help his pupils can give him. When teacher and pupils take time to plan together in advance so that tasks are understood by all, work is usually more productive. Children who understand both the long-range and immediate goals of a program are usually more highly motivated than children who do not. When children understand goals, discipline problems are usually minimized.

Classroom furniture, teaching materials, and schedules should be arranged so as to provide optimum learning opportunities for children. Furniture sometimes needs to be moved for the seating of small groups, or for convenience when working with materials, or for large-group participation.

Materials should be stored in compact containers and labeled so that children can take care of distribution and storage with little loss of time. The schedule must be flexible enough to take care of the needs of all. Children who work fast should be allowed to go on to more difficult tasks in mathematics or to other tasks while children who work more slowly have time to complete tasks.

The curriculum must be flexible; it must contain work for the individual who works above grade level and work for the individual who works below grade level. Since it is impossible to teach the same problems to all of the children in a classroom, textbooks are usually written for the average student. The problems are not problems to the fast learner; he already knows the answers. The problems are not problems to the slow learner; he does not understand them. Thus, textbook problems are usually appropriate for only about one-third of a class.

When children of similar abilities are placed in small groups within the regular classroom, they usually enjoy working together and are highly motivated if problem situations are worthy of their efforts.

When the teacher works with the fast learners, he needs to be a resource person and challenger. He also needs to use mathematics in relation to other subject areas of the curriculum. Skills should be practiced in the framework of science, social studies, and other subjects. He needs to see that the learning of skills does not become incidental, but that children learn the more difficult skills and use them in more and more mature ways in the solution of problems. Graphs, equations, and other procedures can be used in the solution of problems. The teacher should help children understand something of how learning takes place, and of how logical thinking is developed, and something of the structure of concept development. Some children can grasp the meaning of Bloom's Taxonomy of Educational Objectives if their teacher helps them to recognize the steps as they work through them in a complicated problem. The master teacher will help bright students recognize the importance of the use of materials in the solution of problems. The space program, for instance, can be helpful in illustrating the use of models, simulation, and open discussion in completing a project.

Children can learn how to gather data, organize it, apply it to other situations, analyze it, make syntheses and evaluate. They improve in their abilities to present material in a logical way if they work in small groups. Evaluation in the small group situation becomes group evaluation and not individual evaluation. Children in upper grades who have thought of evaluation as grading will probably be slow to venture into depth evaluation with the teacher present, but the teacher can set the stage, give students a model *via* video tape or film, and let them operate on their own for a short time. If the teacher is helpful, but not critical, he will probably be accepted by the group as a participating member.

Children who are slower learners need a different kind of attention. Many children will not discover very much if left completely alone with a problem; some children need a great deal of help. The teacher can supply this help in many ways if he plans the curriculum so that it is flexible enough to provide both for the child who is capable of abstracting and grasping mathematical concepts and for the child who will need a more practical approach, more leading questions, and more time with models and manipulative materials. The teacher should help the student plan a way of attacking a problem through questioning, if possible, but directly, if need be. He should plan so that every child can have a measure of success. Vincent R. Rogers reports in his book, *Teaching in British Primary School* that teachers make use of the old proverb: I hear and I forget. I see and I remember. I do and I understand.

The teacher must make sure that every pupil is able to make a contribution to his group and that he is challenged by the other members of the group—but not overchallenged. Group participation can be maintained only if the pupils do not become individually competitive. For the teaching of skills, a classroom group will often fall into two parts: the average and above, and the average and below. When the teacher places children in groups, he should make it clear that a child may move from one group to another as he needs or desires. If a child who is in the faster group misses school, he may need to go back and work with the slower group for a time; he may even want to work with both groups. One way of grouping children is to introduce a topic to the total class; then, as the children begin to apply their skills in solving problems on their own, the teacher can place himself in a convenient spot (near the chalkboard, for example) and ask children who need help to come to him. They will come one by one, and thus a group will be formed. This group will probably remain intact as long as its members are working on a particular concept, since pupils who do not need help will be progressing more rapidly. In this way the teacher can ensure that every child has the help that he needs and that faster-moving students are not impeded by slower students. It is usually true that little by little some children will fall behind or just not be able to go as far in one concept as others in the class. They will not feel the same pressures that they may feel in a subject such as reading—where one child is reading in one book and others in a more advanced one—if less emphasis is placed on the number of problems a child works, and more upon the child's understanding of what he does work. The child who is pushed in order to keep up with the group is often undermining his own understanding. He may need time to work longer with the concrete materials than others in the class. No stigma is placed upon him, however, if the materials are handy and he can get them as he needs them. (This assumes, of course, that appropriate materials are provided at all times and that the child understands their use.)

Probably the best classroom would be one in which each child could work at his own rate. This is only possible, however, in a classroom in which a decreased emphasis is placed upon completing an assignment and upon grades. For instance, the youngster who can work only two problems, but knows what he is doing, is better off than the child who tries to work five or six and simply does them by memory or, in doing them, uses incorrect procedures. By the same token, some children are bored if they are not permitted to go ahead, and this may result in a classroom discipline problem and a lowering of morale. Also, if too much emphasis is placed upon assignments and grades, then some children will try to make others feel inadequate by talking about the number of problems that they have worked correctly. It is probably best to have the fast group working more difficult problems, but about the same number of problems as the slower group. Sheer numbers of problems will not help the fast group achieve competence unless it is working at its highest level of capability.

While the procedure of giving children more difficult problems may cause the teacher to do more work in preparation (such as devising other problems) it may be possible for him to obtain workbooks on many levels so that each child can have work appropriate to his level of learning. Such books should not be used as workbooks but, rather, as texts. Children who are not capable of working at the grade level of others in the class can then use a workbook that is on a lower level, while children who are working on a higher level can use workbooks of a different series from the standard class text that will provide problems for them to work in the skill they have just learned, but on a higher level. It is thus possible to give all children the same subject—such as geometry, equations, or addition—with some children in the class being given more difficult problems than others. Children should be pushed, and the word *pushed* is used advisedly, to attain the highest level possible for them. They should not, however, be pushed to the point of frustration. There must be some tension for learning, but this tension should not reach a level dangerous to the child's self-concept.

The teacher needs to plan work so that skills are taught during class and necessary practice takes place under his supervision. In this way he can make sure that the child understands the use of a certain skill in problem situations, he can clarify concepts if a pupil has difficulty, and he can set problem situations that challenge the pupil but do not defeat him.

In the more traditional programs, teachers often assigned a great amount of drill to develop and reinforce skills. This practice work was often sent home with the child to be computed and brought back next day, the assumption apparently being that students could work problems at home that they were unable to work at school. This, of course, is not the case.

Most students should be able to complete their assignment in class under the supervision of the teacher; at home they should not have to ask for assistance. Most adults consider that eight hours work each day constitutes a full work day, yet school children spend from six to eight hours a day in class and then often have to spend three to four additional hours doing homework. Such a workload leaves them very little time for other activities—that is, time to just be children.

If children become interested in a problem or project, they may sometimes work on these at home, and there is no reason they should not do work at home if they so desire. But the teacher should make sure that they do not have to repeat work at school that they have already done at home. This will require careful planning on the part of the teacher, but there are many books available that suggest enrichment projects. (Some enrichment activities are suggested in Chapter 11 of this book.)

The point is that the learning of skills in mathematics is far too important to be left to the chance that home conditions will be such that the child can learn better at home than at school. Some parents do too much work for their child, and thus do not help the child learn, while other parents are unable to help their children for a variety of reasons: being away from the home, busy with own work, helping other children in the family with homework, or, in some cases, an inability to read English. If provision is made for the practice of skills at school, the child can use his time at home for reading, recreation, working on projects, and other activities.

It may be objected that under such circumstances the child is not learning the worthwhile habit of work. On the other hand, there is much evidence to indicate that when children are given much busy work, they will often give up in high school and will either leave school or will fail because they refuse to do the unnecessary.

The habit of work efficiency can be developed through assigning the work to be done during the class period and requiring that it be finished at school. If the work is well-planned, most students will finish it during class rather than after school. Forty minutes should certainly be time enough for an elementary mathematics program period. Children are called upon during the day in other subjects, such as social studies and reading, to interpret quantative situations, and they should not be put in the position of having to carry work home that they do not understand and upsetting their parents about the fact that they are having difficulty. Parents who request that their children bring work home should be invited to school for a conference. The teacher should explain why he prefers not to give homework in mathematics. Papers that the student does at school can be sent home so that the parents can keep informed about the progress of their child.

Materials

The selection and use of concrete and semiconcrete materials in the teaching of elementary school mathematics cannot be overemphasized. The use of appropriate materials by children as they learn a new mathematical process corresponds to the simulation training of astronauts. The child sets up the model, thinks through the problem situation, moves the material, and thus solves the problem. He may engage in some trial and error in the process of learning and/or problem-solving. He will learn the reversibility of thought and, it is to be hoped, he will learn to respect his own ideas and be willing to try them out. He will learn that errors can be corrected or reversed and that there are often several ways of solving a problem.

The materials used for teaching elementary school mathematics should be simple, structured, and well administered. The term *structured material* is defined here as a material that has a basic unit of constant size and shape. An example of such structured material would be the cube, or block; two blocks would be exactly twice as large as one block, proportions held constant. A second example would be a number line which would have equal units marked on it:

A third example would be rods, such as the Cuisenaire rods, which are made of wood. The unit rod is a cube of one centimeter in dimension. The second rod has a cross section of one centimeter square and a length of two centimeters. Each rod has one centimeter in length added to it through the length of ten centimeters (see Fig. 2.1).

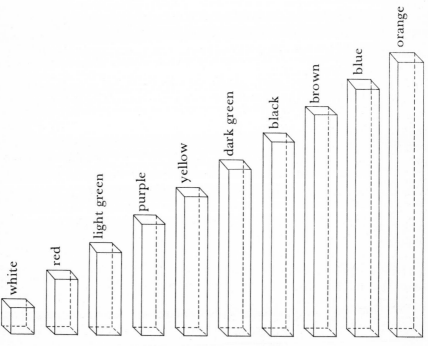

Figure 2.1. The Cuisenaire Rods.

The block is called a *digital material* because it is used as something to be counted. Many uses for the block will be discussed in other chapters describing different teaching processes. The number line is usually referred to as an *analog* material because it is most often used for measuring. The spaces of a number line are sometimes counted, however, in which case it would be used as a digital material. Rods are usually used as analog materials.

The materials mentioned would probably be adequate for the development of concepts in basic operations with whole numbers. As other materials are needed to teach concepts in geometry and other topics, such as graphs and charts, they should be added. The two necessary qualities of any material would be: first, is this the best material to enable the child to understand this concept? and second, is it free from social connotation?

The experience of the child is his background for understanding numerical situations. The very intelligent child can often learn by rote certain formulas and ways of working, but that child needs to experiment with concrete materials to gain a real understanding of a process and to develop generalizations; he needs to verbalize what he has done. Some children will need to use concrete materials much longer than others. The child should decide when he is ready to work without a model.

The teacher can learn much about what the child understands and what concepts need to be clarified as he watches the child organize materials for the solution of a problem and listens as the child expresses his ideas. Cognitive structure and its development can be studied through watching the child manipulate concrete materials and listening to his verbal expressions. The logical thought of the child is often expressed through his motor actions as he organizes the concrete materials. The teacher should carefully observe how the child manipulates concrete materials, and then plan learning situations in terms of these observations and select content to be learned that will be in keeping with the child's intellectual functioning. There is no inherent value in a block or a number line, it is the operation which the child makes that is of value.

The guiding rule should be to make it possible within the environment of the classroom for the child to go on as he is ready and still to feel like a worthwhile person if he is unable to master a concept at a particular time. It is also very important that the teacher spend time on teaching the concept that the developmental stage of the child will permit him to learn so that the teacher's time is not wasted in trying to force him to learn something for which he has no readiness. A great deal of leeway must be given to the individual teacher, since it is impossible to predict at what age children will be ready for certain concepts. We often underestimate the ability of children; on the other hand, we sometimes try to force them to undertake work they are not ready to understand.

"Readiness" is a word we usually—and erroneously—associate with the first grade. In mathematics there must be readiness at every level for each new concept. Some children will undertake one type of mathematics more readily than another. There is a theory that boys have greater readiness for geometry than girls because they have usually played with more blocks and building materials and have taken apart more toys than have little girls. Whether or not this is true, we do not leave the child at his present state of readiness. We set up the environment and learning situations so that he learns new concepts each day, works with new materials, and thus attains readiness for new concepts. It is often necessary for a teacher to devise games or other motivating situations so that children will become interested in a particular subject.

Blocks, number lines and rods will be used almost daily. Small blocks can be cut from wood, and many school woodworking shops will do this at small or no cost. Blocks may also be obtained from school supply houses. The Ideal Company, for instance, manufactures plastic cubes in boxes of 1,000; one box will equip two classrooms with an adequate supply.

Plasticized number lines may also be secured from school supply houses. A number line placed high in the room is of no value since children cannot see it in proper perspective. It should be placed at the eye level of the students. Most rooms do not have a space suitable for the number line except the chalkboard area. If the number lines are made on sentence strip paper, they can be secured to the chalkboard with masking tape and then taken down and rolled up when not in use. In the upper grades, there should be some number lines without numerals, simply even markers; the marks or numerals can be placed above the number line on the chalkboard. In this way the same line can be used for base ten and other bases. On other occasions a no-numeral line can be used for a fraction number line by placing numerals above the marks on the chalkboard. Some teachers may want number lines for each type of work; this need not be expensive, since one roll of sentence strip paper can serve for all the number lines necessary.

It is not appropriate for children to spend a great deal of time making teaching materials, though it will be profitable to them to spend a few periods in making materials, especially if this can be combined with the concept that is being taught. If children are being taught to measure carefully, they can make a number line with great profit. If they are learning to construct figures such as perpendicular lines in order to make a square or rectangle, lines that are parallel to other lines so as to make different kinds of parallelograms, or constructing different kinds of triangles, then they might produce these figures on construction paper or tagboard and cut them out to be used by lower-grade teachers or for bulletin board displays. Children in the fourth, fifth and sixth grades take great interest in learning to construct figures and putting these figures together in attractive forms for the bulletin board. They soon learn to construct figures from boxes or by gluing paper together to make pyramids, cylinders, prisms, and other forms. If they make these materials, it should always be as part of a learning situation, not as busy work, as is sometimes the case.

Children in the fourth grade can usually begin to use a compass, while second-grade children can sometimes use a ruler in drawing. A straight edge can be made from heavy cardboard or even lightweight plyboard, and children can work with it on the floor; one child holding the straight edge, another child drawing by it. Second-grade children can usually begin to measure with the simple ruler, but it is usually better to start with one marked only with the inches, progressing later to one that has both inch and the half-inch markings. Not until fourth grade should children have the complicated ruler usually seen in the classroom.

It is comparatively easy to make many of the materials necessary for a classroom if the teacher has newspapers, a small amount of tagboard, a roll of sentence strip paper, some construction paper, and a willingness to do the job. The materials necessary for teaching geometry can be made from construction paper; wire may be used for making the figures so as to help a child see the difference between a figure such as a triangle and the triangular region. Solid figures may be bought from school supply houses; but many of them can be gathered from the home—for example, boxes and cans of different sizes.

CHAPTER 3

THE DISCOVERY METHOD AND STRATEGIES FOR TEACHING

Modern mathematics in the elementary school has focused much attention on what is popularly known as "the discovery method," yet often teachers do not understand the meaning or implications of this method. To further complicate the situation, different interpretations of what constitutes the discovery method have emerged as well as the interchangeable use of other terms with the term *discovery*. There probably are as many different explanations of the discovery method as there are people to explain it. This does not mean that there is not general agreement concerning the theory of learning by discovery, however. Rather, the difference seems to occur at the level of explaining and implementing discovery—what may be teaching by discovery to one person may not be to another. Consequently, the interpretation of the discovery method presented in this chapter represents the thinking of the authors and is not intended as the only way to view this method. Other terms (such as *inquiry, inductive method,* and *problem-solving*) have been used synonymously with discovery and through such usage have come to mean relatively the same thing as discovery. The use of other terms for discovery is probably of no great consequence as long as they accurately communicate the intended meaning, but *discovery* and *inquiry* seem to be the more descriptive terms.

The Discovery Method

The theory of learning by doing is by no means of recent derivation. Many ancient proverbs of the Hebrews and Chinese reflect various aspects of this theory, as does the work of Socrates and others. A more recent survey of the history of education would reveal a number of persons who also advocated learning from firsthand experience. John Dewey, one of America's pioneer educators, strongly advocated that students should learn from firsthand experience. Although he did not label it as discovery, much of his work described student learning in terms very much akin to what we now know as the discovery method. For a time Dewey's work seemed to be all but forgotten; but the more recent work of Jean Piaget, Jerome Bruner, and others have once again focused attention on the importance of the quality of the student's learning experience and his involvement in the learning process, as well as on the method that enables learning to take place.

Learning is often defined as the acquisition of facts or knowledge. Apparently, to some people, what can be done with this knowledge is not as important as it is to stockpile it in the mind. The explosion of knowledge which has resulted from advances in technology is threatening to engulf us in a tidal wave of factual information. It has been estimated that every day enough new facts are discovered to fill six full sets of *Encyclopaedia Britannica*. With all of this new knowledge, *how* shall we select the facts to be learned and *who* will determine which facts will still be pertinent when our students become adults? During a commencement address at a medical school, the dean warned the graduates to remember that half of all that they had been taught was wrong. He added that the problem was that the faculty did not know *which* half was wrong. If one agrees that determining which facts are most important is likely to be impossible, the definition of learning at the beginning of this paragraph is inadequate.

Another group of people would contend that learning is the development of skills. For example, consider the young child who can count by rote to one hundred. According to this group, the child has learned how to count because he can repeat the number names in the correct sequence—yet in all likelihood this child has not recognized that he can determine the number of objects in a group by counting. The fact that meaning and understanding have been omitted makes this definition of learning also inadequate.

Still another group contends that learning is the merger of experience and knowledge into meaning. That is, the learning experience is processed or structured by the learner's mind in such a way that it can be recalled in a useful form. Advocates of this definition of learning would contend that the important thing is not how much one knows, but how useful that knowledge is. Many educators would agree with the latter definition of learning and contend that probably the most important task in education today is guiding students to learn how to learn by using their rational powers.

Man seems to have the ability to store huge quantities of information in his brain. This information is stored at various levels of meaning as a result of certain experiences. The more meaningful the experience, the more likely it is that information about this experience will be recalled, while the less meaningful experiences are more easily forgotten. Rote learning, which is less meaningful learning, is likely to be stored at a somewhat superficial level, in contrast to learning of a deeper nature, which is likely to be stored at a more structured level. Most of this stored information can be recalled with the aid of suggestions or cues, but it is sometimes difficult to recall this information without such external aids. The key to recalling or retrieving stored information and applying it to a problem situation seems to be the manner in which it was acquired and how it was organized when it was stored. Information that is organized and stored by a technique unique to the individual is probably more easily recalled than memorized facts or information.

The main tenet of the discovery method is that pupils will learn more effectively and remember best that which they discover for themselves. During the process of discovery, the learner seemingly organizes information in a manner not only designed to discover patterns and structures, but also to promote accessibility to this information. Discovery is apparently one of the best methods for an individual to organize and store his information uniquely so that it can be recalled with a minimum of cues or aids. Jerome Bruner[1], the American psychologist who was largely responsible for the recent renewal of interest in learning by discovery, does not believe that individual discovery should be limited to that which has been unknown to mankind, but should also include gaining or uncovering knowledge for the first time for ourselves by utilizing the rational facilities of our own mind. In using the discovery method, teachers are not necessarily trying to develop something new in mathematics; rather, they are trying to guide and assist pupils to uncover, in such a way as to be most meaningful to them, those principles, concepts, and structures which already exist. In mathematics, for example, students using the discovery method may eventually use the same systems of calculation as were used in traditional mathematics. This is true because these systems of calculation have been refined to such a point, over a period of hundreds of years, that it is doubtful they can be made more efficient unless machines are used for calculation.

It is probably unfortunate that we have systems of calculation that are simple enough to learn to use without actually understanding them. A word of explanation and caution seems to be appropriate at this point. The *algorisms* (schemes with which to calculate) are reasonably easy to master, but the understanding of *why* we are able to do these calculations is usually less than obvious. Others invented, developed, and refined the algorisms that are in use today. This means that the

---

1. Jerome S. Bruner. "The Act of Discovery," *Readings in the Psychology of Cognition* edited by D.F. Ausubel and R.C. Anderson, (New York: Holt, Rinehart & Winston, Inc., 1965). p. 627.

elementary teacher's task is one of helping to guide students into the adult world by assisting them in understanding and adapting a most important adult tool—mathematics. People who are efficient in calculation have developed this ability, not overnight, but over a period of years—and were able to because they understood what they were doing.

Basically, there are two types of discovery: *incidental* and *guided.* Incidental discovery could almost be classified as "accidental," because it results without much planning or synthesizing of what has happened. For example, the young child who is trying to learn to ride a bicycle struggles with mastering this skill. One day, after many attempts, the child discovers that he can ride the bicycle a short distance. There probably was not much detailed planning on the part of the child to learn this skill, and after he had this learning experience he probably did not rationalize what he had learned. It should be fairly obvious then that we cannot depend upon the casual experiences of the child to provide all of the necessary learning experiences he will need in order to develop meaning and understanding.

In contrast to incidental discovery, controlled or guided discovery is planned; there will be certain understandings that result from the learning experience. Not only is guided discovery planned, but it also provides an opportunity to extend learning by combining the parts into a more complex whole. Guided discovery does not mean taking the initiative away from the pupil, but it does mean that the teacher guides the pupil at a level where he is capable of achieving a reasonable amount of success. A pupil's discoveries, if made without help or guidance, will usually be superficial and restricted in nature because of his limited background and experience. Most pupils, because of their natural curiosity, will go about discovering things for themselves within certain limits; but these pupils very likely have not developed sufficient self-direction to be left on their own.

The focus must always be upon the needs of the individual. The teacher is responsible for setting up situations that will be motivating to children of differing mathematical abilities and for children who learn in different ways. The fast learner, for example, is often intrigued by the ambiguous, while the slower learner usually prefers situations with more structure. It is the teacher's responsibility to plan, guide, stimulate, and assist pupils in making discoveries, and to help pupils extend the scope of their discoveries; and although it is the teacher's responsibility to guide and extend pupil discovery, his goal will be determined by the method of pupil discovery desired and/or needed. Through observation of the child as he develops and uses mathematical knowledge, the teacher makes his judgment of the sequence of concepts to be taught.

Kersh[2] suggests that there are two methods of obtaining guided discovery. The first method focuses on finding correct answers, while the second focuses on the inquiry, or the searching for a plan, that will lead to a solution. If teachers are interested primarily in right answers, then they will be likely to encourage discovery for correct answers only. If they are interested in the broader, more encompassing aspect of discovery, they will encourage their pupils to learn to search effectively. The basic difference between the two discovery methods is that the second is a plan for action on the part of the child, while the first is concerned merely with how to do it in order to get a desired or previously decided upon answer. For example, a teacher who is concerned primarily with correct answers might say, "There are five chairs in the reading circle and there are eight children in the next reading group. How many more chairs are needed?" Almost everything has been supplied but the solution. Another teacher, who is concerned about pupils learning to search effectively, might say, "How can we know if every pupil in the next reading group will have a chair?" The second teacher causes his pupils first of all to decide on a plan before attempting to arrive at a solution. *While correct answers are very desirable, they are not necessarily the most important aspect of the learning process.* The understanding and insight that is developed from searching for a correct answer and understanding *why* it is a correct answer rates a much higher priority than finding the correct answer alone, since the procedure of inquiry and searching for principles can be applied to many other situations. (It will also lead to correct answers.)

Conversely, the search for correct answers alone applies to only one particular set of elements or circumstances—which means that the method of searching for correct answers should be incorporated as an integral part into the inquiry method, but it should not be used as an end in itself. At this point the discovery method can be viewed as a search in which the pupil does the actual discovering. This search, usually with guidance, but sometimes without, can be either for an answer or for a plan of action.

THE PUPIL'S ROLE IN DISCOVERY

Discovery is essentially an active process requiring involvement of both teacher and pupil. The pupil's role in discovery requires and encourages the utilization of as many of his senses as possible. The pupil, in effect, takes an active part in the formulation of plans and decision-

2. Bert Y. Kersh. "Learning by Discovery: Instructional Strategies," *The Arithmetic Teacher* 12 (October 1965):414-17.

making. At times he assumes the principal role in searching for a solution, while at other times the search is more a cooperative venture, with the pupil's planning and the teacher's guidance. The pupil should not be expected to be sufficiently self-directive in the beginning stages of learning discovery to be left to his own devices, however, Bruner[3] insists that the pupil must develop an attitude of wanting to discover. This attitude of discovery results from the expectancy that there will be something to discover. A student will not know in advance what he will discover, but he must anticipate that his activity will be worthwhile and lead to some understanding that will be of value to him. Then he must devise ways, uniquely his own, of searching and finding regularities and relationships. Thus, as Bruner sees discovery, it can result only from the well-prepared mind. If the mind is prepared, it becomes a matter of rearranging and transforming information and evidence so that it can be reassembled for additional insight. What a person discovers, then, is actually a translation of his physical and mental experiences into some higher type of conceptual framework that has added meaning for him. The child who is flooded with unconnected bits and pieces of information becomes confused and discouraged because he does not see or know how to organize this information into useful units. The child who can discriminate which information will be of value and can also organize it into his cognitive structure will be able to gain insight and understanding from his learning experiences.

A child can learn to organize and internalize information through practice in discovering for himself. At first he will gradually acquire the skill of assimilating information that will be more readily available for problem-solving. Later, when this skill is more fully developed, he not only will be more efficient in solving problem situations but he will also be able to conceptualize alternate solutions, if need be. Learning by the discovery method seems to ensure that the pupil will not only learn better but that he will also use what he has learned effectively. The pupil's role in discovery, then, is of an active nature, requiring involvement, use of physical and mental facilities, a desire to search, and a willingness to begin again when failure occurs.

THE TEACHER'S ROLE IN DISCOVERY

Just as the pupil's role requires active involvement, so must the teacher's role be that of active involvement, but it will be involvement of a different kind. As mentioned, only two ingredients are necessary

3. Jerome S. Bruner. *The Process of Education* (Cambridge, Mass.: Harvard University Press, 1962), p. 33.

for learning to take place—the learner and the experience. A third ingredient, the teacher, may or may not be present. When the teacher *is* present, however, and uses the proper methods and strategies, discovery becomes guided rather than incidental—and the method of intervention the teacher uses will often determine the quality of the learning experience. We are more and more coming to realize what students have been telling us indirectly for years—that program and materials alone are not adequate components of a good learning situation. The catalystic actions of the teacher are necessary to involve children in the learning process.

Phil Jackson[4] has described teaching as having two dimensions: the preactive and the interactive phases. The preactive phase is the deliberate, rational phase of teaching in which planning, selection, and preparation of activities take place. The teacher preparing for discovery-type learning will select and plan those activities that provide the student with firsthand experiences in the learning situation. It is this phase of teaching that generally occurs without students being present. The interactive phase occurs when the teacher carries out his lesson plans with the students. When guiding discovery, the teacher must interact with students in such a way as not to be a detriment to learning, and at the same time he must build the students' self-confidence to the point that they feel it is safe to have ideas and to try them out. (The importance of developing a positive self-concept will be discussed in greater detail later in this chapter in the section on strategies of teaching.)

Interaction between teacher and students can be either verbal or nonverbal. It takes place several thousand times each school day, and over a period of time the manner in which a teacher interacts with his students will have either a positive or a negative effect on the students' self-concept. The teacher's involvement in discovery requires the teacher to be interested, enthusiastic, and ego-involved. By the time children enter school, they have become experts at reading adults' attitudes and actions, so pupils must be shown that teachers place importance on mathematics.

Teachers often teach things they do not intend to teach by their actions and attitudes. It is very easy for teachers to consistently shortchange mathematics by allowing other activities to encroach upon time that should be spent on learning mathematics. If they do, children will soon recognize that although the teacher says he believes math is important, his actions and attitudes say otherwise. If teachers are not inter-

---

4. Philip W. Jackson, *The Way Teaching Is* (Washington, D.C.: Association of Supervision and Curriculum Development, 1966), pp. 7-27.

ested and enthusiastic about their teaching, then why should students be expected to be enthusiastic in their learning?

For the discovery method to be successful, the key element is the teacher—his approach to teaching, his ability and desire to have students make successful discoveries, and his recognition of and respect for children's unique ways of working and learning. It might even be argued that the discovery method is more the philosophical spirit with which a teacher approaches teaching than a method as such. Nevertheless, this philosophical spirit is an integral and fundamental part of the discovery method. A teacher using modern mathematics material and subject matter with the traditional *tell all* teaching method probably cannot recognize any difference between the way his pupils are learning and reacting to the newer materials and the way former pupils did to traditional materials. A modern mathematics program, however, shifts emphasis from the mechanical, or *how* aspect alone, to the understanding, or *why* aspect, as well as the how. This shift of emphasis requires a change in the role of the teacher. No longer should the teacher be expected to *know and tell all;* rather, the teacher should now assume a role similar to that of a guide. The term *guide* implies that one knows his territory, and because of his previous experiences and training knows how to choose the area or place in which his clients are most likely to have successful firsthand experiences. Can you imagine a hunting or fishing trip where the guide did the hunting and fishing while his clients merely watched? Or, even worse, where the guide went on the hunting and fishing trip alone and only told his clients of his experiences when he returned. The clients in such a situation would feel cheated, just as pupils are cheated when they are placed in a passive role in learning. We use a guide to show us the way because we do not know it, and to help insure and assist in successful firsthand experiences. Too often,

B.C.   By JOHNNY HART

Reprinted by permission of Field Enterprise, Inc. Copyright ©1968.

classroom teachers fail to plan for and provide these firsthand experiences that are so vital to learning. Their pupils, like the hunting and
fishing party whose guide had all the firsthand experiences, are forced
into the inactive role of observing and listening. Thus, it is the teacher
who sets the stage, but it should be the pupil who is the star performer.
In a study of some 60,000 public school students of all grade levels,
Fritz Redl[5] reports that the students' greatest expectation of their
teacher was that they wanted someone who enjoyed watching *them*
learn.

In seeking to guide pupils to discover correct answers, the teacher
concentrates on giving bits of information that are pertinent to the
problem, and appropriate materials, but always withholding just enough
so that the pupil will discover something for himself. Given sufficient
information, most pupils will eventually discover an answer, though not
always the correct answer. Such answer seekers usually have developed
rote ability and will depend on this to enable them to give the expected
answer, rather than relating information to their cognitive structure so
that their learning will be their own. In far too many instances the
answer-seeking students are merely trying to read the teacher and give
back the answer they think the teacher wants, rather than processing
their information and then thinking through the situation to a logical
conclusion.

On the other hand, in guiding pupils in inquiry, the teacher concentrates on encouraging pupils to look at the various aspects of the problem, to formulate a plan in solving it, and then attempting to solve it. If
the pupil's plan is unsuccessful, an alternate plan should be sought and
tried. Teaching by the discovery method may seem to take longer,
because the student is allowed to grope and flounder about to some
extent. He is encouraged to generate his own ideas and to try them out,
even to the extent of what might be called an orderly, organized "mess-
ing about."

In guiding pupils in inquiry, the teacher also withholds certain information, but this information is of a different nature from that withheld
in the answer-seeking method. For example, in inquiry the teacher
might supply hints pertaining to ways that the pupil might approach
the problem, or he might ask pertinent questions that would help in
finding a way to approach it. The advantage of the approach focused on
inquiry is that if a pupil should forget either the *how,* or the algorism
needed to solve a problem, he can utilize and employ past experiences
in searching for a way to solve the problem. This ability is becoming

5. Fritz Redl. "What do Children Expect of Teachers?" *Conference Speeches, 1954* (New
York: Bank Street College of Education, 1954), pp. 46-47.

increasingly important because we are living in an ever-changing world where much factual material loses its relevance, while the ability to search effectively will be useful in many situations.

Friedlander[6] warns that after a pupil has made a discovery, it is often necessary that he have help in combining and incorporating this new information into a systematic context. It is at this point that the teacher, with his knowledge and experience, can help the pupil refine and construct an orderly scheme of meaning from the new knowledge, leading the pupil to a fuller realization of the significance of his discovery. Wheeler, Ballenger, and Hollis[7] point out that initially the teacher must plan, develop, and arrange an environment conducive to learning and discovering, but it is the pupil who must do the actual discovering of relationships and solutions for himself. Most pupils have had little, if any, previous practice and experience within their formal education in discovering things for themselves—and many classroom teachers have had practically no experience in guiding pupil discoveries. Teachers have stressed facts to be memorized, and if understanding of *why* somehow came about, it was by accident and not by plan. As a result, pupils have been relegated to an inactive role in the learning process. The teacher's role in discovery should be of an active nature, one requiring involvement, enthusiasm, encouragement, a willingness to view incorrect answers in such a way as to encourage the child, and also a willingness to set up an environment conducive to pupil experimentation and involvement.

The Approach to Discovery

Four things are of importance in the approach to discovery: establishing the proper classroom atmosphere; understanding how children learn; the use of concrete materials; and skillful questioning.

The discovery method is based on the mutual respect of teacher and students. Without such mutual respect, the discovery method cannot flourish and prosper in a classroom. The classroom atmosphere should be one where it is safe for students to have ideas and try them out; one where correct answers are not unduly emphasized; one where learning is kept at a level appropriate to pupils' ability; one where recognition and praise are given for accomplishment, while encouragement is given

---

6. Bernard Z. Friedlander. "A Psychologists Second Thoughts on Concepts, Curiosity and Discovery in Teaching and Learning," *Harvard Education Review* 35 (Winter 1965):18-19.

7. Olive B. Wheeler; Ballenger, Marcus; and Hollis, Loye Y. *Elementary School Mathematics: A Transitional Program* (Lubbock, Texas: The Texas Tech Press, 1965), p. 25.

when failure occurs; and one where each student can enjoy a reasonable amount of success. When the proper classroom atmosphere has been established, the actual use of the discovery method involves providing certain bits of information and withholding other bits.

Learning and understanding are rarely, if ever, the result of all-or no insight. The psychology of learning indicates that in learning mathematics one generally progresses from the use of concrete objects to the use of semiconcrete materials, and then to the abstract level of symbols. Since most of mathematics is based on abstract ideas, recognizing these steps in learning is important. For example, if asked to describe or tell what a glozwif is, could a student do it? Probably not. But if he were allowed to examine a glozwif (a nonsense term), that is, touch, feel, see, taste if necessary, and so forth, some perceptual image or structure of a glozwif would be formed in his mind. The best mental or perceptual images are formed at the concrete level when an object has actually been examined with the senses. It is at this time that proper concrete experiences provide students with the opportunity to construct and store mental models of a concept. If, a short time later, the student was to see a picture of a glozwif, it would be fairly easy for him to associate this semiconcrete picture with the previously formed perceptual image of the concrete object. After sufficient contacts with concrete and semiconcrete objects the abstract word-symbol, glozwif, has meaning for the student in his own terms and through his own experiences. In other words, the perceptual structure has freed the key elements and allowed them to be shifted into a new perspective that is meaningful within the range of his ability and past experiences.

The third point of consideration in the approach to setting up the discovery method is the use of concrete materials. Since discovery implies the actual involvement of the pupils in the learning process, and this involvement can usually be brought about and encouraged best by the use of concrete materials, especially at the elementary level when new or broader concepts are being introduced. Such concrete or objective materials should be used and manipulated by the pupils as long as necessary for them to gain understanding of a particular concept, for if understanding is not developed, then the learning that takes place is likely to be superficial. Therefore, the passing over lightly or omission of any one of the concrete to semiconcrete to abstract levels of learning may jeopardize the pupil's understanding and insight. Individual differences in pupils will allow some to proceed from one level to another much faster than others. It will usually be the faster pupils who proceed at the faster rate, because they have the ability to see and form the perceptual structure necessary for efficient thought on the abstract level. Slower pupils must have more time to work at the concrete and semiconcrete levels.

There are those who feel that the persistent use of objective materials by pupils may cause the pupil to become highly dependent on them, to use them as a "crutch." For example, some teachers are quite concerned when some of their pupils add by counting on their fingers. Yet, it would seem to be of little value to take away a pupil's only way of calculating. Would it not be better to help him gain a more efficient way of calculating, so he will not be dependent on his crutch? When a pupil has developed sufficient readiness and perceptual structure, he usually realizes that he can work much faster at an abstract level without the concrete materials and he will no longer use them for that particular operation.

The automobile industry spends a large sum of money each year advertising preventive maintenance programs. What they are saying is that with some thought and planning many problems can be prevented. It would seem that this idea of preventing problems before they happen would also apply to teaching. There are several things that a teacher can do to prevent certain problems. One factor that can be a problem in learning is the use of materials. In the previous chapter on the discussion of the role and nature of materials to be used, the importance of using materials that do not inhibit or hinder learning was emphasized. A second factor that could be a problem in learning is the method of teaching used by the teacher. The method that a teacher uses in teaching can also either facilitate or interfere with learning. The method of teaching that is being presented in this chapter, as well as the rest of this book, is based on the premise that the teacher and his method should not be a barrier to learning. A third factor that can inhibit or hinder learning is the way the subject matter itself is presented. This particular point, as well as the other two inhibiting factors, will be discussed in greater detail in later chapters, but for the present it is enough to know that the inhibiting effect of these three factors can usually be prevented by the teacher.

The teacher should use probing, less-than-obvious questions in guiding pupils to discover for themselves. This ability to ask thought-provoking questions challenges a teacher's ingenuity, because some pupils will need more clues and more obvious clues than others, yet the teacher must reserve or withhold various types of information. Some pupils will need a clue as to what they should do next, and others may need more specific information in finding a solution. The teacher's best efforts will sometimes fail with some students and he may have to reveal the secret to them. This does not mean that the discovery attempt was a complete failure, however, since both teacher and pupils will now be better prepared to discover in another situation. Psychologists warn that sudden insight into a puzzling or confusing situation does not occur in a haphazard fashion; there must first be sufficient readiness; proper attention must be given to the relationships operative in the whole; and the task must be made meaningful and within the range of the pupil's ability.

Strategies of Teaching

Basic to all the newer mathematics programs is an emphasis on the structure, concepts, and language of mathematics. The teacher, in planning for and guiding discovery should, therefore keep this emphasis constantly before his pupils. The ability to compute is not the end result sought; rather, it is a means of helping achieve the goal of understanding. Certainly we want pupils to be able to compute effectively and accurately, but if we have correctly guided development of understanding, the ability to compute will result from this understanding.

Not only is understanding important, so is the ability to communicate these discoveries in mathematical language. Teachers who insist that pupils memorize formal definitions usually cause students to become so ensnarled in almost meaningless terminology that little or no learning takes place and a combination of confusion and frustration results. But as pupils are guided in developing concepts inductively, they will realize a need for naming the concepts. It is then that proper terminology can be introduced in a meaningful way. For example, students who have been adding two numbers together can be guided to the realization that it makes no difference in the answer if you add the first number to the second, or add the second number to the first. After they can verbalize this idea in their own terms, they can then be told that this is called the commutative property of addition. New terms must become a part of the student's listening and speaking vocabulary first and then, at a later time, a part of his reading and writing vocabulary.

After introducing the proper terminology, the teacher should set a good example by using it, providing opportunities for the pupils to use it, and encouraging pupils to use it. The teacher should not, however, become unduly concerned if pupils do not always use proper terminology. Pupils are great imitators and if they have a good example to follow and are encouraged to use these terms they usually will have little difficulty in developing and using a mathematically precise vocabulary. One thing that helps set man apart from the rest of the animal kingdom is his ability to use and understand language. Shulman and Keislar[8] point out that animals have little or no way of correcting their mistakes because they have little or no language. Thus, with animals it is generally all or none, right or wrong. Man, on the other hand, can correct his mistakes because language makes correction possible; not only what not to do, but also positive suggestions of what can be done. As the language becomes more precise, so does the precision in correction.

A second aspect of teaching strategy is the use of class discussion and conversation so that students feel that any contribution they make is important. The lecture, or tell-all method, relegates pupils to an inactive role in learning. A teacher should strive to develop the feeling in his classroom that he and the students are partners in a learning adventure. If he can develop such a partnership feeling, the teacher does not have to assume an authoritarian role, and the student does not have to hesitate to try new ideas. The student is secure enough to realize that, if necessary, he can retrace his thinking and that he can get help when it is needed.

If students begin to get bored, a change of pace may be needed. Some teachers are so concerned with covering the material in the textbook that they are often the only ones to cover the material, since the pupils "tune them out." When a teacher becomes aware that students are beginning to lose interest, a new topic for a short time will provide the needed change, and after a short interval with it, the original topic can then be profitably resumed and completed. (Many of the activities in chapter 11 can be adapted for this purpose.)

A fourth aspect of teaching strategy is the planning for and providing of experiences which allow opportunities for success by each student. When students become frustrated from working at a level for which they are not ready, they will gradually lose interest. Jack Frymier,[9] a leading authority on academic motivation, reports that research indicates that a student's self-concept is directly related to his motivation level. Those students who have a high, positive self-concept usually have a desirable level of academic motivation, while those students who have a negative self-concept usually have a low level of academic motivation. Since there is such a high correlation between self-concept and motivation, it would seem that if we are going to attempt to raise a student's

8. Lee S. Shulman, and Keisler R. Evan (eds.), *Learning by Discovery: A Critical Appraisal*, Chicago: Rand McNally and Co., 1966. p. 96.
9. Jack R. Frymier. "Motivating Students to Learn," *NEA Journal* 57 (February 1968):37-39.

motivational level, we must also do something to raise his self-concept. There probably is no better way to raise a student's self-concept than to help him be successful. Success breeds confidence, and confidence builds a good self-concept.

Fifth, and probably as important as any of the other teaching strategies, is the skillful use of questions. Through asking the *right* questions, the teacher can guide students to discovery and understanding. The ability to ask the right questions comes largely because the teacher has enough mastery of the subject matter to be competent and has also gone through a somewhat similar experience in learning.

In order to keep students actively involved, a teacher should refrain as much as possible from giving the answer. When a teacher tells an answer, students often feel that this is the final word and the door is closed to any extending discussion. Sometimes it is a good strategy to answer a question with a question. In this way, not only is the answer withheld, but the student is reinvolved in the thought process, and the door is left open to further discussion.

CLASSROOM QUESTIONING AS A TEACHING STRATEGY

Pate and Bremer[10] point out that there are basically two types of questions, convergent and divergent. The convergent question is generally simple in nature because it focuses on one specific answer. Because of this narrow focus, the student can usually answer this type of question with little thought. Also, the thought process that is required is of such a shallow nature that the power of rational, logical thought is not needed. An example of a convergent question would be when a teacher asks, "How much is four and four?" The answer to this question is focused on one specific answer, and probably requires only simple recall on the part of the child to answer it. It may even be a conditioned response, so that when the child hears the stimulus words "four and four" he knows, by conditioning, that he must respond with "eight."

The divergent question, on the other hand, is broader in scope and focuses generally on more than one potential answer. An example of a divergent question could be when a teacher asks, "How could we find how much four and four are?" At this level of questioning the child must formulate some plan of attack before attempting a solution. He is required to use a more analytical level of thought, and is also allowed to pursue the avenue which seems most logical to him in leading to a

---

10. Robert T. Pate and Bremer, Neville H. "Guiding Learning Through Skillful Questioning," *Elementary School Journal* 67 (May 1967):417-22.

solution. Pate and Bremer warn, however, that in the final analysis it is the student's interpretation and response to a question that determines whether it is divergent or convergent.

There is a place for both types of question in teaching, but in the typical classroom the convergent type is used predominately. There is evidence to suggest that in a typical classroom, a teacher will use the convergent type of question more than 95 percent of the time. This predominance relegates the pupil to an inactive role in learning and leaves only about 5 percent of a typical school day when he must utilize his rational powers of thought. If we agree that one of the most important goals of education is to assist students in learning how to utilize the power of rational thought, then it seems that causing a student to use this level of thought only 5 percent of the time is an ineffective method of teaching.

There is probably no one best ratio between convergent and divergent questions, but perhaps a desirable level would be about 25 to 30 percent divergent questions to 70 to 75 percent convergent. After asking a divergent or open-ended question, the teacher could then guide students with convergent questions. Some possible divergent questions might be:

"What could you do if such and such failed?"
"What do you think would happen if we tried such and such?"
"Why do you suppose this did (or did not) work?"
"How do you know this to be true?"
"Can you show me another way to solve this?"

Such questions can be used to guide discovery.

Not only is the type of question the teacher uses important, but also what happens when a pupil replies to a question. The teacher who is using a divergent question quite often gets unexpected replies because the student may not understand the question as the teacher intended it; he may see implications or facets the teacher did not, or he may be completely off base with an attention-seeking reply. If the teacher responds in an abrupt, impatient manner, then very likely students will become hesitant in replying to other questions; the teacher becomes a barrier or obstacle to pupil discovery and learning. On the other hand, the teacher who responds to pupil's reply in a respectful, cordial manner not only does not alienate the student, but also leaves the door open for further inquiry.

Davis[11] suggests that teachers are less likely to interpose themselves

---

11. Robert B. Davis, *Discovery in Mathematics: A Text for Teachers* (Reading, Mass.: Addison-Wesley Publishing Co., 1964), pp. 8-17.

as authority barriers when they pass as little judgment as possible on students' responses. It would seem that if a student is to get a rebuff for his reply, it is much better that it come from mathematics itself (in the form of a solution or answer that does not work) or from his classmates. When teacher judgments are made, positive judgments are preferable to negative judgments.

Davis suggests five strategems to encourage pupils. These incorporate the basic idea of passing judgment as little as possible, and then primarily positive judgment. The five strategems are:

1. Teacher: "Well, let's see if it works."
   (In this response the teacher sounds interested and optimistic about the outcome.)
2. Teacher: "You know, this sounds like a great idea.
   Do you think it will work?" (In this response the teacher sounds as if an even better idea is about to come along.)
3. Teacher: "What?" (This response by the teacher is in the form of a friendly challenge.)
4. Teacher (turning to the rest of the class): "Now, let's see—is this right?" (In this response the teacher is basically optimistic, but acts a little unsure. If a rebuff comes, it will come from classmates, not the teacher.)
5. The teacher thoughtfully considers the response, but is in no hurry to give a reply. Davis calls this playacting, pure and simple. The teacher, while considering the response, gives other children an opportunity to contribute their ideas for a solution. All the time the teacher is giving the impression that the response is worthy of consideration, and that even the teacher must sometimes stop and consider.

These responses should be used with both correct and incorrect student responses, since it is as important for a student to know he is right, without being told, and to be able to defend his position, as it is to realize that he is wrong. If the strategems are used only with incorrect responses, it will not take students long to recognize this and the result will be the same as telling them outright that they are wrong.

The astute teacher learns to question pupils individually in ways that will encourage rather than discourage, since the question or answer that challenges a fast learner may be discouraging to the slower pupil. The teacher must also recognize that because one student understands and makes the desired response, the material may not be equally clear to all students. After a correct response, the teacher could turn to another student and ask him if he understands what the first student meant. If he says he does not understand, the first student is asked to explain it again. If he says he does understand the first student's explanation, then he may be asked to repeat that explanation to the teacher. The strategy of having a second student explain another student's idea or response can also be used quite effectively with students who are only seeking attention. By using this strategy with attention-seekers, the teacher avoids passing judgment and becoming a barrier to learning, while allowing the student's peers to react to his response.

There are also some effective strategies to help students who after a reasonable length of time still seem to be bogged down or who do not know what to do. The teacher could give a hint by saying "I wonder what would happen if you tried such and such?" or, "I noticed some of the students doing such and such. What do you think would happen if you did that?" Thus, teachers can intervene in a manner that does not present an authority-type barrier to the students. In this role, the teacher can both applaud worthy efforts and suggest alternate ways when the desired outcome is not achieved.

Bloom's Taxonomy

In the late 1940s Benjamin S. Bloom and a committee of educators and psychologists recognized that one of the many obstacles faced by education was the lack of understanding of the goals of education except in the most general terms. He and the committee sought to clarify the goals of education by describing and classifying what seemed to them to be a hierarchy of learning behavior based on sequential learning. The result of the committee's work was published in 1956 and has influenced the design and structure of the newer curriculum programs developed in the 1960s and will likely have considerable impact on curriculum revisions in the 1970s. The *Taxonomy of Educational Objectives*[12] (commonly known as "Bloom's Taxonomy") has come to serve not only as a model for the sequential order of objectives but also is a model for understanding and planning for academic learning.

The committee recognized three major domains of the intellect: the *cognitive* domain (dealing with the development of intellectual skills and abilities); the *affective* domain (dealing with values, interests, attitudes, and the like); and the *psychomotor* domain (dealing with the development of motor skills). The cognitive domain is the area most directly affected by curriculum development, though the advocates of this taxonomy point out that while in theory it is possible to separate

---

12. Bloom, Benjamin S., *Taxonomy of Educational Objectives*. New York: Longmans Green Co., 1956.

learning behaviors into arbitrary categories, in actual practice there is usually a great deal of overlapping between adjacent categories.

The learning behaviors in Bloom's taxonomy are divided into six major categories:

1. Knowledge
2. Comprehension
3. Application
4. Analysis
5. Synthesis
6. Evaluation

This arrangement of the hierarchy is from the simple to the complex, a basic premise being that learning at the higher levels will probably utilize and be based on learning found in all of the preceding lower levels.

The committee also suggested that cognitive behaviors occur at a rather high degree of awareness on the part of the student, as opposed to affective behaviors, which seem to occur at a much lower level of consciousness. As learning behaviors become more complex, there seems to be more awareness of their existence on the part of the individual. Here, briefly, is an amplification of the six categories:

1. *Knowledge:* that which develops almost directly from one's experiences, particularly those experiences at the concrete level. *Remembering is the key intellectual process involved.* The student is expected to store certain facts derived from an experience and then at some later time be able to recall this information with minimum help.

2. *Comprehension:* the student is expected to derive the meaning and intent of a communication and to make some use of this information. It is thought that at this level the skills and abilities of subjects such as mathematics are developed. This learning behavior may take any of the following forms: the translating or rephrasing of an idea based largely on the literal meaning of the given communication, the reorganization of ideas according to their relevance and relationship to get implied meanings, or the extrapolation or projected meaning of a communication (making judgments, inferences, or predictions based on the given information).

3. *Application:* requires the learner to remember and comprehend and also to apply the proper generalization at the right time and place. For example, there is a great deal of difference in knowing *how* to subtract and knowing *when* to subtract. Application requires the student to go beyond correctly demonstrating a skill—he must be able to apply the appropriate abstraction without being told or shown.

4. *Analysis:* is the breaking down of the material into its constituent parts in order to gain fuller comprehension and application. Analysis may be thought of as containing the following three levels: breaking down the whole into its parts, determining the explicit relationships of the parts within the organization and structure of the communication, and recognizing the organizing principles which give meaning to and hold the communication together.

5. *Synthesis*: the putting together of parts to form a meaningful whole or generalization that was not clearly evident from the individual parts. At the preceding levels, the work is generally done with parts which constituted a whole in themselves. At the synthesis level, the learner must utilize his past experiences in combination with given parts and put them in a structure that was not obvious before, and at the same time produce a product that is more than the parts he began with. An example of this type of synthesis would be when students inductively develop a generalization such as the commutative property of multiplication.

6. *Evaluation*: involves the making of judgments, appraisals, and the like by using some criterion and/or standard to determine the worth of the end result. The criteria and/or standards may be determined by the individual or they may be supplied from some outside source. Evaluation usually involves some combination of the other behaviors. It is, in one sense, the end product of cognitive behavior, while in another sense it is the major connecting link between cognitive and affective behavior. While evaluation is generally considered an end result, it can occur at almost any stage of any level and possibly as a prelude to some levels. For example, as a result of evaluation, a person might realize the need for more knowledge or greater comprehension.

EDUCATIONAL IMPLICATIONS

Most, if not all, of what is taught in the schools today is intended for application to problem-solving in real life. Few teachers or administrators would argue this point. Yet in far too many instances the level of learning that takes place in classrooms seldom rises above the knowledge level. Factual knowledge can serve as the basic building blocks for higher levels of thought, but until it is assimilated by the mind and put to use in rational thought, it is of little value. As information begins to have meaning, it also begins to be useful in productive thinking, skill development, and learning. It is only after sufficient understanding and insight that the learner can successfully apply his learning to new situations in what psychologists call *transfer of learning*. Thus, one measure of the effectiveness of the education that students are receiving would be how successfully they choose the appropriate generalization for application in situations not encountered in the learning process.

Research studies indicate that comprehending a generalization or abstraction is no guarantee that a student will be able to apply it correctly or in the appropriate place. Students apparently need many opportunities to practice restructuring and classifying situations so that the appropriate generalization can be applied. There seems to be a consensus that training will transfer to new areas more readily when students are taught in such a way that they learn effective methods of attacking problems, when they learn concepts and generalizations rather than how to use specific factual information in certain situations, when they develop proper attitudes toward work, and when they develop a positive self-concept.

Extending Your Thinking

1. Rephrase the following teacher replies to student responses so that you are not passing judgment on the student's response or, if you must pass judgment, so that it is positive:

   a. "Don't you know that nine and seven are sixteen?"
   b. "What a bonehead stunt you pulled, adding instead of subtracting!"
   c. "That's wrong. Any idiot knows eight times nine is seventy-two!"
   d. "Keep quiet until I call on you!"
   e. "What do you mean you don't know how?"
   f. "No, you can't work it that way!"
   g. "I don't care what you did, the answer is still wrong!"
   h. "If you can't work these simple problems how do you expect to get a passing grade?"
   i. "Now why would anyone want to work this problem by addition when it is a multiplication problem?"
   j. "Why has it taken you so long to work your problems?"

2. Restate the following so that the student must decide on a plan of action that will lead to a solution:

   a. "Is adding three sets of three the same as three times three?"
   b. "If four plus seven equals seven plus four, does nine plus two equal two plus nine?"
   c. "Do you think the two triangles are equal?"
   d. "Can you always divide any number by one and not change the number's value?"

e. "Since subtraction is not commutative, can we say nine minus four is equal to four minus nine?"

3. What strategies could you, as a teacher, use in the following situations so that you do not become a barrier to learning?

  a. There is a small group of students who react to many of your questions with "cute" (wrong) answers seeking to gain attention from their classmates.
  b. There is a small group of students in your class having difficulty in mastering concepts and working their problems as quickly as the rest of the class.
  c. A student tells you that he (or she) is not a good student in math because his parents were not good in math.
  d. The class as a whole generally enjoys geometry activities, but you, the teacher, do not feel adequate or confident in geometry.
  e. The class as a whole groans when you tell them that they are going to work again today, and as many days as necessary, on stated problems because they still do not know how to work them.

4. What are at least three alternatives to the following situations?

  a. There are some students in your class who generally finish their problems with ease and much quicker than most of the class. These students could be given additional problems (busy work) or . . . .
  b. Your class is very unusual this year in that there seem to be no average students. They all seem to be either very good math students or very poor in math. You can teach the material in your math book and probably bore the fast group and discourage the slower group, or . . . .
  c. There are a few students in your class who generally get most of their problems wrong. These students can be assigned the task of reworking these, or similar, problems until they get them correct, or . . . .
  d. Your class has completed the first six chapters of the textbook, but the next chapter does not seem to be appropriate for your students, at least at this time. You can go ahead with the next chapter, or . . . .
  e. The other teachers in your building who teach the same grade level that you do have indicated that their students are considerably further along in the math textbook than your students. You can push your students harder to catch up, or . . . .

Related References

Dewey, John. *Experience and Education.* New York: Macmillan Co., 1938.

———. *How We Think.* Boston: D.C. Heath Co., 1910.

Piaget, Jean. *Psychology of Intelligence.* Patterson, N.J.: Littlefield, Adams and Co., 1963.

———. *The Child's Conception of Physical Causality.* Patterson, N.J.: Littlefield, Adams and Co., 1965.

Shulman, Lee S., and Keisler, Evan R., eds. *Learning by Discovery: A Critical Appraisal.* Chicago: Rand McNally & Co., 1966.

UNIT TWO
DEVELOPMENT OF BASIC SKILLS AND CONCEPTS

CHAPTER 4

SETS

While the idea of sets is relatively new to the field of mathematics, it is even newer to the field of elementary mathematics. Consequently, many parents and some teachers are not familiar with sets and their use, particularly as they relate to elementary school mathematics. The ideas of number and counting are among the most fundamental ideas in mathematics, yet they are abstract ideas and are not easily perceived by young children. Consequently, some concrete way of assisting children to develop these abstract ideas is needed so that they will gain understanding along with their skills. Since sets can be composed of physical objects (as well as abstract objects) they represent a method by which children can gradually make the transition from physical objects to the formulation of abstract ideas.

If we think of mathematics as a system of related ideas, sets become even more important, since they serve as the unifying concepts of mathematics. With them, children develop better understanding of numbers and can also be guided to a clearer and more functional understanding of the existing relationships that occur regularly through mathematics—relationships such as those that exist between number ideas and geometric ideas.

Perhaps an even more important reason for sets being used in elementary school mathematics derives from what we know about the way children develop mathematical ideas. The young child's first idea about numbers seems to come from his perception of a group or set. As children handle, arrange, and manipulate objects, their first notions about number are being developed. From this fundamental beginning, more mature ideas can emerge and unfold.

George Boole developed the basis of the concept of sets in symbolic logic about 1840. It was not until the 1870s, however, that George Cantor further expanded symbolic logic to include numbers and began the development of set theory as we know it today. Set theory has been used primarily in higher mathematics. It was not until the late 1940s that mathematicians and educators recognized that elementary school pupils could understand operations with numbers, basic ideas of number and numeral, principles of mathematics, and the unity of mathematics through the study of sets.

Meaning of Set

A set generally means a collection or grouping of things which can be described accurately enough so that we can determine whether or not an object belongs to it. Objects themselves do not make or constitute a set until we think of them as belonging to a set; thus, the determination of sets is a mental process.

We have in everyday life a large number of examples of sets; for example, we speak of a set of dishes, a set of golf clubs, or a set of books. The list of examples could be extended indefinitely, but the method of grouping is more important than the listing of examples.

Method of Grouping

Since the grouping of objects into a set is a mental process, let us examine three sets and see if there are some rules for making sets. If the first set we consider is the set of basal readers in a certain room, then very likely each member of this set would be essentially the same, or alike. Since these books are classed as a set, it can be concluded that sets can contain members that are all alike. If next we examine a set of dishes, we would see that there are eight identical dinner plates, eight identical saucers, eight identical cups, and so forth. There are members of this set that are alike, but the cups are not like either the saucers or the dinner plates. Yet these dishes are classed as a set. From this example we could conclude that a set may be a combination of things both alike and different. The third example is a set of golf clubs. In examining this set we find that there are no identical members because in a normal set of golf clubs no two clubs are exactly alike. Yet in this case these golf clubs are also called a set. From this example we could conclude that a set may be composed of members that are entirely different. Thus a set may be made up of objects all alike, all different, or a combination of characteristics both alike and different.

Not only can the objects of a set be alike, different, or in combination, but the grouping of these objects may be an actual physical grouping (for example, the set of students in a certain grade in a particular school), or the grouping may be done mentally (for example, all the fourth-grade pupils in a certain city). This idea of grouping can be further extended because the set may be composed of actual physical objects or of objects that are grouped abstractly, such as a set of all the stars visible on a certain night.

A child's ability to determine whether or not things belong in a certain set is a skill that needs to be developed, since this ability is a form of readiness for a most basic thought process, that of *classifying*. Students use the process of classifying in many ways both in the classroom and in everyday life. For example, one phase of reading readiness seeks to help children determine how certain things are alike or how they are different. At another time when students study parts of speech, they will need to determine whether or not a word, or group of words, have certain characteristics, such as functionality. In social studies, students may need to group (classify) countries by certain economic characteristics. Other similar situations requiring this skill can be found in almost any area of the curriculum as well as everyday life situations. The student must be able to distinguish which things belong and why they belong to specific sets.

Since the young child's first idea about number develops from his perception of a group (set), the initial activities that would be used with young children should be directed toward developing understanding of a set or group. These activities would start with the children working with and manipulating physical objects that can be easily grouped. Gradually the child can be guided to the understanding that because of a particular grouping scheme, some objects belong to this particular set and some objects do not belong.

Initially the teacher could describe a set and then ask if certain objects could belong to that set. For example, when working with the counting blocks, the teacher could have the children show their set of red counting blocks and then ask, "Can this blue block belong to this set?" After discussing various answers, such as how the children know that a blue block cannot belong to the set of red blocks, other colored blocks can be used and it can be determined if an object meets the requirements for set membership. At a later time, when the students are reasonably skillful in determining if things are members of a particular set or not, students can be given practice in verbally describing sets and then having other students name what they think would be members of this set. If the set is described accurately enough, the other students should have no trouble identifying members of the set. There are numerous other activities that can be used in developing this ability. The following activities provide some ideas and the teacher can then expand on them, as well as using ideas of his own.

Placing Objects in Sets. In this activity the teacher (or a student) starts by placing objects in two or more groupings (sets), while the remaining students attempt to guess the rule that is being used in placing the objects in the various sets. Probably the simplest rule would be to decide to place objects according to one characteristic, such as size, shape or color. For example, the teacher decides to group the objects by using the characteristic of being red or not being red. The activity might proceed as follows:

Teacher: "I am placing some of these objects in one group or the other." (After having placed about five or six objects in each group, select another object.) "Now, I want you to tell me in which set (or group), you think this object should be placed."

A student is selected to respond, and after receiving his response, a check is made to see if several of the other students agree with him. If there is disagreement among students about the placement of the object, the teacher may want to withhold the object for awhile until more agreement can be reached. Regardless of whether or not the students correctly determine the placement of the object, the teacher should place the object in the group in which most students believe it should be placed. If it is apparent that the students have not determined the selected rule, or characteristic, the teacher might place a few more objects in each group and then give the students other opportunities to tell in which group an object should be placed. After all objects have been placed in one of the two groups, the teacher should ask several students if they agree with the placement of all of the objects. This will provide an opportunity to correct mistakes in the placement of objects. When all objects are in the correct group, the teacher then asks the students to tell him the rule used to determine in which set to place the objects. This activity can be developed with varying degrees of difficulty, such as using three or more categories.

Going to London. This activity is a game that has been played by children for generations. The object of this activity, as in the preceding activity, is to determine the rule being used to designate set membership. The teacher could start this activity, after discussing how the game is played, as follows:

Teacher: "We are going to play a game called 'Going to London.' I am going to London and I am going to take an apple and an ant. Who would like to go with me?" (The teacher then calls on various students to determine if they could go.)

Student A: "I want to go to London and I want to take an apple, an ant, and an orange."

Teacher: "I am sorry but you cannot go this time."

Student B: "I want to go to London and I want to take an apple, an ant, and an airplane."

Teacher: "You may go."

Student C: "I want to go to London and I want to take an apple, an ant, and a banana."

Teacher: "I'm sorry but you cannot go this time."

Student D: "I want to go to London and I want to take an apple, an ant, and an autoharp."

Teacher: "You may go."

Other responses that would permit students to go to London are:

automobile	atom	aspirin
abacus	acorn	apron

Responses that would not permit students to go to London are:

ship	camera	brush
grapes	doughnuts	football

A student is allowed to guess more than once in the event his first answer is incorrect. After a reasonable time, in which there have been several correct answers, and the rule has probably been discovered by most of the students, the teacher asks the students to state the rule. The activity can be repeated numerous times, using a different scheme each time. For example:

Teacher: "I am going to London and I am going to take a pear and a grape. Who would like to go?"

Responses that would permit students to go are:

orange	plum	grapefruit
apple	banana	peach

Responses that would not permit students to go are:

basketball	comb	shirt
hat	bus	shoes

The rule for this game was to name a fruit, but it could also have been to name something edible. Another variation would be:

Teacher: "I am going to London and I am going to take an apple and a bat. Who would like to go?"

The next reponses that would permit a student to go are:

cart	cookie	can
cape	car	cartoon

Responses that would not permit a student to go are:

shoes	map	infant
Yo-Yo	bed	lamp

The rule this time was to name objects in alphabetical order according to their first letter. After initial *c* responses would come initial *d* responses, and so on, through the alphabet.

Methods of Describing Sets

To help us communicate our ideas about sets, we can describe sets orally, in writing, or by drawing pictures of the members. The method chosen will generally depend on the situation; mathematically, any one of the three methods is applicable. With young children it is probably best to describe a set orally and at the same time to physically group actual objects to help communicate the idea of a set along with a description of its members. When we list the members of a set, the elements of a set are enclosed within braces. If we are talking about more than one set, it often becomes difficult and/or cumbersome to list the entire set each time. It has become accepted procedure and common practice to denote sets with capital letters, such as set B = {the boys in Mrs. Jones' third grade}.

The teacher will be able to guide the understanding of young children about sets by providing many opportunities for them to group concrete objects. As students develop understanding with concrete materials, they will also be building mental models that will enable them to transfer this understanding to pictorial representation of sets. At still a later time, their understanding will extend to the more abstract representation of sets using numbers or letters. It should be remembered, however, that it is organized experiences with concrete materials that lay the foundation for later understandings, since manipulation of concrete materials requires thought and generates thought. The use of language is then needed to describe and communicate this thought.

Subsets

There are occasions, when parts of a set can be used without using the entire set. This leads to the idea of a *subset*; that is, a part of a set, or a set within a set. This is not quite the complete meaning of subset, however, since a subset can mean more than just part of a set. A set is said to be a subset if it contains no members that are not in the original set. It is possible then, according to this definition, for the entire original set to be a subset of itself. The *empty set,* or *null set,* is also a subset of every set because it has no members and consequently cannot contain any members that are not in the original set. The implied meaning of subset, then, is that it can consist of part of the members of the original set, all of the members of the original set, or the empty set which contains no members. It should be noted that in most instances when subsets are used, they are parts of the original set. Some people have found it convenient to designate those subsets that are different from the original set and the empty set as *proper subsets*. The symbol ⊂ is used to mean "is a subset of." For example, if set A were all the letters in our alphabet and set V were all the vowels, then set V would be a subset of set A. It would be written like this: V ⊂ A, and read: "V is a subset of A."

Prenumber Idea of Sets

Thus far in the discussion of sets very little has been said about numbers being associated with or used in sets. This does not mean that numbers are not important in relation to sets, or that they cannot be used with sets. Rather it was intended to help emphasize one of the more important features of sets, the *prenumber idea*—that is, that several things may be done with sets that do not involve numbers or counting. It is very likely that this prenumber idea is one of the first concepts developed by young children in developing readiness for numbers and mathematics. It is also very likely that early man went through similar stages in developing his ideas about numbers.

The prenumber idea involves a comparison of two sets without counting or using numbers. It should occur *before* the concept of number is developed and it is in fact part of the readiness for developing the concept of number. Early man probably had some need or reason to distinguish between groups of one and more than one. It was when he finally conceived the idea of manyness, or plurality, that he was ready to develop the concept of number. Young children apparently must go through a similar learning experience before they are ready to develop the idea of manyness in contrast to the oneness of a single object. Then there likely must be the development of the idea that things can be compared so that the manyness of one group can be compared to the manyness of another group. From this kind of comparison, there must eventually develop the idea of equality and inequality.

To develop this idea, each child begins comparing sets of physical objects by mapping (matching) each object of the first set with one, and only one, object of the second set. For example, if the child is comparing a set of blue counting blocks with a set of red counting blocks, he would match each object of the first set with one object of the second set by having each object touch the object with which it was paired in the other set, as shown in Figure 4.1.

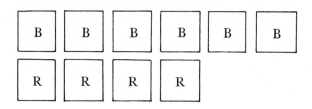

Figure 4.1

From this type of comparison, the child should begin to develop rudimentary ideas about greater than, less than, and equivalent to. The children should be guided in the initial phase of developing the idea of greater than and equal to, because less than is a concept that is more difficult for them to acquire, probably because the comparison of less than requires them to form an abstract image of objects that are not there in order to make the comparison. After the children have developed the concept of greater than and equal to, they usually have less difficulty developing the idea of less than.

The teacher can have the children rearrange the order of the objects in each set and then repeat the mapping of objects. The students could then determine that the relationship of the sets remains the same (that is, the larger set remains the larger) regardless of the arrangement. After considerable experience in matching physical objects to compare sets, the children could then be guided to compare sets of objects in the classroom and verbalize how they know whether or not the sets are equivalent. At a later time, the children can compare pictures of sets by matching one object of the first set to a corresponding object of the second set by using connecting lines. Figure 4.2 shows how pictures of objects might be matched by connecting lines. From similar experiences, children will gradually develop the idea of a one-to-one correspondence, and the understanding of the concept of one-to-one correspondence is vital to the future development of other mathematical ideas based on comparison. At some future time, after children understand one-to-one correspondence, they can develop the idea of a many-to-one correspondence, for example, the set of children in a particular classroom to the teacher of that class, or the set of shoes in a particular classroom to the set of children in that room.

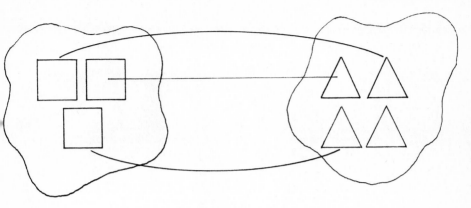

Figure 4.2

Through such experiences it should become more and more obvious that when we compare any two sets by matching the members of one set with the members of the other set, we will find that there will be one of three possibilities: the first set could be equivalent to the second set; the first set could be greater than the second; or the first set could be less than the second. When each of the members of one set has been matched or paired with a member of the other set so that no member in either set remains unmatched, we have in effect put the members of these sets into a *one-to-one correspondence,* and we can say that the sets are matched or equivalent (but not necessarily equal).

An illustration of the comparison of sets without counting would be when a mother gives her young child a handful of cookies to share with a friend. The two children would probably divide the cookies on a "one-for-me, one-for-you" basis until there are no cookies left to share. By using this "one-for-me, one-for-you" method, the children divide the cookies into two equal sets without counting or knowing much about numbers. If in the matching of two sets we find that we have matched every member of one set with a member of the other, but that there are still some members of the other set that are not paired, we would then know that these two sets were not equal or equivalent. An example of unequal sets would be when a group of children are seated in the reading circle and there are chairs in the circle that are not occupied. It is fairly easy to determine, without counting or numbers, that the set of chairs is greater than the set of children at the reading circle.

When a teacher is guiding children in readiness for understanding numbers, the children must have many opportunities and experiences in handling and manipulating concrete materials. In developing the concept of three, for example, children must work with many collections of three to develop the mental concept of the threeness of three. If three balls are placed into a set they are not the only set to have the characteristic of threeness. In progress toward the concept of number, students must be guided to the eventual realization that the threeness of three or the fourness of four is a characteristic of a whole group of sets that contain that number of objects or members. If the concept of equality and inequality are to be developed meaningfully, students will probably need concrete experiences that focus attention on the necessary conditions to form a one-to-one matching.

Sets have been identified as a collection of things: books, stamps, people, numbers, etc. In mathematics the word *set* refers to a collection of definite, distinct objects in our perception or in our thoughts. Sets may be compared and/or matched without involving numbers. If two sets are matched, the order or arrangement of the individual members within each set is not important.

Properties of Sets

As prehistoric man progressed in his development, it became necessary for him to determine *how many* objects were in certain collections. It was no longer sufficient to know that collections were the same size, or that one was larger than the other. Apparently early man became aware that equivalent groups had a property of being alike in some way. From Figure 4.3, it is not difficult to become aware of this likeness.

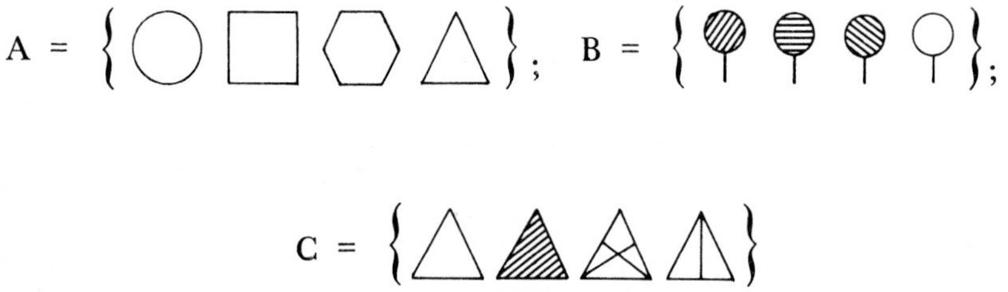

Figure 4.3

Thus it is that all equivalent sets share a common number property. This common number property is known as the *cardinal number* of the set. It is the cardinal number of the set that tells us how many are in a set. The idea of the cardinal number will be further refined when the child begins counting, but at this phase in his development of the concept of number he is beginning to develop an intuitive notion of cardinal numbers. After he develops the concept of cardinal number and counting, he can then be guided to understand ordinal numbers and how they differ from cardinal numbers. (An *ordinal number* designates or specifies a particular thing in a sequence, such as the fourth child in line.)

Although number is an abstract concept, man has invented ways of representing numbers. These representations of numbers are called *numerals*. The words or number symbols that we use are merely name tags that we are attaching to the abstract idea of number. It has also been shown that sets can be compared to determine if one set is less than ($<$), equivalent to ($\equiv$), or greater than ($>$) the other set. If we look at the properties of numbers, we see that numbers have, for all practical purposes, the same properties as sets. Consequently, in working with sets we are developing readiness for numbers and numerals. In effect, sets provide a connecting link between groups of physical objects and abstract numbers.

Not only do sets have common properties with numbers, but sets can also be arranged in order from smallest to largest according to the number of elements in each set. If we have four sets ($\{\boxtimes, \otimes, \otimes\}$; $\{\triangle\}$; $\{a, b, c, d\}$; and $\{\bigcirc, \square\}$), Figure 4.4 illustrates the ordering from the smallest to largest:

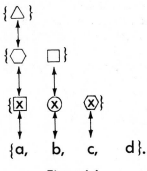

Figure 4.4

Since sets can be ordered, and since they also have common properties with whole numbers, we now conclude that whole numbers can also be ordered and thus used for counting.

Counting

Counting is the most basic operation in arithmetic. The methods of computing (algorisms) in addition, subtraction, multiplication and division are simply shortcuts in counting. Any problem in addition, subtraction, multiplication, or division can be solved by counting, if we want to take the time to do it. Some people have not understood counting nor its importance in mathematics and they believe that when a child can recite the number names in the correct sequence, the child is counting. But counting is a more complicated process than just saying certain words in a particular sequence. Before a child can learn to count rationally, he must first develop the concept of number (that is, the twoness of two, the threeness of three, and so forth). Closely allied with the concept of number are the ideas that one, and only one, number tells how many are in the set and that the number which is associated with a given set is also associated with each other set which is equivalent to the first set. The physical characteristics of the members of a set (color, shape, size, and the like) do not affect the number that is associated with the set. As children develop the understanding that a number tells us how many members are in a set, the teacher should encourage them to verbalize and explain their understanding. In this way he obtains some indication of the child's level of development of the number concept. If need be, assistance may be given in further refining the concept by guiding the child into other appropriate experiences.

If we have a set and want to determine how many members are in this set, we are in effect trying to match this set with its equivalent set of ordered counting numbers.

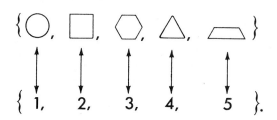

Figure 4.5.

An important property of pairing the members of the set of geometric figures and the members of the set of ordered counting numbers in Figure 4.5, for example, is that the last number we use in this pairing not only names the number of these equivalent sets, but it also tells how many members are in the set. This is a most important concept in counting, yet it is sometimes not taught at all.

Cardinal and Ordinal Numbers

One of the prime purposes of counting is to find the answer to the question, "How many?" It is the *cardinal number* that establishes *how many* objects or things are in a set. Since the ability to find how many is so fundamental, the concept of cardinal numbers is developed first. At a later time, the concept of ordinal numbers is developed. As children develop skill in counting, the teacher must diligently guide students to the full realization of the usefulness of this skill. The students must have many experiences involving counting to find how many before they have a command of this skill.

In the beginning stages, the teacher and children should count sets of physical objects by touching each object, when possible, as the number name is given. After the last object has been given a number name, the teacher assists the students in establishing that the last number named also tells how many are in the set. The astute teacher will provide many opportunities for children to practice counting to find how many during the entire school day, rather than just during the math period. For instance, when a group of children come to the reading circle, they can count and find how many are in that reading group. At lunch time, the children can count to find out how many are going home for lunch, how many brought their lunch, and how many are going to buy their lunch. Or, when preparing to go home, they can count how many wore coats and how many wore sweaters. Thus, many times during the day the teacher can provide opportunities for practice and reinforcement in developing skill and understanding of counting.

As children develop proficiency in counting, they can further refine their understanding by being guided to the realization that it makes no difference which object we start with in counting, as long as each object in the set is counted. Figure 4.6 illustrates this:

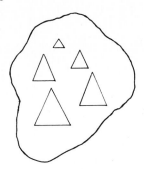

Figure 4.6

The teacher has the children count the objects in the set in Figure 4.6 by starting with the smallest object. After the number of objects has been determined, the students then count the objects beginning with the largest and find that they have counted the same number of objects either way. After many similar experiences, they will realize that where counting a set of objects was started does not affect the cardinal number of the set, provided each object is counted. Gradually, the idea of cardinal numbers should be expanded into the idea that the cardinal number of a set identifies a particular family of sets, all of which have the same number of members. For instance, a set of five blocks would belong to the same family as a set of five balls, or a set of five cats, or any other set of five things. Thus, the cardinal number of a set names the particular family of sets to which that set belongs.

Understanding ordinal numbers is a bit more complex, and it is necessary to have a reasonable understanding of cardinal numbers and counting before developing the concept of ordinal numbers. An *ordinal number* identifies *which one* in a particular sequence or arrangement. Many children come to school with some ideas of ordinal numbers—they may know they are the *second* child in their family, for instance, or that they are in the *first* grade. Most children will need guidance in refining these immature ideas into more mature concepts.

Since an ordinal number tells which one, it allows us to extend the idea of counting by introducing a means of identification and/or discrimination that is not possible with cardinal numbers. It thus adds another type of precision to our communication, and just as the teacher provided many experiences in counting to find how many opportunities of a similar nature will be needed to determine which one in a particular arrangement—the *fourth* block from the top, the *second* triangle from the bottom, the *third* red book, and so on. The teacher guides the children in understanding that the counting used with ordinal numbers is somewhat different from the counting used to determine cardinal numbers and that usually it is not necessary to count the entire set, but only as far as the designated ordinal number. To illustrate the difference, the teacher would designate a certain position, such as fourth, and count up to that position. If he were using a set like that in Figure 4.7, he would say, as he touches each object,

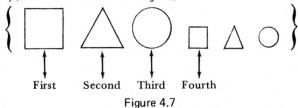

Figure 4.7

There would probably need to be some explanation that with this type of numbers the words "first," "second," "third," "fourth, . . ." are used instead of "one," "two," "three," "four, . . ."

After some discussion of the similarities between the two types of counting, the children should be ready for practice in counting and in naming positions in an arrangement.

Set Terminology

1. Braces ${ }$ are usually used to enclose sets and are read "the set whose members are . . ." For example, $\{a, b, c\}$ would be read "the set whose members are a, b, and c."

2. Capital letters are customarily used to specify certain sets. For example, $A = \{a, b, c\}$ would be read, "set A, whose members are a, b, and c."

3. Each thing in a set is called a *member* or *element* of that set. To indicate set membership, the symbol $\in$ is used. *Nonmembership* in a set is indicated by $\notin$ The symbol $\in$ is read "is an element of . . .," and the symbol $\notin$ is read, "is not an element of . . ."

4. Each set has at least one subset, and usually more than one. As the name suggests, a subset is part of an original set. In a subset, there can be no member of the subset that is not also a member of the original set. The symbol $\subset$ is used to denote a subset and is read "is a subset of." For example, in Figure 4.8 then $B \subset A$ because every element (member) of B is also a member of A.

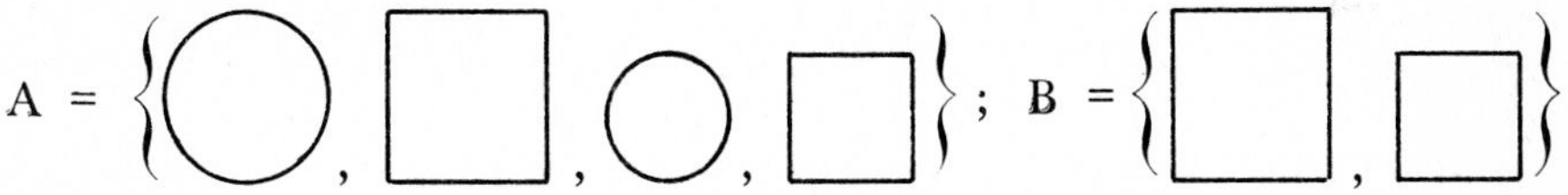

Figure 4.8

5. The *empty* or *null* set is always a subset of every set. The empty set is written ${ }$ or $\emptyset$. This concept of the empty set is sometimes confusing. As an example of the empty set, we are sorting a group of marbles so that all the red marbles are placed in a red box, blue marbles in a blue box, and orange marbles in an orange box, and if after sorting this group of marbles we find that all of the marbles are either red or blue, then the set of marbles in the orange box would be described as the empty set. Or to describe the empty set in still another way, there is

quite a difference between an empty box and no box at all. The key idea is that the empty set exists even though it has no members. Many children tend to confuse the empty set with nonexisting sets. The teacher should first give many examples of the empty set and gradually encourage students to give and describe other empty sets.

6. The set, or class, of things under consideration is often referred to as the *universe,* or *universal* set. The universe is usually denoted by the capital letter U.

7. Sets that have the same number of elements are called *equivalent sets.* The sets are equal if the members in one set are exactly the same as the members in the other. If we have three sets, A = $\{a, b, c, d\}$, B = $\{d, a, c, b\}$, and C = $\{w, x, y, z\}$, then all three sets are equivalent, but only A and B are equal.

8. *Intersecting sets* are sets having at least one member in common, while *disjoint sets* are sets having no members in common. For example, given set L = $\{l, m, o, p, q\}$, set M = $\{a, e, i, o, u\}$, and set N = $\{1, 2, 3, 4, 5, 6, 7, 8, 9\}$, then L and M would be intersecting sets because they have at least one member in common (the letter o). Sets L and N would be disjoint sets because they have no members in common.

9. A *finite set* has a definite number of members and can be counted, while an infinite set has so many members that it cannot be counted. An example of a finite set would be

$$A = \{ \triangle \ \triangle \ \triangle \ \triangle \}$$

while an example of an infinite set would be the set of natural numbers,

$$N = \{1, 2, 3, 4, 5, 6, 7, 8, \ldots\}.$$

(The three dots indicate that the set continues unendingly in like manner.)

10. *Venn diagram* is a pictorial representation of sets using goemetric figures. This method of representing sets is often used to help interpret sets and visualize relationships among sets. Rectangles are generally used to denote the universal sets and circles are used to enclose the members of the set under consideration. (Although rectangles and circles are commonly used, other geometric shapes could be used.) In Figures 4.9 and 4.10, U is the set of counting numbers, A is the set of the first five counting numbers, B is the set of numbers from the fourth through the eighth counting number, X is the set of the first five even counting numbers, and Y is the set of the first five odd counting numbers.

Example 1

U = { the set of counting numbers }

A = { 1, 2, 3, 4, 5 }

B = { 4, 5, 6, 7, 8 }

A ∩ B

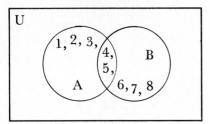

Figure 4.9

Example 2

U = { the set of counting numbers }

X = { 2, 4, 6, 8, 10 }

Y = { 1, 3, 5, 7, 9 }

X ∩ Y

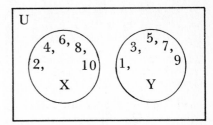

Figure 4.10

Figure 4.9 shows the intersection of two intersecting sets, while Figure 4.10 shows the relationship of two disjoint sets. The size of the circles is not used to represent the magnitude of sets, only to show the relationship of the sets.

Union of Sets

Probably one of the most fundamental of basic operations to be performed with two sets would be to join these two sets into a new super-set containing the two original sets. This operation is called the *union of sets*. The symbol ∪ is used to indicate the union of sets. An example of union of two sets could be:

Set A = { boys in your classroom }

Set B = { girls in your classroom }

A ∪ B = { all the boys and girls in your classroom }

or { all the children in your classroom }

Another example of union could be:

Set E = { 2, 4, 6, 8, 10 }

Set O = { 1, 3, 5, 7, 9 }

E ∪ O = { 2, 4, 6, 8, 10, 1, 3, 5, 7, 9 }

In the first two examples the sets are *disjoint sets* (having no members in common), while in the example in Figure 4.11 they are *intersecting sets* (they have one member in common, the square). Although the square is in both sets, it is only listed once.

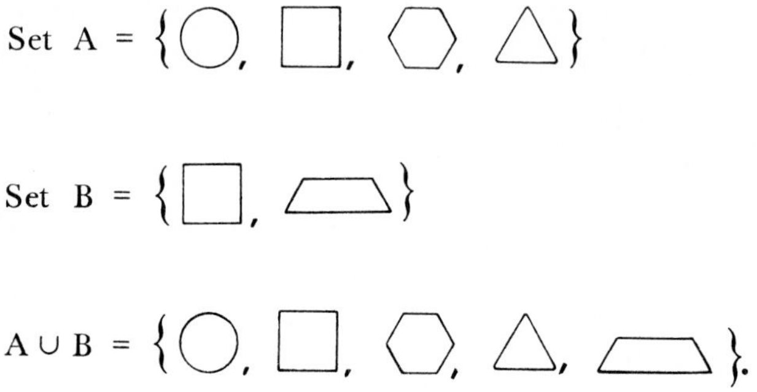

Set A = {◯, ☐, ⬡, △}

Set B = {☐, ⬭}

A ∪ B = {◯, ☐, ⬡, △, ⬭}.

Figure 4.11

A key teaching idea to assist in the understanding of the union of sets is that when the two sets are put together they usually create a new, larger set. For example, after students have performed the union of a set of red and a set of green blocks, as in Figure 4.12, they can

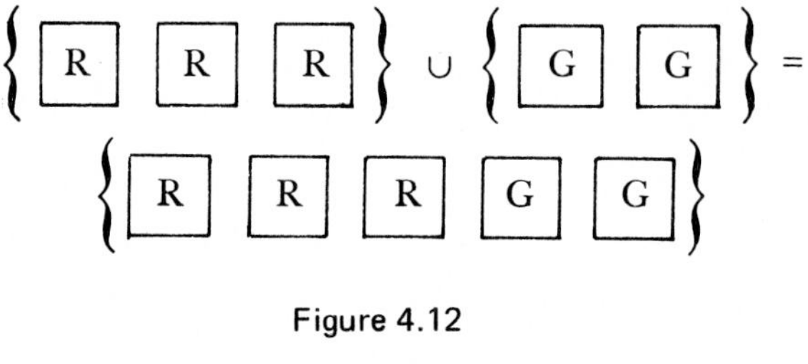

{ R R R } ∪ { G G } =

{ R R R G G }

Figure 4.12

then be guided to the realization that although they can still see the set of red blocks and the set of green blocks within the new set, they have created a new set containing both of the original sets.

The union of two disjoint sets is the basis for developing concepts of addition. Figure 4.13 will help to illustrate how sets can aid in developing concepts of addition.

Set S = $\{ a, b, c \}$

$\boxed{N_3}$ (Denotes cardinal number of set S)

Set T = $\{ d, e, f, g \}$

$\boxed{N_4}$ (Denotes cardinal number of set T)

S ∪ T = $\{ a, b, c, d, e, f, g \}$

$\boxed{N_7}$ (Denotes cardinal number of S ∪ T)

Figure 4.13

The union of two sets can further be shown in relation to addition as in Figure 4.14. (This time the number line will also be involved.)

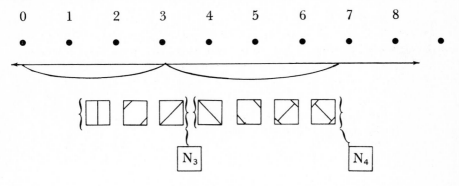

Figure 4.14

While it is apparent that adding is just a quick way of determining how many are in the new set resulting from the union of two sets, this relation of addition and union is true only when *disjoint sets* are involved. The following illustration should help to clarify this: a teacher asked her children to bring some Christmas books and Christmas pictures for the classroom. The children brought items as shown in Figure 4.15.

Set B   (books) = $\{$ John, Jane, Sam, Ann $\}$

$$\boxed{N_4}$$

Set P   (pictures)   = $\{$ John, Ann, Charles $\}$

$$\boxed{N_3}$$

Figure 4.15

When we determine how many children brought pictures or books, we see that only five children (John, Ann, Jane, Sam, and Charles) brought them. We saw in earlier examples, however, that sets with cardinal numbers of four and three united to form a new set of seven. The reason the example in Figure 4.15 does *not* add up to seven is that the two sets are not disjoint sets, but intersecting sets. It should be remembered that addition is an operation on two numbers, while joining is an operation on sets. In joining we unite two sets to form a third set, while in addition we add two numbers to get a third number. Thus addition of two numbers is considered in terms of joining two disjoint sets.

Remainder Sets

The remainder set operation is a binary operation that is primarily concerned with a set and its subsets, and it can be used to help build the concepts of inverse and of subtraction. But there are differing opinions about the value of using remainder sets when first beginning to develop concepts of subtraction because the remainder set is very similar to comparison-type subtraction, while take-away subtraction is the subtraction often taught. Therefore, remainder set is presented as only one of the methods of developing subtraction.

If we consider a set of children in a certain reading group to be as follows:

Set R =$\{$John, Ann, Richard, Charles, Sally, Sue, Bob, Homer $\}$

then the set of boys in this reading group is a subset of the original set R:

Set B = $\{$ John, Richard, Charles, Bob, Homer $\}$
and B $\subset$ R

If we take all of the boys out of this reading group and check who remains in the original set R, we see that it is the set of girls (which is also a subset of set R). Thus the *remainder set* is considered to be a set of all the members remaining in the original set that are not members of the specific subset. Or, to state this in another way, the original set was separated into two subsets. One subset contains the designated members of the original set while the other subset contains the remaining members of the original set.

In the preceding example, when the boys (the designated members of the original set, the reading group) were taken out of the reading group, the subset remaining, or remainder set, was the girls. Thus it can be seen that by the nature of this operation the remainder set must be a subset of the original set. The main idea to be developed about remainder sets is that a total, or whole, set is separated into certain specified component parts.

After children have developed an understanding of the operation that unites sets, they can then experience the separating or parting of a certain subset from the total set. For instance, when working with a set of red and green blocks, if the set of red blocks is taken out of the total set, the set of green blocks remains, as in Figure 4.16.

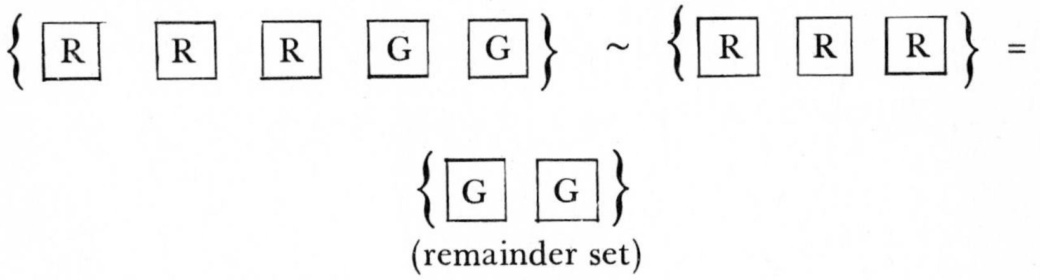

$$\{ \boxed{R} \quad \boxed{R} \quad \boxed{R} \quad \boxed{G} \quad \boxed{G} \} \sim \{ \boxed{R} \quad \boxed{R} \quad \boxed{R} \} =$$

$$\{ \boxed{G} \quad \boxed{G} \}$$
(remainder set)

Figure 4.16

The symbol $\sim$, read "but not in," is used to denote the operation that produces remainder sets. You will note that the more familiar minus symbol $-$, is not used here, it is reserved for use with numbers.

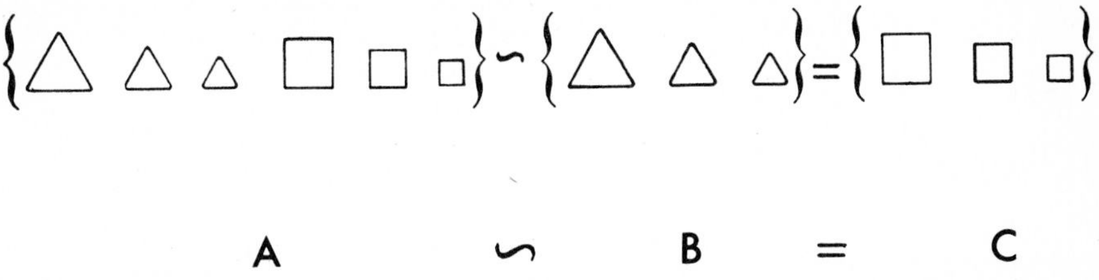

$$\{ \triangle \quad \triangle \quad \triangle \quad \square \quad \square \quad \square \} \sim \{ \triangle \quad \triangle \quad \triangle \} = \{ \square \quad \square \quad \square \}$$

A $\quad\sim\quad$ B $\quad=\quad$ C

Figure 4.17

In Figure 4.17, if we take the set of triangles (set B) out of Set A, then all that remains of the original set is the set of squares (set C).

Remainder sets may be viewed another way by matching all of the members of the designated subset with themselves in the original set. then all of the members of the original set that remain unmatched will be the remainder set. An example using matching (with the same sets used in Figure 4.17) is shown in Figure 4.18.

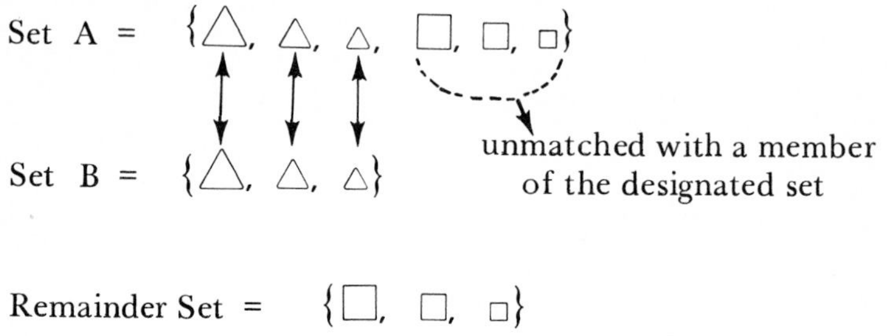

Set A = $\{\triangle, \triangle, \triangle, \square, \square, \square\}$

Set B = $\{\triangle, \triangle, \triangle\}$

unmatched with a member of the designated set

Remainder Set = $\{\square, \square, \square\}$

Figure 4.18

Now we can start developing the concept of *inverse*. We will do this with Figure 4.19, using the previous example of a set of triangles and squares.

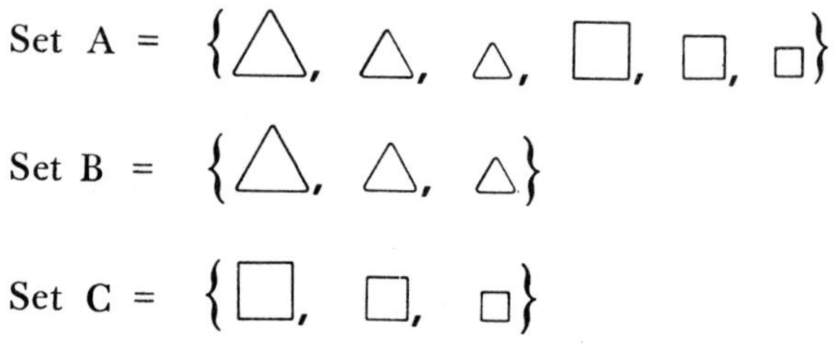

Set A = $\{\triangle, \triangle, \triangle, \square, \square, \square\}$

Set B = $\{\triangle, \triangle, \triangle\}$

Set C = $\{\square, \square, \square\}$

If we form the remainder set A ~ B

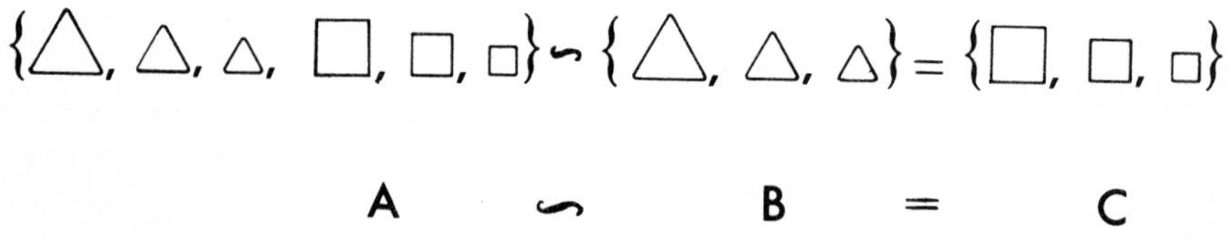

$\{\triangle, \triangle, \triangle, \square, \square, \square\} \sim \{\triangle, \triangle, \triangle\} = \{\square, \square, \square\}$

A ~ B = C

Figure 4.19

and then join the remainder set C with set B, the result will be set A, (Figure 4.20). We are right back where we started because the union of set B with remainder set C has undone, or reversed, the previous operation.

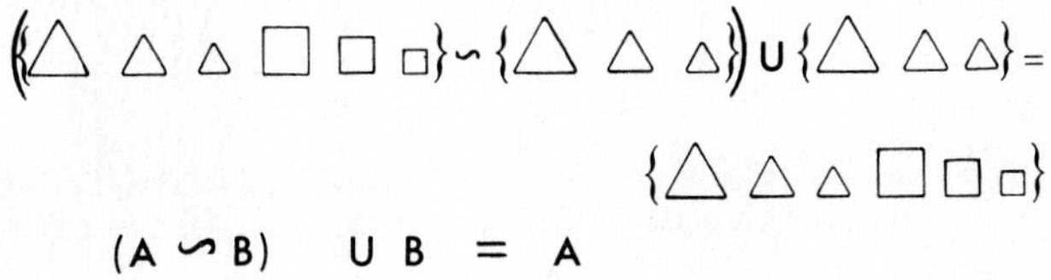

$$\left(\{\triangle \ \triangle \ \triangle \ \square \ \square \ \square\} \smile \{\triangle \ \triangle \ \triangle\}\right) \cup \{\triangle \ \triangle \ \triangle\} =$$

$$\{\triangle \ \triangle \ \triangle \ \square \ \square \ \square\}$$

$$(A \smile B) \qquad U \ B \ = \ A$$

Figure 4.20

Also, since (A ~ B) is the same as (or equal to) C, we could do the following:

$$(A \sim B) \cup B \ = \ A$$

since $(A \sim B) \ = \ C$, we substitute C for $(A \sim B)$

thus $C \cup B \ = \ A$

When two sets are joined, as in Figure 4.21,

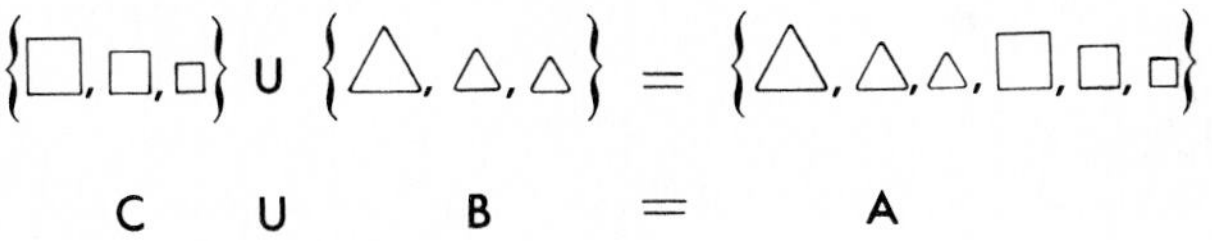

$$\{\square, \square, \square\} \cup \{\triangle, \triangle, \triangle\} \ = \ \{\triangle, \triangle, \triangle, \square, \square, \square\}$$

$$C \qquad U \qquad B \qquad = \qquad A$$

Figure 4.21

we have an operation with sets that undoes (or that is the inverse of) another operation.

The concept of an inverse operation is one of considerable importance in mathematics. Consequently, in developing this concept, care should be taken to ensure that this concept is developed as an undoing operation rather than as of one being an opposite. Other examples of inverses may help to clarify this concept. We can find many examples of nonmathematical inverses in everyday life. If our car motor is running and we stop it, the stopping of the motor undoes the original condition of running. So the inverse of the running motor, in this case, would be the stopped motor. If we should again start the motor, this undoes the condition of its being stopped, and in this instance the starting of the motor is the inverse of its being stopped. Another example of inverse might be found in the child's game "May I?" If a child is told he can take two giant steps and he takes the steps forward without saying "May I?" he would have to go back to his original location by taking two giant steps backward. Thus the two steps backward would be the inverse of the two steps forward because they undo the operation and return the child to his original position.

In mathematics, inverse relationships exist between addition and subtraction, and to an extent between multiplication and division. Addition is thought of as a putting-together process while subtraction is thought of as a taking-apart process. If we have put together two sets, we would then have a new set containing both of the original sets. Now, suppose for some reason that we wish to have our two original sets separated, or back in their initial arrangement. We must then undo the putting together or perform the inverse of putting together and separate the two sets. This concept of inverse will be explored again in later chapters on the four basic processes.

Cartesian Products

Just as the union of sets is the basis for building the concept of addition, so Cartesian products can be used as a basis for building the concept of multiplication. A Cartesian product is a pairing process in which each member of one set is paired with each member of the second set until all possible pairings have been made. We could think of a *Cartesian product* as all of the possible ordered pairs using one member from each set so that the first member of the ordered pair comes from the first set and the second member comes from the second set. To state this in still another way, each member of the first set is paired, in turn, with each member of the second set. While Cartesian products can be used in developing the concept of multiplication, they are generally considered to be too abstract to be used effectively in developing concepts in any but the higher elementary grades. For this reason, multiplication is generally introduced in the elementary school as the putting together of equal size sets (or equal additions). Also, the equal additions concept of multiplication is encountered many times more often in daily life than is the pairing concept found in Cartesian products. Since some textbook programs present multiplication as an extension of Cartesian products, however, the topic is included in this chapter as background information for the teacher. The symbol for a Cartesian product is $\times$, read "cross."

If we have three children and three books, as in Figure 4.22, how many possible pairings can be made?

Set 1 = $\{$ John, Charles, Jim $\}$

Set 2 = $\{$ Book A, Book B, Book C $\}$

	Book A	Book B	Book C
John	John Book A	John Book B	John Book C
Charles	Charles Book A	Charles Book B	Charles Book C
Jim	Jim Book A	Jim Book B	Jim Book C

Figure 4.22

There are nine possible pairings from three boys and three books. This should not be too surprising since we know the product of 3 $\times$ 3 is 9. Another way the Cartesian product can be shown is as shown in Figure 4.23.

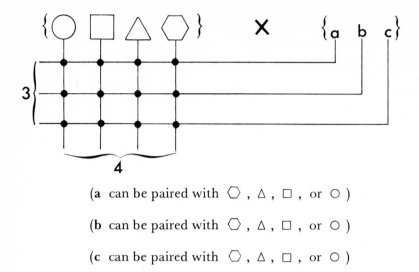

(a can be paired with ⬡ , △ , □ , or ○)

(b can be paired with ⬡ , △ , □ , or ○)

(c can be paired with ⬡ , △ , □ , or ○)

Figure 4.23

In Figure 4.23, where the lines intersect showing the pairings of members of one set with members of the other, we have a rectangular array (things arranged in rows and columns) formed by the intersection of the lines. The arrangement of things in a rectangular array approaches very closely the concept of putting together equal size sets. The rows indicate the size of each equal set, the columns the number of equal sets being put together.

There would be twelve possible pairings from the two sets of four and three. Would it change anything if we matched from the first set to the second, instead of from the second to the first?

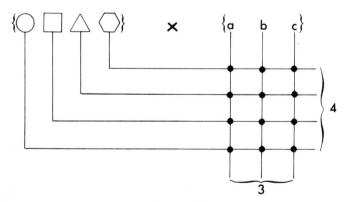

Figure 4.24

As Figure 4.24 shows, there are some things that changed. This also illustrates the commutative property of multiplication.

Looking back at Figures 4.23 and 4.24 and some of the pairings, we cannot conclude that these two illustrations are exactly the same, although we did find twelve possible pairings in both examples. For example, in the pairings of Figure 4.23, (a, ○) [read "a is paired with the ○ "] , (a, △), (a, □) or (a, ○), while in Figure 4.24, (○, a), (○, b), (○,c). We can see that in the case of (a, ○) and (○, a) the same members of each set are used in the pairings, but the order is not the same and therefore we cannot say that these pairings are exactly the same. Since these pairings are not exactly the same, we cannot conclude that 3 × 4 is exactly the same as 4 × 3 (three sets of four is not exactly the same as four sets of three). We can get out of this dilemma fairly easily, however, because although 3 × 4 is not exactly the same as 4 × 3, the product is the same; therefore, we can conclude that if we are seeking the *product* of two numbers, it makes no difference in which order we multiply.

One of the more important features of Cartesian products is that with them we can illustrate very graphically that the product of any number and zero is always zero. This concept is one that is often difficult for children to perceive. Figure 4.25 illustrates 7 × 0 = 0. It can be seen very easily that there are no pairings, because one set (the empty set) does not have any members with which to form a pair.

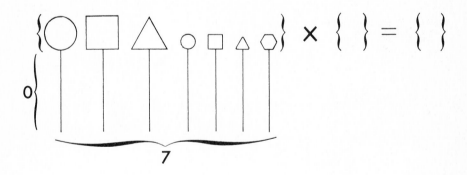

Figure 4.25

Intersection of Sets

Another binary operation of sets is that of intersection. It will be recalled that the union of sets was a joining of two sets to create a new super-set so that both of the two original sets become subsets of the new super-set. The intersection of sets determines a set that is a common subset to both original sets. The symbol "∩" is used to indicate intersection. Since the intersection of streets is understood by most everyone, Figure 4.26 is used for illustration.

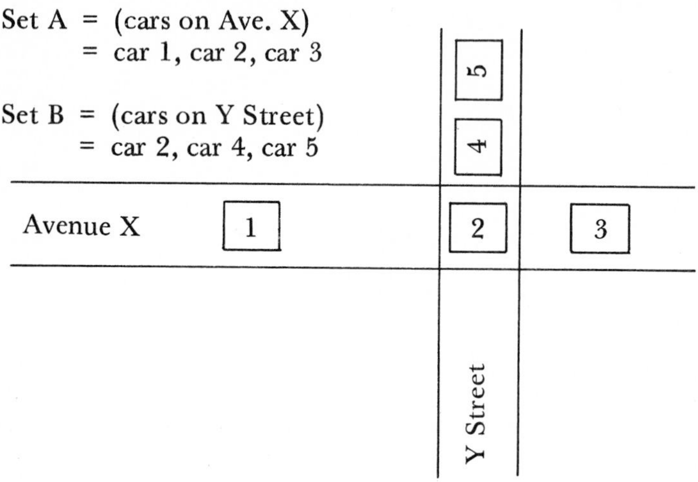

Set A = (cars on Ave. X)
 = car 1, car 2, car 3

Set B = (cars on Y Street)
 = car 2, car 4, car 5

Avenue X

Figure 4.26.

Are there any cars on both Avenue X and Y Street? It can be seen that car 2 is at the intersection of Avenue X and Y Street, so it can be considered as being on both. The intersection (written A ∩ B) will be the member, or members, common to both set A and set B. This can be written as follows:

$$\{Car\ 1,\ Car\ 2,\ Car\ 3,\} \cap \{Car\ 2,\ Car\ 4,\ Car\ 5\} = \{Car\ 2\}$$

$$or\ A \cap B = \{Car\ 2\}$$

Another example of intersection would be:

$$Set\ P = \{1,\ 2,\ 3,\ 4,\ 5,\ 6,\ 7,\ 8\}$$

$$Set\ Q = \{2,\ 4,\ 6,\ 8,\ 10\}$$

$$\{1, 2, 3, 4, 5, 6, 7, 8\} \cap \{2, 4, 6, 8, 10\} = \{2, 4, 6, 8\}$$

$$or\ P \cap Q = \{2, 4, 6, 8\}$$

Figure 4.27 illustrates what happens when disjoint sets are used.

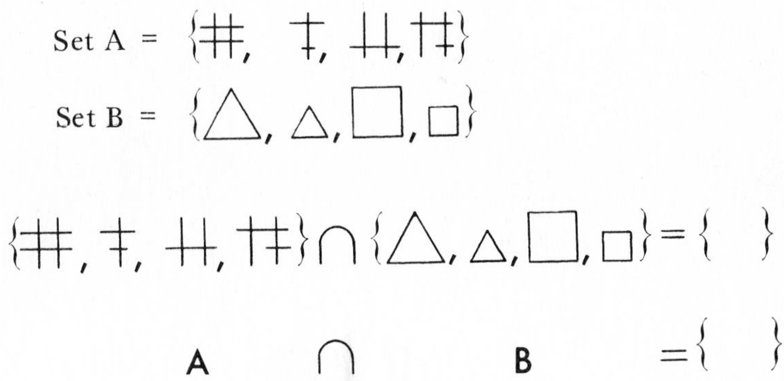

Figure 4.27

Since there are no members in A that are also in B, and no members in B that are also in A, the intersection of A and B would be the empty set (remember the empty set is a subset of every set) because the empty set is the only common subset of sets A and B.

Union and remainder sets were shown relating to addition and subtraction. Intersection of sets, however, does not relate to the basic processes as do union and remainder sets. The operation of intersection becomes important in working with truth or solution sets.

Solution Sets

Solution sets are not operations on sets, but they form the set necessary to make an open sentence true. Solution sets in mathematics are sets of numbers, but solution sets are also used in nonmathematical open sentences. For our purposes, we are only going to be concerned with solution sets as they pertain to mathematics. If we were seeking the solution set to the equation, $3 + 1 = \square$, we must determine the set of numbers that can be placed individually in the blank and each number which makes the equation a true statement. The only number that we can place in the blank and make the equation a true statement is 4, so we would say that $\{4\}$ is the solution set to $3 + 1 = \square$.

In the preceding example the solution set had only one member, but it is possible to have solution sets that have two or more members, for example: $3 + 1 > \square$. This problem asks, "3 + 1 is greater than what number or numbers?" After some checking we find that $3 + 1$ is greater than 3, and 2, and 1, and 0. Thus any one of those numbers can be placed in the blank and make $3 + 1 > \square$ a true statement. We can now say that the solution set to $3 + 1 > \square$ is $\{3, 2, 1, 0\}$. It is also possible to have a solution set that contains no members. The following examples will be helpful in understanding solution sets:

open sentence	solution set
1. $5 + 3 = \square$	$\{8\}$
2. $6 + \square = 10$	$\{4\}$
3. $3 + 2 > \square$	$\{4, 3, 2, 1, 0\}$
4. $\square \times \triangle = 12$	$\{(12, 1), (6, 2), (4, 3),$ $(3, 4), (2, 6), (1, 12)\}$
5. $5 \times 2 < \square + 3$	$\{8, 9, 10, 11, 12, 13, \ldots\}$

Solution sets are also referred to as *truth sets* because they are the sets necessary to make true statements out of open sentences.

Extending Your Thinking

1. Two children, who do not know how to count, want to share a sack of gumdrops equally. Illustrate at least *two* different ways that these children could share the gumdrops without having to count.

2. Illustrate with two sets how you could show without counting that:

a. one set is greater than the other
b. one set is equivalent to the other
c. one set is less than the other

3. Illustrate with five sets, each of a different size, how sets can be ordered from smallest to largest.

4. Show how you would illustrate:

a. two equivalent sets
b. two equal sets
c. intersecting sets
d. a finite set
e. an infinite set

5. Illustrate with a Venn diagram:

Set B = the set of freshmen boys at State College

Set G = the set of freshmen girls at State College

Set R = the set of red-headed freshmen at State College

6. Answer a through e, given these four sets:

Set A = {△, △, △}

Set B = {▢, ▢, ▢, ▢, ▢}

Set C = {△, △, △, ▢, ▢, ▢}

Set D = {◯, ◯, ○}

      a. A ∪ B =

      b. B ∩ C =

      c. B ∪ D =

      d. D ∩ A =

      e. C ∪ A =

7. Show, by use of Cartesian products, all the possible choices of:

    a. three boys and five different flavors of ice cream
    b. two girls and four sweaters
    c. four salesmen and four cars
    d. two painters and five paint brushes

8. Identify at least four situations in which children could be guided to describe a set precisely enough so that it can be determined whether or not an object or thing is a member. How could the teacher guide the children in extending this idea into the more general idea of classifying?

9. Describe and list five activities that would require children to utilize the prenumber idea. Now, can you modify these activities so that the children must also order the sets from smallest to largest without counting?

10. Describe a sequence of learning activities that will assist children in developing the concept of number (that is, the twoness of two, the threeness of three, and so on). How would a teacher then relate this to the process of counting?

11. How could children be guided to distinguish between matching (or mapping) of objects and a one-to-one correspondence of objects?

Why is the matching (or mapping) of objects considered the more fundamental of these two processes?

ANSWERS TO SELECTED QUESTIONS

2a.

$$A = \{ \bigcirc \bigcirc \bigcirc \bigcirc \bigcirc \bigcirc \}$$
$$B = \{ \triangle \triangle \triangle \triangle \}$$

(Set A is the largest because some members in it remain unmatched.)

4a. Two equivalent sets:

$$\{ \bigcirc \bigcirc \bigcirc \} \equiv \{ \square \square \square \}$$

5.

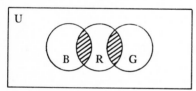

6a. A ∪ B

$$\{ \triangle \triangle \triangle \} \cup \{ \square \square \square \square \} = \{ \triangle \triangle \triangle \square \square \square \square \}$$

7b. Cartesian Product

	Pink Sweater	White Sweater	Yellow Sweater	Blue Sweater
Sally	Pink Sally	White Sally	Yellow Sally	Blue Sally
Mary	Pink Mary	White Mary	Yellow Mary	Blue Mary

or

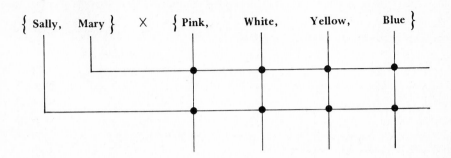

Related References

Banks, J.H. *Learning and Teaching Arithmetic.* 2nd ed. Boston: Allyn & Bacon, Inc., 1964. Chap. 6.

Dwight, Leslie A. *Modern Mathematics for the Elementary Teacher.* New York: Holt, Rinehart & Winston, Inc., 1966. pp. 14-74.

Educational Research Council of Greater Cleveland, *Key Topics in Mathematics for the Primary Teacher.* Chicago: Science Research Associates, 1962. pp. 9-17.

McFarland, Dora and Lewis, Eunice. *Introduction to Modern Mathematics for Elementary Teachers.* Boston: D.C. Heath & Co., 1966. pp. 7-30.

The National Council of Teachers of Mathematics. *Topics in Mathematics for Elementary School Teachers.* 29th Yearbook. Washington, D.C.: 1964. pp. 1-42.

School Mathematics Study Group. *Studies in Mathematics.* vol. 9, rev. ed. Palo Alto, Calif.: Stanford University Press, 1963. pp. 1-21.

Van Engen, Henry; Hartung, Maurice; and Stochl, James. *Foundations of Elementary School Arithmetic.* Chicago: Scott, Foresman and Co., 1965. pp. 11-40.

CHAPTER 5

NUMERATION SYSTEMS

Before proceeding with a discussion of numeration systems, it will be helpful to operationally define some of the basic terms used in this chapter:

1. *Number* is an abstract concept that is a characteristic of all sets of the same quantity.

2. *Numeral* is the symbol or word we use to represent a number.

3. A *numeration system* (or *notation system*) refers to the numerals and to a systematic scheme for arranging a set of symbols to convey the concept of number.

4. The *number system* is the universal set of all numbers (such as the set of natural numbers, the set of integers, the set of rational numbers, and so on) that man uses in quantitative thinking. The number system (or what was known of it at any given time) has remained the same down through the ages, and from civilization to civilization. Only the method of symbolizing and communicating numbers has changed.

As civilizations develop and become more complex, so do their numeration systems. Scientific discovery and technical development cannot flourish without the related mathematical concepts and a system of notation that can adequately explain them, and for this reason, new systems have been developed in recent years. The electrical structure of the computer has made the use of a base ten notation system impractical because of the mechanical processing necessary before it can be used; therefore, a numeration system was developed that would be functional in computers. Today's children are growing up in a civilization of computers and related scientific developments. They will spend their adult life living in and adjusting to this technical environment. Today's students must, then, know about and understand these systems if they are to participate effectively in their society. In this chapter we shall be concerned with the historical background of earlier numeration systems, with the characteristics of a functional numeration system, with descriptions of our numbers, and with nondecimal systems of numeration.

History of Early Numeration Systems

When prehistoric man developed the thought capabilities necessary for language, he was apparently only a short step away from the level of mental thought necessary for the development of mathematical ideas. Ancient history not only seems to confirm this, but today's educational research findings have revealed more than a coincidental relationship between language development of children and their mathematical ability. Since language and mathematics are seemingly so closely related, it seems logical that many people consider mathematics to be a language. Mathematics is used in record keeping and calculation and it is also a vehicle of communication. It is considered by many to be the most universal language of all. A person could go into almost any elementary school in any country in the world, write $2 + 2 = \square$ on a chalkboard, and be understood by the students. The language of mathematics transcends most geographical boundaries. In a broad sense, numeration systems are the alphabet for expressing the language of mathematics. A well-developed numeration system seems to generate and open up new avenues of productive thought which are necessary for the advancement of society. As numeration systems have become more precise, man's ability to develop and communicate rational thought has become more refined and precise.

Primitive man probably had little need for a system of numeration because he was kept busy simply trying to survive in what must have been a hostile environment. In such a primitive, nomadic existence, man probably used the numbers one, two, and possibly three; anything larger would have been "many" to him. With the development of the idea that two sets could be compared by matching in a one-to-one correspondence and the idea of manyness, or plurality, man acquired the ability to develop the rudimentary concepts of number. With the establishment of communities and the development of domesticated flocks and herds, the limited numeration systems that had previously been used were no longer adequate. There came a time when knowing that one thing was more than something else was not enough. Man needed to know how *much more* one thing was than another. Man also needed an accurate method of keeping records of his flock or herd, and a dependable method of deciding when to plant certain crops.

Very likely man first developed a simple tally system that took the form of placing a pebble in a pouch for each of his sheep, or cutting a notch in a stick for each day, or scratching marks on a large rock to denote something. The simple tally system which prehistoric man used probably looked something like this:

Probably man's first significant advance toward a system of numeration came when he realized that grouping the tallies made them easier to work with and to keep track of:

$$\text{H\!H\!H} \quad \text{H\!H\!H} \quad \text{H\!H\!H} \quad /\!/\!/$$

As significant as such a first step was, it still did not provide man with a system of numeration that was efficient and functional. The next major breakthrough probably came when man realized the need for a set of basic symbols to represent different numbers. With symbols to represent numbers, man could save time in writing and calculating both small and large numbers. One of the earliest recorded sets of number symbols were the hieroglyphics (picture writing) used by the Egyptians in about 3000 B.C. Some of the picture symbols used by the Egyptians were as follows:

1	$/$	stroke
10	$\cap$	arch (or heel bone)
100	$\mathcal{G}$	coiled rope
1,000	$\mathcal{P}$	lotus flower

The ancient Egyptians had other symbols for numbers larger than 1,000, but we will only utilize the first four of their symbols in order to understand how their system probably influenced the development of our own system of numeration. The Egyptian system was based on ten, but it did not have a symbol for zero, nor did it have positional notation. The number symbols could be arranged in any order, since the value of the symbol did not depend on its position in the numeral. If the Egyptians wanted to write 2,316, they could write it in any of the ways shown in Figure 5.1.

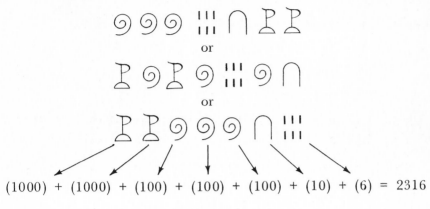

$$(1000) + (1000) + (100) + (100) + (100) + (10) + (6) = 2316$$

Figure 5.1

The nonpositional aspect of this system is apparent, as well as another most important feature, the *additive property*—that is, the values of the various symbols are added together to make the total number.

It is very likely that the Babylonians, who rose to prominence after the decline of the Egyptian civilization, learned the best features of the Egyptian system, namely a set of basic symbols to represent numbers and the additive property of a numeration system. Not only did the Babylonians incorporate these features into their own system, but they also made innovations and improvements. Their numeration system was based on sixty. The impact that their base sixty has had on our present-day lives can be seen by recalling how many seconds make a minute, how many minutes make an hour, and so on. The choice of the base sixty caused this system to be a bit unwieldy to work with, but it was probably the first to make use of the concept of *place value*, or positional notation.

Briefly, the concept of place value means that the value of each symbol is determined by its position in the numeral. The Babylonian numeral system used only two basic cuneiform (wedge-shaped) symbols, (V and <), to write all of their numerals. Just as in the Egyptian numeration system, however, a major defect in the Babylonian system was that it had no zero concept, nor a symbol to represent an empty place. Consequently, the symbol < could represent 10 or 60 or some number even larger. The context in which the symbol was used was expected to make the intended value clear. At a later time, the Babylonians apparently recognized this deficiency and made an attempt to compensate for lack of a zero concept by leaving a blank or empty space in the notation of a number. This solution was only partially effective, however, because when the zero or empty space occurred at the end of a numeral it was difficult to tell how many zeros were intended. History does not record whether or not they successfully resolved this problem.

Roman civilization came into prominence about 500 B.C. By using letters to represent number symbols, the Romans chose a different approach to a numeration system. It is generally believed that the Romans developed and patterned their numeration system after the numeration system of the Greeks. Earlier in historical time the Greek civilization had developed a system of numeration using letters to represent numbers, rather than creating an entirely different set of symbols to represent numbers. The Roman system used only seven symbols—I, V, X, L, C, D, and M. By combining these and using either the additive or subtractive property, they appeared to be able to make all of the numerals they needed. For example, if the first of two symbols represented a larger value than the second, the additive feature was used— that is, the value of the first symbol was added to the value of the second symbol, as in the case of VI, XI, and so forth. If the first of two symbols represented a smaller value than the second, the subtractive feature was used—that is, the value of the first symbol was subtracted from the value of the second symbol, as in the case of IV, IX, and so forth.

The Roman system did not have a zero concept and was not easy to use; in fact, it was quite unwieldy. This unwieldiness was due largely to the fact that the Romans' system of numeration was nonpositional (as were the Egyptian and the Greek). A number symbol always represented the same value, regardless of its position in the numeral. For example, 1971 would be written MCMLXXI. Calculations were very difficult to perform. It is interesting to note that although there were many significant achievements by the Romans, this civilization is not noted for its accomplishments or contributions in the field of mathematics. It may have been that the Romans were not mathematically inclined in their thinking; it may have been that their system of numeration had such severe limitations that it discouraged the development of higher mathematical thought; or it may have been a combination of both factors. On the other hand, the Greek civilization is recognized as having attained many noteworthy mathematical achievements, particularly in the area of geometry. It should be recognized, however, that neither the Romans nor the Greeks probably made any significant impact on the development of our system of numeration.

At least two other major civilizations, the Chinese and the Mayan, developed fairly complete systems of numeration. The Chinese civilization flourished at about the same time as the Egyptian and Babylonian civilizations. Although the Chinese achieved many notable accomplishments, their remoteness and isolation from the other parts of the then civilized world probably prevented them from influencing the development of western systems of numeration. For essentially the same reason, the Mayan civilization of Central America (fl. 300 A.D.), though more recent in time, had little or no influence on the development of our present system of numeration. It can be noted, however, that the Mayans had an amazingly advanced system of numeration that included the zero concept and a symbol to represent it.

By about 200 B.C., the Hindus had developed a system of numeration based on nine symbols. Hindu mathematicians were fascinated with large numbers and they found that other systems of numerations were too restrictive or cumbersome to be efficient and functional. Consequently, they devised and developed a system designed to overcome the defects present in other systems. Sometime prior to 700 A.D., the Hindus incorporated the zero concept (the tenth symbol) into their system and thus captured a concept that had long eluded others. Not only did the Hindu system have the zero concept, but it also had a scheme for place value that was based on grouping by tens or multiples of ten. This grouping (base) by tens used only ten digits or symbols that could be repeated within the numeration, and the value of each symbol was determined by the position of the numeral in the symbolization of a number. With this development of a functional, efficient system of numeration, it became possible for man to count larger amounts more easily. At the same time, he could keep track of his place in counting because of his awareness of the inherent pattern built into the system. No longer did he have to recognize many different symbols, only a few basic symbols and the rule or pattern for combining them. Very likely it was man's awareness of the importance that patterns play in learning and remembering that enabled him to develop this numeration system.

Man could now not only count effectively, but he soon realized that because of the pattern and consistency of this numeration system it was possible for him to speed up this counting process by developing written systems or schemes of calculating. These written schemes or systems of computing are called *algorisms*. By the fifteenth century man had developed and was using these written systems in making computations.

The Hindu achievement might, like the Chinese and Mayan numeration system, have gone unnoticed, had it not been for the nomadic Arabs. The Arabs, who often came in contact with the Hindus in trading, were impressed with the ease with which the Hindus could work with numbers, particularly large numbers. As a result, they adopted the

Hindu system of numeration and soon caused it to spread westward to the Mediterranean and European civilizations. There is evidence to suggest that the shape of the various numerals probably changed several times during this westward movement, but the fundamental laws upon which the Hindu system was based remained the same. With the invention of the printing press during the fifteenth century and the use of the Hindu-Arabic system in the newly printed books and documents, a standardization of number symbols evolved. The symbols we use today have actually changed very little from those earlier symbols used in the first books.

Table 5.2 reviews and compares the numeration systems of the various civilizations that have been discussed.

Table 5.1

Number Name	Egyptian Numeral	Babylonian Numeral	Roman Numeral	Hindu-Arabic Numeral
Zero				0
One	/	∨	I	1
Two	//	∨ ∨	II	2
Three	///	∨ ∨ ∨	III	3
Four	////	∨ ∨ ∨ / ∨	IV	4
Five	/// //	∨ ∨ ∨ / ∨ ∨	V	5
Six	/// ///	∨ ∨ ∨ / ∨ ∨ ∨	VI	6
Seven	// // ///	∨ ∨ ∨ / ∨ ∨ ∨ / ∨	VII	7
Eight	//// ////	∨ ∨ ∨ / ∨ ∨ ∨ ∨	VIII	8
Nine	// /// ////	∨ ∨ ∨ / ∨ ∨ ∨ / ∨ ∨ ∨	IX	9
Ten	∩	<	X	10
Twenty	∩ ∩	< <	XX	20
Fifty	∩ ∩ ∩	< < < / < <	L	50
One Hundred	၅	∨ <	C	100
One Thousand	႒	< ∨ <	M	1000

It took man untold centuries to finally develop a truly workable system, yet today some people expect all children to become experts in the different systems of computing in their first ten years of life. It is true that many children achieve reasonable mastery of these skills, but the important point to remember is that numeration systems and systems of computing (algorisms) are inventions of the adult mind in an adult world. In the elementary school, the teacher must guide and assist students in making the transition from the child's world into the adult world of symbols, algorisms, and logic.

Characteristics of a Functional Numeration System

The characteristics that make the system of numeration we use so functional and efficient are: a basic set of symbols, a method of grouping or a base, a zero concept, and a place value concept.

First, a functional numeration system must have a basic set of symbols to represent different numbers. Without some method of representing numbers (other than tally marks), we would have great difficulty in working with larger numbers; the algorisms (written patterns or systems of calculation) that we use would probably also be severely limited. The Hindu-Arabic system does have a set of ten basic symbols; they are 0, 1, 2, 3, 4, 5, 6, 7, 8, and 9. Because there is no *single* symbol to denote the chosen base, ten, we combine the two symbols 1 and 0 to make 10. By combining the basic symbols 0 through 9 in a systematic way, numbers greater than 9 can be represented.

The second feature of the Hindu-Arabic numeration system is the manner of grouping, or its base. This system generally groups by tens or multiples of tens (that is, tens, hundreds, thousands, and so on). It will be pointed out in the section on nondecimal numeration systems that this numeration system can be functional and efficient in other bases as well as base ten. The fact that we generally use base ten, however, and that we normally are endowed with ten fingers is too obvious to be considered a coincidence.

It soon becomes evident that there is more involved than just a method of grouping. Not only must there be a method of grouping, but if a number system is to be functional and efficient, the same method must be used *consistently* throughout the system. For example, we do not group by tens in the first grouping, by fives in the next, and by eights in the next. Instead, we group by tens *each* time (that is, *ten* ones are grouped into one group of ten, *ten* tens are grouped into one group of one hundred, *ten* hundreds are grouped into one group of one thousand, and so on). Not all groupings in systems we encounter are as consistent. In measurement, for example, when we have twelve inches, we group that into one foot; when we have three feet (not twelve feet) we group that into one yard; five and one-half yards (not three yards) are grouped into one rod, and so on. It is the consistent use of the same method of grouping throughout the system that allows patterns to develop and be used.

The third characteristic of a functional efficient system of numeration is that it must utilize the zero concept and have a symbol to represent it. Without this concept, the Hindu-Arabic system would probably be just as ineffective as previous systems of numeration. In some of the earlier attempts to take this concept into consideration, space was left between the symbols, but not everyone left the same amount of space and if this empty space came at the end of the numeral, even more difficulty was encountered in understanding the number representation. The development of the zero concept and its symbol is considered by many as one of mankind's greatest achievements.

These, then, are the first three characteristics of a functional and efficient system of numeration: a basic set of symbols, a method of grouping or a base, and the zero concept and symbol. The fourth characteristic of a functional, efficient numeration system is that it must have a scheme or plan for combining symbols to represent various numbers larger than the chosen base. This merely implies that the system must make some use of the concept of positional notation and place value.

The place value characteristic encompasses a difficult concept to understand. The concept of place value and positional notation means that symbols can be repeated within a number and that the value of each symbol is determined by its position in the symbolized number. Because of the place value concept, the Hindu-Arabic decimal system ("decimal" means ten) needs only ten different basic symbols to represent any number, no matter how large or small. Not only can each symbol be repeated within the number, but each digital symbol performs two functions. First, each symbol serves as a place holder, since it holds a place, or position, in the number represented. Second, it serves as a cardinal number, because it tells "how many" of the units of a specific positional value is present in any given numeral. Or, to state this in another way, each basic number symbol has two values: a positional value and a cardinal or face value. (It should be noted that in this place value system it is possible to write numerals that are not whole numbers, as in the case of decimal fractions.) The numeral 333 means the following:

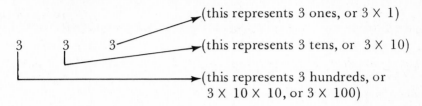

3   3   3   (this represents 3 ones, or 3 × 1)

(this represents 3 tens, or 3 × 10)

(this represents 3 hundreds, or
3 × 10 × 10, or 3 × 100)

Or in the expanded form 333 would be (300) + (30) + (3).

From this example we can see that the three on the left represents a value ten times larger than the three in the middle (and a hundred times a larger than the three on the right). The three in the middle represents a value exactly ten times larger than the three on the right, but it represents a value only one-tenth as large as the three on its left.

Not only does the position a numeral occupies help determine its value, but the value of the individual digit also enters into the determination of the value represented. In the example of 333, it was noted that each symbol to the left of any symbol represented a value exactly ten times larger than the symbol on its right. In the case of 248, however, the number represented by the digit two is a product. It is the product of the number two and the place value assigned to its position, 100. In a similar fashion the number represented by the digit four is the product of the number four and the place assigned to its position, ten; and the number represented by the digit eight is the product of the number eight and the place value assigned to its position, one. The entire numeral, 248, represents the sum of these three products. Thus there is a number symbol assigned to each position within the numeral and each digit of the numeral represents the product of the number it names and the place value assigned to its particular position. Consequently, it is the place or position (such as the ones' place, tens' place, hundreds' place, and so on) that is represented as exactly ten times larger than the position or place on its right. For example, the hundreds' place represents a position ten times larger than the tens' place to its right, but at the same time the hundreds' place represents a position one-tenth as large as the place on its left. Only in the special case where the same symbol is repeated in the next adjoining position does the symbol on the left represent a value exactly ten times larger than its neighbor on the right.

Also inherent in the place value characteristic is the additive feature of the Hindu-Arabic system of numeration, which means that the representative positional values added together comprise the total value of the number. The following example will illustrate this additive feature:

$$\begin{array}{ccc} 2 & 4 & 8 \\ \downarrow & \downarrow & \downarrow \end{array}$$
$$(200) + (40) + (8)$$

Here, the two represents two hundreds, the four represents four tens, and the eight represents eight ones. When these values are added together they total 248. These same digits can be combined in several different ways to represent several numbers of differing value, such as 284, 428, 482, 824, and 842. So in this and other combinations of the basic digits, three elements determine the total value of the numbers: the positional value, the number of units of each position as indicated by the individual digit, and the combined sums of these products.

Writing 248 in the form of (200) + (40) + (8) is known as the expanded form. It is possible to write numerals in the expanded form because of the additive feature of the Hindu-Arabic system.

Using a place value chart (Fig. 5.2) promotes understanding of how powers and exponents are an inherent part of the concept of place value. It can be seen that starting at the far right in Figure 5.2,

ten thousands	thousands	hundreds	tens	ones
2	1	4	6	7

7 represents 7 ones (7×1)

6 represents 6 tens (6×10)

4 represents 4 hundreds $4 \times (10 \times 10)$

1 represents 1 thousand $1 \times (10 \times 10 \times 10)$

2 represents 2 ten thousands $2 \times (10 \times 10 \times 10 \times 10)$

Figure 5.2

and moving to the left, each succeeding place represents a position ten times larger than the place to its right. The two, which represents two ten thousands, could be written as $2 \times (10 \times 10 \times 10 \times 10)$, which is rather cumbersome. The larger the number, the more cumbersome and unwieldly this method becomes. Mathematicians, seeking a shorter method of writing large numbers, developed the concept of *powers*, or *how many times a number is used as a factor.* A small number written to the upper right of another number indicates how many times a number is used as a factor, and is known as an *exponent*. An exponent indicates the power to which the number is raised. For example:

$$100 = (10 \times 10) \text{ or } 10^2$$

$$1,000 = (10 \times 10 \times 10) \text{ or } 10^3$$

$$10,000 = (10 \times 10 \times 10 \times 10) \text{ or } 10^4$$

The timesaving feature of using powers and exponents becomes more apparent as the numbers become larger. It is much quicker to write 10^4 than $(10 \times 10 \times 10 \times 10)$. Another timesaving feature of powers and exponents is that numbers such as hundreds and thousands can be multiplied or divided by each other much faster, as follows:

$$1000 \quad \times \quad 100 \quad = \quad 100,000$$

$$(10 \times 10 \times 10) \times (10 \times 10) = (10 \times 10 \times 10 \times 10 \times 10)$$

$$10^3 \quad \times \quad 10^2 \quad = \quad 10^5$$

In order to multiply $(10^3 \times 10^2)$, we actually add exponents. In the case of division, the following will illustrate:

$$1000 \quad \div \quad 100 \quad = \quad \frac{1000}{100} = \frac{10^3}{10^2} = \frac{10^1}{1} = 10$$

$$(10 \times 10 \times 10) \div (10 \times 10) = \frac{(10 \times 10 \times 10)}{(10 \times 10)} = \frac{10}{1} = 10$$

$$10^3 \quad \div \quad 10^2 \quad = \quad 10^1 \quad \text{or} \quad 10$$

To divide $(10^3 \div 10^2)$, we actually subtract exponents.

An interesting thing happens if we divide a number with exponents by itself, such as $10^4 \div 10^4$, or $6^2 \div 6^2$.

$$\frac{10^4}{10^4} = 10^0 \quad \text{or} \quad \frac{6^2}{6^2} = 6^0$$

We know that any nonzero number such as 10,000 (which is 10^4) divided by itself is one. Further, 36 (which is 6^2 or 6×6) divided by itself is also one. (Division by zero gives a quotient to which we cannot really attach meaning, and will be discussed in more detail in Chapter 6.) Therefore, we can conclude that any nonzero number to the zero power is always one.

We will reexamine the place value chart by placing the numeral 21,467 in Figure 5.3. It can be seen that as we move from right to left, the ascending order of each position is in powers of ten.

10^4	10^3	10^2	10^1	10^0
(10 × 10 × 10 × 10)	(10 × 10 × 10)	(10 × 10)	(10 × 1)	
ten thousands	thousands	hundreds	tens	ones
2	1	4	6	7

Figure 5.3

In the expanded form this can be written:

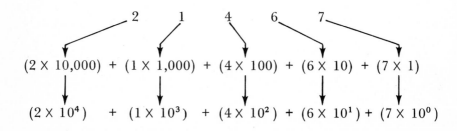

$$(2 \times 10,000) + (1 \times 1,000) + (4 \times 100) + (6 \times 10) + (7 \times 1)$$

$$(2 \times 10^4) + (1 \times 10^3) + (4 \times 10^2) + (6 \times 10^1) + (7 \times 10^0)$$

Thus, place value is a scheme for combining symbols to represent various numbers larger than the chosen base. In this scheme the value of each symbol is determined by its position in the symbolized number and a number symbol is assigned to each position within the numeral. Each digit in the numeral represents the product of the number it names and the place value assigned to its particular position.

In summary, the characteristics of a functional, efficient system of numeration are:

1. A set of basic symbols with which to represent numbers.
2. Some consistent, specific method of grouping, or a base.
3. A zero concept and its symbol.
4. A place value concept that provides a scheme for combining basic symbols to denote various numbers.

THE IMPORTANCE OF THE UNITS' (ONES') PLACE

Children and teachers have often missed or overlooked the importance of the units' place, probably because of a failure to fully understand the place value system of notation. In developing the place value system, each position to the left of the units' position derives its value in relation to the unit. For example, eighteen derives its value because it is eighteen times greater than the unit (one). With decimal fractions, the place value system is extended to the right of the units' position and, in a similar fashion, fractional numbers also derive their value in relation to the units' place. The decimal fraction .3 derives its value because it is three-tenths as great as the unit (one). Thus, the units' place is the reference point of our numeration system, since any number derives its value by its relationship to the unit (one).

Description of Our Numbers

Much of the material presented in this section and this chapter is *not* intended for presentation in the elementary classroom to elementary pupils. It is intended to help teachers and prospective teachers develop a better understanding not only of our system of numeration, but mathematics as well. If this understanding is developed, then perhaps a better view of the structure and completeness of mathematics will also come about.

In viewing the vastness of our system of numbers, one can hardly fail to be impressed. Man has not always known such a vast complicated system, however. It was only after man found a need for a larger, more complete field of numbers that these numbers were developed, usually as the result of a gradual and somewhat hesitant evolution. At times, man reached a point where certain problems were unsolvable with the numbers he had; consequently, man could either accept the problem as unsolvable, or he could attempt to develop the number tools to make a solution possible. Since the extension, or expansion, of man's concept of number was so gradual, no one person can be credited with its development. It is important to realize, however, that it was man's need for more freedom in formal calculation that brought about the expansion of the number system. This expansion had to develop in such a way that the original rules and properties of the basic numbers were maintained and preserved in the larger domain.

This section will be concerned primarily with the sets of natural numbers, integers, and rational numbers, because these are the sets of numbers used almost exclusively in the elementary school mathematics program. In the expansion of the number systems, the natural and rational numbers were among the first sets to be developed, while the set of integers was among the last. Mathematicians had long realized that something was missing in the total system, but it was not until the concept of negative numbers was fully developed that this void was filled. These sets are:

1. The set of *natural numbers*, made up of numbers that we normally use in counting. This infinite set of whole numbers begins with one and each succeeding member is one greater than the previous number.

2. The set of *integers*, composed of all the whole numbers. This infinite set not only contains the natural numbers, but the negative whole numbers, and zero as well.

3. The set of *rational numbers*, composed of all fractions that can be expressed in the form of $\frac{a}{b}$, when b is not zero. This infinite set contains not only the set of integers, but all of the common fractions as well.

4. The set of *irrational numbers*, which cannot be expressed in the form of $\frac{a}{b}$. These numbers will be presented very briefly to illustrate relationships of different sets of numbers in the total number system. This infinite set contains such numbers as $\sqrt{2}$, the value of π (pi), and others.

5. The set of *real numbers*, composed of the sets of irrational numbers and rational numbers.

NATURAL NUMBERS

This set of numbers is often referred to as the set of counting numbers because these are the numbers used in counting. These are the numbers that were first developed by man, and they are often considered the most basic of all numbers. All other numbers are usually defined in terms of natural numbers. This infinite set of whole numbers begins with one and each succeeding number is one greater than the previous number. Thus, the set of natural numbers would be N = {1, 2, 3, 4, 5, 6, 7, 8, 9, 10, 11, 12, ...} (Remember that the three dots mean that this set continues unendingly in like fashion.) Zero is not usually considered a natural number.

Early mathematicians recognized that some natural numbers possessed some interesting characteristics that others of these numbers did not possess. They found, for example, that when using as many concrete objects as indicated by the number, certain numbers of objects could be arranged into rectangular arrays (that is, having at least two rows and two columns). Other numbers of objects could not be arranged into a rectangular array no matter how the objects were arranged. Those numbers that could be arranged into a rectangular array became known as *composite numbers* because they can be expressed as the product of two or more smaller numbers. Those numbers that could not be arranged into a rectangular array were considered to be the basic building blocks for the composite numbers and they became known as *prime numbers.*

A teacher can guide his students to discover this characteristic of numbers by having them arrange various numbers of concrete objects, such as counting disks, in an attempt to see which number of objects can be placed in a rectangular array and which number cannnot. The examples in Figure 5.4 illustrate how objects can (or cannot) be arranged in a rectangular array:

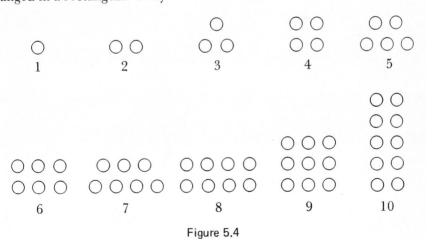

Figure 5.4

From this limited number of examples, the pattern starts to appear. The results may be tabulated in a chart, as in Figure 5.5.

Numbers that cannot be arranged in a rectangular array	Numbers that can be arranged in a rectangular array
1	4
2	6
3	8
5	9
7	10

Figure 5.5

Children should work with many more examples than those just illustrated so that the characteristics of the prime and composite numbers become more obvious. At a later time the children can be guided inductively to develop a definition of each of these numbers, using student terminology. The definitions will probably be somewhat similar to these:

1. A prime number is a number that cannot be broken or factored by any other number other than itself or one.

2. A composite number can be broken or factored into two or more prime factors.

There will be more discussion of prime and composite numbers in Chapter 8. Among the uses presented in that chapter will be a method of finding common denominators using prime numbers and prime factorization. It will be necessary for students to have more than just a casual acquaintance with prime numbers before they can be expected to work with them. Since children will regularly encounter prime and composite numbers after their second year in school, teachers from the second and third grade upward should plan to provide their students with numerous opportunities to work with prime and composite numbers.

INTEGERS

The set of integers is normally thought of as the set of whole numbers, which includes positive numbers, negative numbers, and zero. Every integer can be written, or expressed, as the difference of two natural numbers. The examples in Figure 5.6 illustrates how integers can be expressed as the difference of two natural.

Integer	Expressed as difference of two natural numbers
17	$(18 - 1), (20 - 3), (60 - 43) \ldots$
5	$(6 - 1), (10 - 5), (22 - 17) \ldots$
0	$(8 - 8), (39 - 39), (83 - 83) \ldots$
$^-4$	$(3 - 7), (9 - 13), (67 - 71) \ldots$
$^-12$	$(9 - 21), (20 - 32), (39 - 51) \ldots$

Figure 5.6

Any number that can be expressed as the difference of two natural numbers is an integer. The idea of expressing a number as the difference of two other numbers may seem a little foreign and strange at first. If we examine the first example in Figure 5.6, we note that $(18 - 1)$, $(20 - 3)$, and $(60 - 43)$ are all naming the same number. It should also be pointed out that these three examples are not the only way that 17 can be named. It can in fact be named in an infinite number of ways. This is one of the many instances in which the concept that "Numbers Have Many Names" is used in mathematics. By describing the members of the set of integers in this particular way, membership in this set is being limited to numbers with a certain specified characteristic—being a whole number. The following number line shows some of the members of the set of integers:

Some authors of textbook series have tried to create a new hybrid set of numbers that includes all of the counting numbers (natural numbers) and zero. They have labeled this set of numbers *whole numbers.* Students are left with the impression that these are the only whole numbers. When they later encounter negative numbers, they are sometimes confused, since they thought they had already met all the whole numbers. One possible solution to this would be to explain to students that because of the difficulty in learning all at once, only part of the set of whole numbers (integers) will be used in the beginning phase.

At the appropriate time the entire set of integers can then be introduced with less confusion. You have probably concluded by now that the set of natural numbers is a subset of integers.

RATIONAL NUMBERS

This set of numbers contains the set of whole numbers (integers) and the set of fractions designated as common fractions. To put it another way, every number that can be expressed as the quotient, or ratio, of two integers in the form $\frac{a}{b}$ (with a and b being integers and $b \neq 0$), is a rational number, as in Figure 5.7.

Rational Number	Expressed as quotient, or ratio, of two integers in form of $\frac{a}{b}$ ($b \neq 0$)
9	$\frac{9}{1}$, $\frac{18}{2}$, $\frac{36}{4}$, $\frac{99}{11}$, $\cdots$
$2\frac{1}{2}$	$\frac{5}{2}$, $\frac{20}{8}$, $\frac{60}{24}$, $\cdots$
0	$\frac{0}{1}$, $\frac{0}{4}$, $\frac{0}{9}$, $\frac{0}{31}$, $\cdots$
$\frac{^-1}{6}$	$\frac{^-3}{18}$, $\frac{4}{^-24}$, $\frac{^-12}{72}$, $\cdots$

Figure 5.7

Recall that all integers can be named as the difference of two natural numbers. The same concept that "Numbers Have Many Names" will be used to express rational numbers as the quotient of two integers in the form of $\frac{a}{b}$ ($b \neq 0$). By using this concept (Numbers Have Many Names) to express rational numbers, even though it may be somewhat strange to us, we are defining and describing a set of numbers that have unique characteristics. At the same time, we are limiting membership in this set to those numbers that can be expressed in fractional form. It will be remembered that we concluded that the set of natural numbers was a subset of the set of integers; we can now conclude that the set of integers is a subset of the set of rational numbers. The following number line illustration shows some of the set of rational numbers.

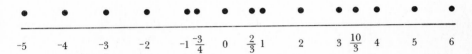

Although the elementary mathematics program is concerned primarily with natural numbers (the basic counting numbers), integers (positive and negative whole numbers and zero), and rational numbers (common fractions), the chart in Figure 5.8 is presented to help give an overall view of the relationships of these and various other number sets.

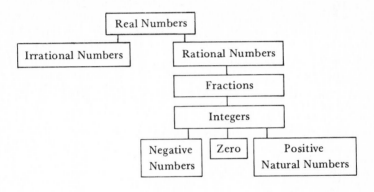

Figure 5.8

Nondecimal Numeration Systems

Nondecimal numeration systems are often referred to as bases other than ten. The importance of bases other than ten to the elementary mathematics program lies in the fact that the Hindu-Arabic system is not dependent upon base ten to be functional. That is, the laws on which this system is built make it a functional, efficient system of numeration in any base except base one. While it is true that we generally associate the Hindu-Arabic system with only base ten, this is probably because most, if not all, of our experiences with and use of this system has been in this particular base. The base that finally gains acceptance by the vast majority generally does so because of the convenience it provides in working with numbers. This was probably the reason that base ten has gained such wide acceptance and use.

The studying and working with bases other than ten should be done primarily to develop an appreciation and understanding of the system of numeration that we use, and not as an end in itself. Generally bases other than ten are not introduced until the intermediate grades or above.

It should be remembered that when we discuss bases, we are talking about a method of grouping. In any place value system of numeration, single-number symbols are chosen for the numbers up to, but not including, the base itself. A numeration system that utilizes the place value concept will have the same number of basic, single symbols as the base. To phase this another way, it will have numerically one less single *counting* symbol (because zero is not a counting symbol) than the base. To write a number as large as the base, or larger, more than one basic digit must be used.

We can find numerous examples of bases other than ten in everyday life. For example, there are sixty minutes in one hour, but there are twenty-four hours in one day, seven days in one week, fifty-two weeks in one year, and so on. Other examples related to measure include the following: there are two pints in one quart and four quarts in one gallon; five pennies in one nickel, five nickels in one quarter, and four quarters in one dollar; twelve inches in one foot, three feet in one yard, and so on. Even working with common fractions is in a sense working with bases other than ten.

If we have a collection of objects, and want to group them by tens, we might group them as follows:

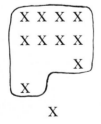
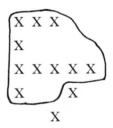

Two groups of ten and three ones equals twenty-three in base ten.

Suppose we decide to group this same collection of objects by sixes instead of tens. We might group them as follows:

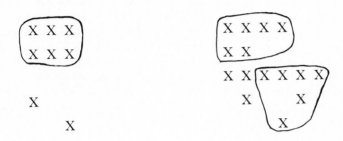

Three groups of six and five ones equals 35 in base six (this would be read: three-five-base-six). What we actually do is to count any six objects into a group and consider this as one group of six. We then count any six remaining objects into another group and consider this as another group of six. Again we count any six remaining objects into still another group of six. After counting the three groups of six, we find that there are not enough objects remaining to make another group of six, so we count the five remaining objects into groups and consider them as five groups of one. The same number of objects are in each collection, but the method of grouping was different. Therefore, 35_{base_6} is the same as (or another name for) $23_{\text{base}_{10}}$. To state this in another way, 23 and 35_6 are naming the same number—only the numerals are different because the bases are different. This is one more instance in which the idea that "Numbers Have Many Names" is used in mathematics.

The idea of naming a number in more than one way is probably not very strange now, especially if we realize that we encounter it in many different forms. To illustrate, the following examples name the same number:

$$(\text{VI}), \left(\frac{12}{2}\right), (6), (7-1), (5+1), (3 \times 2), (\text{six}), \ldots$$

The fact that numbers can have many names is usually intriguing and fascinating to students. Children usually have little difficulty or hesitancy in accepting this idea because most of them have a given name and a nickname and it intrigues them that it is also possible for numbers to have more than one name. While the idea that "Numbers Have Many Names" is less than obvious to most students, the recognition and development of this idea by students can become one of their most powerful mathematical tools. Working in a base other than ten means that we now group according to the number of the new base rather than by tens.

Mathematicians have agreed that when working in a base other than ten, they will write a small numerical subscript by the numeral to denote which base is being used. If no small numerical subscript is used by the numeral, it is understood to be base ten. The examples used previously of three groups of six and five ones would be written as 35_6, or 35_{six}.

Another look at the original collection of objects may help clarify this concept of grouping. This time we will group by threes.

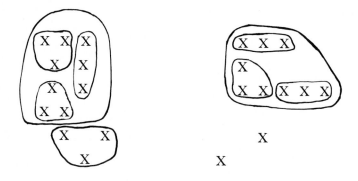

Two groups of nine, one group of three and two ones equal 212 in base 3. It will be noted that in grouping by threes, three groups of threes are regrouped into a larger group of nine. Or, to state it another way, we group first by threes, then group the three threes into groups of nines; then the groups of nines are grouped together in groups of twenty-seven, and so on. If we reexamine our base ten system, we notice that we group first by tens, then when we get a group of ten tens, we regroup this into one hundred and so on. For example, 212 and 212_3 are compared in the charts in Figure 5.9 Although the same numerals are used in both examples, the twos on the left and the ones in the middle represent entirely different values. This is because of the place value feature of our number system. If we once again compare the two charts, it can be noted that there are some similarities. Both columns on the far right of each chart represent the units, the column to the left of it represents the base being used, and the next column to the left of the base column is the base squared column, and so on. Therefore, for the

Base$_{10}$			
10^3	10^2	10^1	10^0
$(10 \times 10 \times 10)$	(10×10)		
thousands	hundreds	tens	ones
	2	1	2

Base$_3$			
3^3	3^2	3^1	3^0
$(3 \times 3 \times 3)$	(3×3)		
twenty sevens	nines	threes	ones
	2	1	2

Figure 5.9

base in which we choose to work, we can use the place value chart given in Figure 5.10.

If we are grouping by sixes and we have one group of six and no units, we would represent this as 10_{six} (meaning one group of six and no units; this would be read one-zero-base-six). Grouping by eight, 10_8 would mean one group of eight and no units. Whatever the base being used, its numerical representation would be 10 in the notation of that base. In nondecimal bases, 10 is not read as "ten" but as "one of the base," or "one-zero." This is not inconsistent with our base ten,

Base$_4$	Base$_3$	Base$_2$	Base$_1$	Base$_0$
Base to fourth power	Base cubed	Base squared	Base	Ones

Figure 5.10

because "one-zero" (10) in base $_{10}$ means one group of ten and no units.

In working with nondecimal bases, certain disadvantages become apparent. If we select a base that is small, such as base two, we must use relatively long expressions to represent small numbers. For example, 35 would be represented in base two as 100011_2. On the other hand, if we choose a base larger than ten, we must develop and use some new number symbols in addition to the ten basic symbols used in base ten.

At this point we might compare the single digits used in various bases. It will be remembered that, because of our place value scheme, the base itself can never be represented by a single digit. The numeral to represent the base will always mean one group of the base and zero ones and written as 10. Table 5.2 aids in comparing the different bases.

Table 5.2

Base	Single Digits in that base	Comments
Base 10	0, 1, 2, 3, 4, 5, 6, 7, 8, 9	Base 10 = 10 single digits
Base 2	0, 1	Base 2 = 2 single digits
Base 4	0, 1, 2, 3	Base 4 = 4 single digits
Base 5	0, 1, 2, 3, 4	Base 5 = 5 single digits
Base 6	0, 1, 2, 3, 4, 5	Base 6 = 6 single digits
Base 8	0, 1, 2, 3, 4, 5, 6, 7	Base 8 = 8 single digits

From Table 5.2, it can be seen that there are the same number of single digits as the number of the base. If we want to know how many single counting digits there are in a base, the number will always be one less than the number of the base (that is, base ten has nine single counting digits; base four has three single counting digits; base six has five single counting digits; and so on). This is true because zero is a member of each of these sets, but zero is not a counting number.

If we want to consider a base greater than ten, such as base twelve, we must create some additional single digits. According to the generalization we developed from Table 5.2, base twelve will have twelve single digits. Since our base ten has ten single digits, we will need two more single digits in addition to the ten single digits used in base ten. The two additional single digits cannot be the same as any of the other ten digits used in base ten, so mathematicians have arbitrarily agreed to use t and e as the two additional symbols. The digits used in base twelve would look like this:

$$0, 1, 2, 3, 4, 5, 6, 7, 8, 9, t, e, 10$$

Converting a Nondecimal Numeral to Base Ten

In working with various bases, it sometimes becomes desirable to change, or convert, a nondecimal numeral to its equivalent base ten numeral. For example, if we want to know what numeral in base ten is equivalent to 546_8, we would first write 546_8 in its expanded form, like this:

$$5 \quad 4 \quad 6_8$$
$$(5 \times 8^2) + (4 \times 8^1) + (6 \times 8^0)$$
$$(5 \times 64) + (4 \times 8) + (6 \times 1)$$
$$320 \quad + \quad 32 \quad + \quad 6 \quad = 358$$

$$546_8 = 358$$

When the base eight numeral is placed in the expanded form and the positional value of each digit is indicated as the product of that digit and a power of eight, then the values being worked with become base ten values. Since there is no one numeral in base eight to represent the base, when we place eight, or powers of eight, in the expanded form, we are working with base ten values.

If we want to check the earlier example and see if 100011_2 is really equivalent to 35, we would first write 100011_2 in its expanded form, like this:

$$1 \quad 0 \quad 0 \quad 0 \quad 1 \quad 1_2$$
$$(1 \times 2^5) + (0 \times 2^4) + (0 \times 2^3) + (0 \times 2^2) + (1 \times 2^1) + (1 \times 2^0)$$
$$(1 \times 32) + (0 \times 16) + (0 \times 8) + (0 \times 4) + (1 \times 2) + (1 \times 1)$$
$$32 \quad + \quad 0 \quad + \quad 0 \quad + \quad 0 \quad + \quad 2 \quad + \quad 1 \quad = 35$$

Now look at this example using still a different base:

Change 325_6 to base$_{10}$:

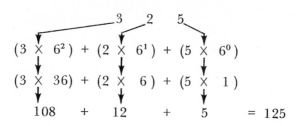

$$(3 \times 6^2) + (2 \times 6^1) + (5 \times 6^0)$$
$$(3 \times 36) + (2 \times 6) + (5 \times 1)$$
$$108 + 12 + 5 = 125$$

When 325_6 is put in expanded form, base ten values are used for the indicated product of the digit and positional values because the numeral six is a base ten value, while at the same time it indicates a place value position of base six in the expanded form of 325_6. Now look at an example of changing a base twelve numeral to base ten.

Change $3t4e_{12}$ to base$_{10}$:

$$(3 \times 12^3) + (10 \times 12^2) + (4 \times 12^1) + (11 \times 12^0)$$
$$(3 \times 1728) + (10 \times 144) + (4 \times 12) + (11 \times 1)$$
$$5184 + 1440 + 48 + 11 = 6683$$
$$3t4e_{12} = 6683$$

Converting a Base Ten Numeral to a Nondecimal Numeral

At other times it becomes desirable to convert a base ten numeral to a nondecimal numeral, which requires the use of an entirely different method of conversion. When converting a base ten numeral to another base, the goal is to determine how many groups of the new base are contained in the base ten number, then how many groups of the base squared are contained in the base ten number, and so on. In the example of 3,427, for instance, we are going to determine how many groups of the base (tens) are contained in this number, then how many groups of the base squared (hundreds) are contained in the number, and so on. Thus, we will start by dividing 3,427 by 10 to see how many groups of ten are contained in this number, then divide the resulting groups of ten by 10 again to determine how many groups of hundreds it contains, and so on until nothing remains to be divided.

$$342 \text{ R } 7 = \text{(Number of groups of ones)}$$
$$10 \overline{) 3427}$$

The resulting quotient, 342, is the number of groups of 10 contained in 3,427. The remainder of seven is the number of ones remaining since there are not enough ones to make another group of tens. The next step will be to divide the number of groups of tens, 342, by 10, which will indicate the number of groups of hundreds in 3,427, as follows:

$$34 \text{ R } 2 = \text{(Number of groups of tens)}$$
$$10 \overline{) 342} \text{ R } 7 = \text{(Number of groups of ones)}$$
$$10 \overline{) 3427}$$

This quotient, 34, indicates the number of groups of hundreds contained in 3,427 and the remainder two indicates the number of tens that are left because there are not enough tens to make another group of one hundred. Now, by dividing the number of groups of hundreds, 34, by 10, the number of groups of thousands can be found, as follows:

$$3 \text{ R } 4 = \text{(Number of groups of hundreds)}$$
$$10 \overline{) 34} \text{ R } 2 = \text{(Number of groups of tens)}$$
$$10 \overline{) 342} \text{ R } 7 = \text{(Number of groups of ones)}$$
$$10 \overline{) 3427}$$

The quotient, 3, indicates the number of groups of thousands contained in 3,427 and the remainder, 4, indicates the number of hundreds that remain because there are not enough hundreds to make another group of a thousand. By dividing once more by 10, the number of groups of ten thousands contained in 3, 427 will be determined:

$$
\begin{array}{rl}
0 \text{ R } 3 & = \text{(Number of groups of thousands)} \\
10\overline{\smash{)}3} \text{ R } 4 & = \text{(Number of groups of hundreds)} \\
10\overline{\smash{)}34} \text{ R } 2 & = \text{(Number of groups of tens)} \\
10\overline{\smash{)}342} \text{ R } 7 & = \text{(Number of groups of ones)} \\
10\overline{\smash{)}3427} &
\end{array}
$$

The quotient, 0, indicates that there are no groups of ten thousands; and the remainder, 3, indicates the number of thousands that remain. It is the remainders in each division that tell how many groups of each positional value there are. The first remainder, 7, indicates the number of ones; the second remainder, 2, the number of tens; the third remainder, 4, the number of hundreds; and the last remainder, 3, the number of thousands.

Another method of accomplishing the same thing is to start dividing by the largest multiple of the base contained in the number. If we are working with a four-place number, the first division will be by the base to the third power, the second division by the base^2, then division by the base, and finally by one. A place value chart of the base being used will be particularly helpful in determining the numbers to be used in each division. Using the same number as in the preceding illustration (3,427), this second method divides it as follows:

10^5	10^4	10^3	10^2	10^1	10^0
100000	10000	1000	100	10	1

$$
\begin{array}{rl}
1000\,\overline{\smash{)}\,\begin{array}{l}3427 \\ 3000\end{array}} & 3 \quad \text{(Number of groups of } 10^3\text{)} \\
100\,\overline{\smash{)}\,\begin{array}{l}427 \\ 400\end{array}} & 4 \quad \text{(Number of groups of } 10^2\text{)} \\
10\,\overline{\smash{)}\,\begin{array}{l}27 \\ 20\end{array}} & 2 \quad \text{(Number of groups of } 10^1\text{)} \\
1\,\overline{\smash{)}\,\begin{array}{l}7 \\ 7\end{array}} & 7 \quad \text{(Number of groups of } 10^0\text{)}
\end{array}
$$

Thus, successive division by a base (or in the case of the second method, powers of the base), results in certain remainders which are the new groups, or numerals, in another base.

In order to change 326 to base 7, it is necessary to see how many groups of 7 are contained in 326, then how many groups of 7 × 7 are contained, and so on, as in the following example:

$$
\begin{array}{lllll}
 & 0 & R & 6 & = \text{(Number of groups of } 7 \times 7) \\
7 \overline{\smash{)}\;6} & & R & 4 & = \text{(Number of groups of 7)} \\
7 \overline{\smash{)}\;46} & & R & 4 & = \text{(Number of ones)} \\
7 \overline{\smash{)}\;326} & & & &
\end{array}
$$

$$326 = 644_7$$

Another example may help clarify this procedure. This time 139 will be changed to its equivalent numeral in base 3, by the process of making successive divisions by the base, or 3.

$$
\begin{array}{lllll}
 & 0 & R & 1 & = \text{(Number of groups of } 3 \times 3 \times 3 \times 3) \\
3 \overline{\smash{)}\;1} & & R & 2 & = \text{(Number of groups of } 3 \times 3 \times 3) \\
3 \overline{\smash{)}\;5} & & R & 0 & = \text{(Number of groups of } 3 \times 3) \\
3 \overline{\smash{)}\;15} & & R & 1 & = \text{(Number of groups of 3)} \\
3 \overline{\smash{)}\;46} & & R & 1 & = \text{(Number of groups of one)} \\
3 \overline{\smash{)}\;139} & & & &
\end{array}
$$

$$139 = 12011_3$$

Using the second method to convert 326 to base 7, the first division will be by the largest multiple of the base contained in the number (in this case the largest multiple contained is 7×7 or 49). The second division will be by the base, 7, and then division by one will follow.

7^4	7^3	7^2	7^1	7^0
2401	343	49	7	1

$$
\begin{array}{r|ll}
49 & 326 & 6 = \text{(Number of groups of } 7^2 \text{)} \\
   & 294 & \\
7 & 32 & 4 = \text{(Number of groups of } 7^1 \text{)} \\
  & 29 & \\
1 & 4 & 4 = \text{(Number of groups of } 7^0 \text{)} \\
  & 4 & \\
\end{array}
$$

$$326 = 644_7$$

Converting 139 to base$_3$ by the second method would be done as follows:

3^5	3^4	3^3	3^2	3^1	3^0
243	81	27	9	3	1

$$
\begin{array}{r|ll}
81 & 139 & 1 = \text{(Number of groups of } 3^4 \text{)} \\
   & 81 & \\
27 & 58 & 2 = \text{(Number of groups of } 3^3 \text{)} \\
   & 54 & \\
9 & 4 & 0 = \text{(Number of groups of } 3^2 \text{)} \\
  & 0 & \\
3 & 4 & 1 = \text{(Number of groups of } 3^1 \text{)} \\
  & 9 & \\
1 & 1 & 1 = \text{(Number of groups of } 3^0 \text{)} \\
  & 1 & \\
\end{array}
$$

$$139 = 12011_3$$

It can now be seen that 139 equals 12011_3 using either method.

CHART OF BASES

The base indicates the number of items grouped as one set. Table 5.3 depicts the grouping and symbolization of bases ten, twelve, eight, five, three, and two.

Table 5.3

Base Ten	Base Twelve	Base Eight	Base Five	Base Three	Base Two
1	1	1	1	1	1
2	2	2	2	2	10_{two}
3	3	3	3	10_{three}	11_{two}
4	4	4	4	11_{three}	100_{two}
5	5	5	10_{five}	12_{three}	101_{two}
6	6	6	11_{five}	20_{three}	110_{two}
7	7	7	12_{five}	21_{three}	111_{two}
8	8	10_{eight}	13_{five}	22_{three}	1000_{two}
9	9	11_{eight}	14_{five}	100_{three}	1001_{two}
10	t	12_{eight}	20_{five}	101_{three}	1010_{two}
11	e	13_{eight}	21_{five}	102_{three}	1011_{two}
12	10_{twelve}	14_{eight}	22_{five}	110_{three}	1100_{two}
13	11_{twelve}	15_{eight}	23_{five}	111_{three}	1101_{two}
14	12_{twelve}	16_{eight}	24_{five}	112_{three}	1110_{two}
15	13_{twelve}	17_{eight}	30_{five}	120_{three}	1111_{two}
16	14_{twelve}	20_{eight}	31_{five}	121_{three}	10000_{two}
17	15_{twelve}	21_{eight}	32_{five}	122_{three}	10001_{two}
18	16_{twelve}	22_{eight}	33_{five}	200_{three}	10010_{two}
19	17_{twelve}	23_{eight}	34_{five}	201_{three}	10011_{two}
20	18_{twelve}	24_{eight}	40_{five}	202_{three}	10100_{two}
21	19_{twelve}	25_{eight}	41_{five}	210_{three}	10101_{two}

Extending Your Thinking

1. Using a set of symbols that you make up and a base other than ten, develop a functional, efficient numeration system.

2. Develop a functional, efficient numeration system using base one.

3. Change each of the following to its equivalent number in base ten:

a. 1110110_2 d. $6t23_{12}$

b. 4601_7 e. 1040_5

c. 3333_8 f. 110101_3

4. Change each of the following base ten numbers to the indicated base:

a. $67 = \underline{\hspace{1cm}} base_5$ d. $317 = \underline{\hspace{1cm}} base_7$

b. $229 = \underline{\hspace{1cm}} base_8$ e. $843 = \underline{\hspace{1cm}} base_{12}$

c. $121 = \underline{\hspace{1cm}} base_2$ f. $192 = \underline{\hspace{1cm}} base_3$

5. Change each of the following to the indicated base:

a. $601_8 = \underline{\hspace{1cm}} base_3$ c. $101101_2 = \underline{\hspace{1cm}} base_7$

b. $2e6_{12} = \underline{\hspace{1cm}} base_8$ d. $3210_4 = \underline{\hspace{1cm}} base_6$

6. Observe the following numeration system:

E, M, R, P, EQ, EE, EM, ER, EP, MQ, ME, . . .

a. What is the base of this system?

b. Is it a functional, efficient numeration system? Explain why you think it is, or is not, a functional, efficient system.

7. Describe the sequential steps that would be used to guide children to discover the relationship between counting to ten and counting to one hundred.

8. List five activities that would provide children with opportunities to use the concept that "Numbers Have Many Names."

9. Identify four classroom or everyday-life situations in which children would need to use a system other than base ten.

10. Describe at least three activities that would assist students in understanding and distinguishing number and numeral.

ANSWERS TO SELECTED QUESTIONS

3a. $11101110_2 = 118$

4a. $67 = 232_5$

5a. $601_8 = 112021_3$

6a. $Base_5$

b. It is a functional, efficient system because: it has a set of symbols to represent numbers (E, M, R, P, . . .); it has a base; it has a zero concept and symbol to represent zero (Q); it has a place value concept (i.e., EQ, EE, EM, ER, . . .).

Related References

Banks, J.H. *Learning and Teaching Arithmetic.* 2nd ed. Boston: Allyn & Bacon, Inc., 1964. Chap. two and three.

Dantzig, Tobias. *Number.* Garden City, N.Y.: Doubleday & Co., Inc., 1954. pp. 1-100.

Educational Research Council of Greater Cleveland. *Key Topics in Mathematics for the Primary Teacher.* Chicago: Science Research Associates, 1962. pp. 17-31.

Kramer, Klaas. *The Teaching of Elementary School Mathematics.* Boston: Allyn & Bacon, Inc., 1966. pp. 45-64.

The National Council of Teachers of Mathematics. *Topics in Mathematics for Elementary School Teachers.* 29th Yearbook. Washington, D.C.: 1964. pp. 102-30.

School Mathematics Study Group. *Studies in Mathematics.* vol. 9, rev. ed. Palo Alto, Calif.: Stanford University Press, 1963. pp. 31-41.

Swenson, Esther J. *Teaching Arithmetic to Children.* New York: Macmillan Co., Ltd., 1964. pp. 33-80.

CHAPTER 6

OPERATIONALISM AND BASIC OPERATIONS

One of the first ideas that the child acquires about number is the idea of the group or set. The child progresses through the process of counting and eventually numeration up to and including ten. After he understands the development of the number idea through ten, he is ready to use his knowledge. As he progresses beyond the idea of ten, the system will become clear, exact, and usable if he is stimulated to explore and discover and is guided toward a more mature understanding each day. The methods of working with sets, or groups, that the child learns will determine the kinds of number ideas he will be able to acquire.

If children are to acquire ways of working that are adequate, clear, and definite, they should be taught to proceed in a systematic way. Both the content and the materials used for teaching should have a structure that the child can understand; he must progress in a way which is meaningful to him. The method of study develops as the child develops more number ideas. A concept does not usually come to a pupil as a mature concept; if he understands a principle in a simple problem situation, he can build on the foundation. Each time the concept is presented, he will understand some new facet of it.

The groups, or sets, with which the child first deals are composed of objects. The objects must be moved about and handled as the child develops his concept of number. We know a great deal about concept formation, but we cannot determine the method of concept development for a particular child. The child begins with what he perceives and goes on to discriminate, and make generalizations about environmental data.

Materials which have some structure are less distracting and more facilitating to the learning process than objects which might be used at random. These materials would include cubes of equal size, number lines with equal units, and rods which are cut in correct proportions. Cubes not more than one-half inch in dimension are to be preferred over larger ones, since the child can see and handle ten blocks which cover a span of five inches more readily than ten blocks which cover a span of ten inches. Extensive research with both Spanish-speaking and English-speaking children using small cubes and the Cuisenaire rods has proven the value of using such materials. When a child can use both digital (can be counted) and analog (can be measured) materials, he is more likely to find the one which helps him most in concept development.

Concepts seem to develop out of actual use of objects in different situations. Abstractions and generalizations will proceed more readily in an environment where the child encounters a variety of stimulating experiences, provided the experiences are matched with the child's neuro-physiological development. It should be emphasized that thought arises out of actions and mathematical concepts arise out of the actions the child performs with objects, and not from the objects themselves. Authorities who have done much experimentation with children indicate that children cannot learn from mere observation. Their own actions must first build up systems of mental operations. When these become coordinated with one another, children can begin to interpret the physical world. Teachers, then, must provide appropriate materials for children and must set up situations in which children can discover relationships within the number system and can learn to solve problems which are provided to extend quantitative thinking.

There is an old saying that teachers teach as they have been taught. This may or may not be true; however, it is true that the student in a teacher education program who gains some mathematical insight through the manipulation of blocks and rods will understand the importance of providing these materials in the elementary school mathematics program.

The authors take a median position in the difference of opinion between those who say that the child must have free range through activities and experiences so that there would be little need for direct teaching, and those who believe that almost all actions with the concrete materials must be directed toward a single goal. Within this middle-ground position the child would probably engage in some trial and error in the manipulation of materials. The teacher would guide and direct through some demonstration, but more through the art of raising questions than by giving specific directions. Children would arrive at correct answers in more than one way. Answers would be questioned so that children could learn to prove and defend correct answers or could discover their own errors and correct them. The process is important, and through the use of correct processes children can learn to find correct solutions.

The child's time is valuable; it would require too much time to allow him to learn what he could with no guidance. Some children will require more guidance than others and guidance is probably most effective when handled through thought-provoking questions. Some examples of such questions are: "What does the problem tell you to do?" "Can you think of ways that you might do this?" "Can you prove that your answer is correct?"

The manipulation of objects is not merely a physical action. When the child picks up his first block, he must decide the direction he must move it in order to accomplish his purpose. Since his action can always be reversed, the child can begin to learn the reversibility of thought. If he can have some freedom of movement he will begin to see that an error can be corrected. When he learns that errors can be corrected, fear and much of the wrong kind of tension can be relieved. The child who learns a way of action and learns to proceed on his own will have the courage to try more; he has a way of solving problems and a way of correcting any errors that he may make.

The teacher need not fear that children will get into the habit of using concrete materials and will, then, depend upon them. Most children walk after crawling because they find they can get around better and they seem to find a certain exhilaration in accomplishing a new developmental task. If a person has to use a crutch for walking, he is usually glad to give it up when he finds that he is able to walk without it. If concrete materials are handled properly, children will use them when necessary and will work without them when they can do so successfully. There will probably never be one specific day when all children in a particular classroom will give up the use of concrete materials while working on a particular type of problem. One by one children will discover that their thought patterns have developed to the point that they have a mental pattern of action which is independent of the objects. The same children will go back to the use of concrete materials when a new concept is developed. The use of concrete models in teaching mathematics is not limited to the elementary school program. Few teachers, even in the most traditional programs, have attempted to teach geometry in high school without the use of models.

The teacher encourages the proper use of materials, uses inquiry to stimulate thinking, and when the time seems to be right, encourages a child to try a solution without concrete materials. He does not demand that a child give up the use of objects at a particular time. Some teachers encourage children to solve problems without objects by placing the concrete materials on a table at some distance from the child. The child has access to them, but will have to make some effort to reach them. The more alert children will often push on to a solution without using materials in preference to making an effort to get them. Many children are anxious to try for solutions without materials as soon as they have understood the process.

An excellent distinction can be made between analytic and constructive thinking. In analytical thinking the individual uses logical thought as far as he is able, so that his concepts are clearly formulated and defined before he uses them. In constructive thinking the child gets an intuitive perception of something which is not fully understood; this rather vague perception urges him on to constructive or creative effort to confirm the intuition. While it may be possible that some children think more analytically than constructively or more constructively than analytically, few individuals will use the same mode of thinking in all problem situations.

It is rather well established that opportunities for manipulating objects and for tactic exploration aid the individual in developing both spatial relationships and accurate concepts of the number system. The understandings established through the comparisons of sets of objects which help the child to understand the smaller natural numbers such as the twoness of two, will help him to make the transition to an understanding of such symbols as 9,245 or 10,129.

Counting

Many children come to school knowing how to count by rote. Many of them may have some knowledge of what the number names represent, but this is not always true. Leslie Dwight defines rote counting as written or oral expressions of a sequence of number names either memorized or in accordance with a systematic plan. Rational counting is usually considered to be a one-to-one correspondence between the elements of a set and the abstract number names. This concept is learned gradually as the child has experience in relating number names to objects.

In developing the rational counting process, the unit is of major importance, since each number is one unit more than the number which is just before it. The use of small cubes, more often referred to as blocks, of the same size when teaching counting helps greatly in the initial stages. The teacher should display one block and ask the child to take one block. The child should have a piece of construction paper or other similar material on the desk or table in front of him so that he has a logical place to display his blocks. The teacher will say, "This is one block." The child should repeat the sentence and place the block on his paper. The child will need to repeat the activitiy many times, but will not usually need to be told the number; if he has different colored blocks, he may be asked to put one red block on the paper. After the child is able to respond to the direction to place one block on the paper, he is ready to work with two blocks, and, so on until he is able to understand counting through ten.

In developing an understanding of the number two, the child would follow the example of the teacher by placing two blocks on the paper, as shown in Figure 6.1. He would then take one block and match it with the two blocks and find that the set of two is greater than, or more than, the set of one. He will also find that if he adds one block to the one block, the two sets are the same, or that two is one greater than one.

Figure 6.1

By placing the blocks in a vertical position the child can find the same information in a different way (see Fig. 6.1). If the models are made in more than one way, it may help those children who did not see it at first to see and understand the presentation, and it will probably help develop the generalization of the concept. The teacher would proceed in the same way in teaching counting through ten.

While he is using the blocks, or cubes, the teacher may also introduce the use of the number line (Fig. 6.2), at first a number line that does not have numerals. The child should understand that he is placing the blocks one at a time and is matching each block to a space

Figure 6.2

on the number line. As he moves the blocks, he counts orally. Allow all of the children in a small group to move the blocks and count aloud at the same time. The teacher can detect mistakes and can ask the group to move the blocks and count again. Mistakes must be corrected at once in order to develop correct concepts, but there is no need to point out the person who made the mistake.

After the children are able to recognize the numerals to ten, the teacher should use a number line that has the numerals on it. From the use of this number line, (Fig. 6.3) the children may learn many concepts:

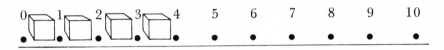

Figure 6.3

1. The numerals tell *how many* spaces.
2. The numerals tell *how many* blocks.
3. There are only nine (9) numerals plus zero (0).
4. The ten is made by using the one (1) and the zero (0).
5. Four is one greater than three, and so on.
6. To find the next number, count up one.
7. The greater the number represented on the number line, the further it is placed to the right on the number line. (Later, children may use different positions for the number line, but the horizontal position is usually used for young children.)
8. There is a reason for the sequence formerly used in rote counting.

If learning situations are well-planned and set up, the teacher will usually find that children learn not only the concept for which the situation was designed, but many other things also. The interest of the child and his intelligence are determining factors in the extent of concomitant learning. One concomitant, a desire to learn mathematics, should be provided for in each lesson plan.

After the child has learned to count, he should learn to place the blocks in groups in some order, or according to some design, so that he will be able to recognize the number of blocks in a group without counting each block. Figure 6.4 illustrates groupings that might be used.

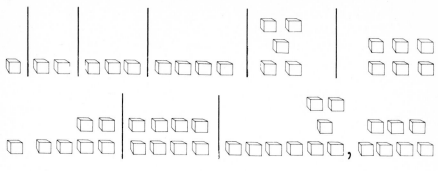

Figure 6.4

Other groupings might be used. The design for ten is fairly standard: four blocks at the bottom four rows, one block at the top.

After the child understands the counting process through ten, can make the one-to-one comparison, and can put the blocks into a design that is recognizable to him, he is ready to count beyond ten. Probably because the names do not indicate the concept, children have great difficulty in learning the meaning of eleven and twelve. Once the child understands that eleven is represented with the blocks as ten-and-one-more and by the numerals as 10 + 1 or 11, he is ready for the concept of ten-and-two-more, or twelve (see Fig. 6.5). Once he understands these two concepts, he usually proceeds quickly through an understanding of numbers through ten-and-nine-more or nineteen.

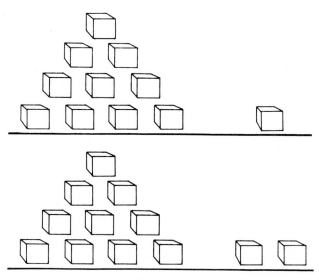

Figure 6.5

The names of the numbers thirteen through nineteen seem to help the child to understand these numbers. Careful teaching of the meaning of twelve and eleven also give the child readiness for further concepts. Children who have seen the representation of numbers with the blocks, have moved the blocks to make these representations, have matched the blocks to space on the number line and have understood that numbers can be represented by adding certain numbers to ten will usually have little trouble in forming the concepts of tens, twenties, and so on through 100. Time spent in developing the initial concepts well will save time and frustration for the child in the future. Not all children will move at the same pace in forming number concepts. Children who learn more quickly than others may go on to more advanced counting and/or may use the concepts that they have developed in problem situations. Children who learn more slowly should not be pushed on until their understandings have developed to a degree of competence that will enable them to learn more advanced concepts without frustration.

0	1	2	3	4	5	6	7	8	9	10	11
•	•	•	•	•	•	•	•	•	•	•	•

12	13	14	15	16	17	18	19	20	21	22	23
•	•	•	•	•	•	•	•	•	•	•	•

24	25	26	27	28	29	30
•	•	•	•	•	•	•

The design for ten, using blocks as well as the number line, would be used to develop the concept of twenty, thirty, and other multiples of ten.

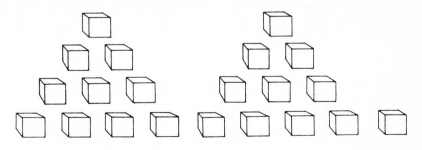

Figure 6.6

Through questioning, the child can be led to discover that two tens would be twenty and that two tens and one would be twenty-one (Fig. 6.6), just as one ten and one was eleven. Some children will make the generalization that three tens would be thirty, but some children will go on using the number line and the blocks to develop the understanding of numbers to one hundred. The child should use concrete materials as long as he needs them.

An understanding of place value is an extension of the counting process. This is a developing concept and can be developed more easily if the child has learned the true meaning of counting. There is no need for children in first grade to be working with large numbers until they have some concept of ten and twenty. If they learn this well, they will gain concepts of larger numbers at their own rates or in small groups.

In going from the use of concrete materials in understanding the meaning of counting, the teacher may use many games which make use of senses other than seeing and touching. He may also use situations in which the child is passive, not active. One such game would involve giving each child a number; one child would go outside the room and knock on the door. If he knocked three times, the child who was number three would go to open the door. All children in the group would listen and count to see whose number was indicated. Other games might involve tapping the child lightly on the head when his eyes are closed and letting him count the number of times you tapped.

Once the child has mastered the counting process using structured materials, he may begin to count things or people in the classroom and in social situations. Limits should not be set on how far he can go; the important thing is that he should be able to answer such questions as:

"Which is greater, 9 or 117?"
"Explain how you know this."
"Which is greater, 18 or 22?"
"How do you know that?"
"Which is greater, 27 or 25?"
"How do you know that?"
"Why do we place the 30 to the right of 29 on the number line?"

It is not unusual to find teachers having children do such tasks as filling blanks such as the following before children have gained the meaning of tens: 57, _____ , 59. Children are required to answer with the numeral 58 when they do not understand what 57, 58, or 59 means and often before they are able to make the numerals correctly. Not only are the children being asked to perform a meaningless task, but there is also the risk of causing retroactive inhibition in the children when they encounter similar problems at a later time.

Overview of Four Operations

In most textbooks, the addition process is the first to receive attention in a formal way. In reality the child probably begins with partition division. In an informal situation children divide many things equally among several children through the process of saying "One for you and one for you and one for me." In this way the child has placed the cookies, candies or playthings into three equal sets; this is a prenumber concept. The sets would be equal only if the total number of objects were divisible by three. The child might be able to count the objects that each child received to see if the sets were equal. He could also match the elements of the sets in a one-to-one correspondence to see if all sets were equal. If the sets are not equal, the child will be in a process of subtraction when he attempts to answer such questions as "How many more are in this set?" or "How many less are in this set?"

Division and subtraction are processes that the child needs and will use often, but the algorisms for the processes are difficult and probably should be left until the child has used the concepts on a prenumber basis for a long time and has developed a deep understanding of their meaning. Only then is he ready to attempt to make symbolizations for the processes.

Addition and multiplication are processes of putting together. The natural situations for the application of these concepts do not arise as often in the young child's social environment as do the division and subtraction situations. Thus, the teaching strategies, demonstrations, and models must be contrived more often than not, but situations can be managed in such a way as to fit the neurophysiological development of the child.

It is probably better to start a formal study of addition before the other three processes. The stage in which the child begins to simulate algorisms through the manipulation of concrete objects is very important and should precede the time when he will use numerals to make the algorisms. The order should probably be: to make the simulations with blocks, to use cards with numerals on them to symbolize algorisms, and then, to begin making the numerals. The child would probably be better off if he did not proceed to the last stage until he is in second grade. There is some evidence that a child will correct a mistake more readily if he can do so by moving a card or plastic numeral than if he needs to erase a numeral that he has written. There is a great deal of evidence to indicate that the child will make better numerals if he does not have to practice making them under a problem situation early in his experience.

ADDITION

Addition is a binary operation, it is the putting together of two sets or two numbers. The meaning of addition is not simple, however; the sums are both quantitative and qualitative. Teachers have been disappointed because children seemed to learn the addition combinations but were often helpless in using this knowledge in solving problems. Much of this difficulty may be attributed to weaknesses in the mathematics programs of the past. Little emphasis was given to the child's verbalization of what he was doing, for instance. When a child talks through a process, he appears to gain a better understanding of what he is doing and seems to be more willing to reverse a process if he sees that he has made a mistake. Nor have enough programs given attention to the qualitative phases of addition; for instance, a child is given little help in understanding the renaming process. Piaget has demonstrated this lack of understanding with wooden blocks, some white and some brown. Children had difficulty in understanding that there were more wooden blocks than brown blocks.

A third weakness of past programs was that number sentences were not understood. The child could usually understand the simple addition sentence "If you had five marbles and I gave you two marbles how many marbles would you have?" He had more difficulty with the inverted sentence, both the mathematical and English meanings. "If you had five marbles and I gave you some marbles and then you had eight marbles how many did I give you?" The wordiness of the sentence, the fact that the sum is given and that it is really a subtraction problem all add to the confusion of the child unless he has a great deal of readiness for understanding both the sentence and the mathematical situation. This understanding can be developed more easily if the child is not confronted with too much at one time. He should be able to explain a process and later tell the teacher how to make an algorism before he attempts to make the algorism himself. The child should first be concerned with many situations where he classifies objects, sorts them out according to as many classifications as possible, and learns to rename some classes: boys and girls are children, brown beads can also be wooden beads, cats and dogs can be pets. It would probably be wise to study the qualitative facets of addition on an oral and operational level only, for a long time after the child has begun to learn the quantitative phase of addition through the use of blocks, number lines and rods.

Counting indicates readiness for quantitative addition. The child adds one block to a set of blocks and counts up one to find how many blocks are in the new set, or he adds one block as he matches the blocks to the unit spaces on the number line (Fig. 6.7). Since the blocks are alike and each space on the number line is like every other space, the child has no decisions to make concerning whether or not a block or a space belongs to a certain set.

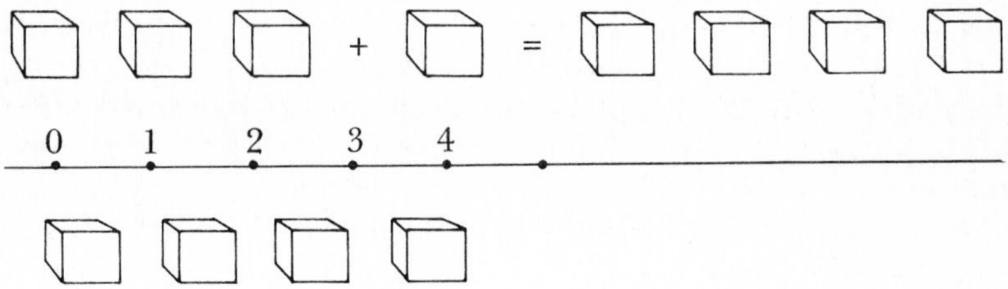

Figure 6.7

There is no renaming; the child is only concerned with the quantity, the number of elements in the new set. The child can see that one block and one block makes two blocks, two blocks and one block are three blocks, and so on. He soon learns that if one is added to a number, one more is counted to get the sum:

$1 + 1 = 2; 2 + 1 = 3; 3 + 1 = 4; 4 + 1 = 5; 5 + 1 = 6; 6 + 1 = 7; 7 + 1 = 8; 8 + 1 = 9; 9 + 1 = 10$

After the child understands the addition of one to a number, he probably understands that addition is a putting-together process. If this concept is learned through the child's manipulation of the blocks and the number line, he will soon learn that when he adds two whole numbers, the sum is a uniquely determined numeral in the set of whole numbers. In symbolizing this on the chalkboard, the teacher demonstrates how the blocks should be placed, how the blocks would be moved, and how to find the total number of blocks (the sum). When the teacher writes $2 + 3$, the child places the blocks into two sets, one set of two blocks and one set of three blocks. He then moves the blocks together and counts to find the number of blocks in the new set. The children tell the teacher and the teacher completes the symbolization of the number sentence ($2 + 3 = 5$). The children should verbalize the process in as many ways as possible. Since the teacher will usually be working with only a few children at one time, all can answer at the same time. They can be taught to keep their voices low so as not to bother other people, and because each child gets to respond every time, a single individual will feel no need to be heard above the rest. The teacher should listen for any incorrect answers and correct them, but he should not call attention to the individual who made the mistake. After the child understands that addition is putting two sets together, and that one counts to find how many in the new set, the teacher should begin to organize the content so that the child will be able to see relationships and eventually begin to retain some of the information.

Figure 6.8 shows a pattern of organization which demonstrates the commutative property of addition. Using the blocks, the child forms two sets, one with two blocks and one with three blocks, then he rearranges the same blocks with three blocks and two blocks.

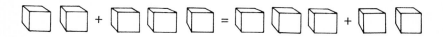

Figure 6.8

In each case he will find that he has five blocks. Using the number line, a measure equivalent to two spaces, and one equivalent to three spaces, he will find that two plus three is congruent to three plus two. He can also measure with the rods and find that the red rod (2) and the light green rod (3) are equivalent to the yellow rod. When he changes the places of the rods and puts the light green one first, he will find that the two rods are still equivalent to the yellow rod.

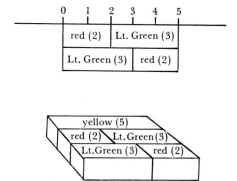

Figure 6.9

The child should soon learn the meaning of the commutative property of addition and should be able to apply the principle to the addition of other whole numbers. For example, if he has three blocks and four blocks and puts them together to form a set of seven blocks, the teacher can symbolize the equation $3 + 4 = 7$. If the teacher writes a second equation, $4 + 3 =$ _____ , the child should be able to recognize that the sum would be 7 because of the commutative property. One by one, children will begin to express the commutative property in different ways. If the teacher says, "We call this the commutative property," but makes no demands upon the children to remember the word or to spell it, he will find them beginning to say "commutative" and using the word correctly. The order in which addition combinations are presented and the way that they are symbolized will help children to see the commutative property, to know how many combinations can be made for a sum, and to see patterns.

If the child takes five blocks and sees how many different combinations he can make using the five blocks, the patterns will be something like the models shown in Figure 6.10.

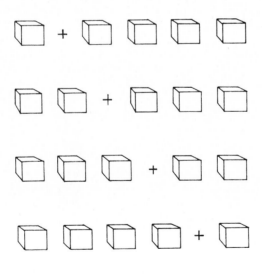

Figure 6.10

The child should talk about what he has done as he arranges the blocks until he can express his observations. Through his own observation and through seeking answers to the teacher's questions, he probably will learn most of the following:

1. If the sum is five, there are four combinations. The child will finally learn, but probably not in the first grade, that the number of combinations is one less than the cardinal number of the sum.

2. As the number on the left (the first number) increases, the one on the right decreases. The child may say that as the first one goes up the second one will come down. Children should eventually be able to explain this process and tell why it works the way it does (see Fig. 6.10).

If children have not been taught to use Cuisenaire rods (see Fig. 6.11), they should be taught at this time. The unit rod (white) is very important in the child's understanding of the other rods. The child should measure each rod using the unit rod as a measure. The red rod is called the "two rod" because it takes two unit (white) rods to be equivalent to the red rod; it takes ten unit rods to be equivalent to the orange rod. The child should work with measuring the rods until he understands what each rod equals. He may not remember a specific length, but he will know how to measure to find a length or equivalence.

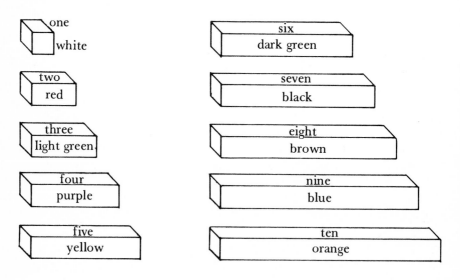

Figure 6.11

The program that should be taught using the rods is one built on the total development of the child. Programs that call for early and difficult symbolization should be discouraged. The master teacher can use the rods to great advantage in a prenumber program, finding relationships such as less than, greater than, equal, and equivalent. The rods are very valuable in teaching addition. The child can see and feel the rods as he puts them together to simulate a sum as shown in Figure 6.12.

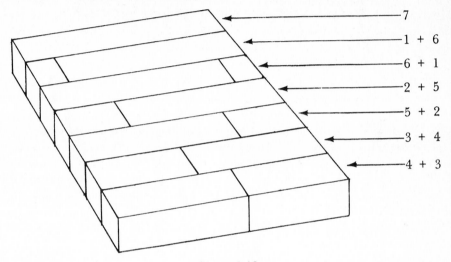

Figure 6.12

Children will make the patterns and will eventually be able to cover the pattern and give the combinations, while learning to use a logical order in making them. A child must learn to recognize when he has completed a pattern. If the sum were an odd number (Fig. 6.12), he would find himself repeating a combination that he had already used. If the sum were an even number (Fig. 6.13), he would end with a double.

The children should learn the combinations up to and including the sum of ten. They will learn through their own operations with the digital and analog materials, rather than by watching demonstrations. Each child should also talk about what he has done and explain each step in his own words. All of these activities should take place before the child writes any algorisms for himself: he tells the teacher how to symbolize the combinations. Only after he has learned to make all of his numerals without difficulty should he be expected to write algorisms. He will probably learn more mathematics if he did not write the algorisms until his second year in school.

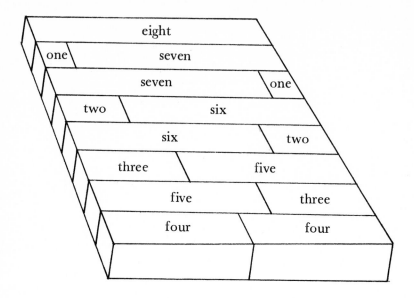

Figure 6.13

A child should not be required to copy numerals from the chalk-board before he is eight or nine years old. His eyes do not mature before that time and he does not have the memory span to look at a number and then write it on his paper without looking back at the chalkboard. Focusing for distant work, reading the numerals on the board, and then focusing for the close work of writing the numeral is very hard on a child's eyes. Some children will become nauseated if the exercise is long. Children often copy wrong because their eyes do not go back to the proper spot on the board. The self-esteem of the student decreases when he hears his teacher shout, "You can't even copy correctly." Unfortunately, the child cannot explain that he is having difficulty because the teacher is expecting him to perform a task that he is not yet physically equipped to do. Also, children often develop poor writing techniques, such as reversing numerals when they are required to write too early.

When the child can see the symbols that the teacher has made, he is free to make generalizations and can become more involved in the solution of problems. For instance, the teacher might diagram sums on the chalkboard as shown in Figure 6.14.

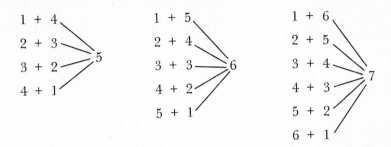

Figure 6.14

Some of the observations that children would make would probably be:

1. There are more combinations for big numbers.
2. With six or an eight, the middle combination is a double.
3. If the sum is even, the middle combination is a double.
4. There is always one less combination than the sum used.
5. If the sum is odd, one number is odd and one is even.
6. If the sum is even, the addends are alike, both odd or both even.

One specific aid to children in learning the commutative law is for the teacher to use an overhead projector and form the pattern (using cubes) for addition of two numbers on a transparent sheet that is not fastened to a roll.

The teacher might ask "How many blocks do I have?" The teacher then turns the sheet so that the set of three blocks is placed first.

The teacher would ask "How many blocks do I have now?" The child would then form the two patterns on a piece of paper placed on his desk; he would make a one-to-one correspondence of the two sets of blocks until he realizes that the sets are equal. He will soon realize that he needs to make only one pattern and can turn the paper to make the other pattern. After he has made the patterns using many set of addends (sums not exceeding ten), he should be asked to state what he has learned. Children will make the statement of the commutative property in many different ways. If the statement is correct, it should be accepted even though it may be stated in a very immature way. Refinement of definition will progress as the child learns more about a property.

The teacher can use the Cuisenaire or other similar rods to develop an understanding of the commutative property. If he took one rod, such as the seven rod shown in Figure 6.15, and found two rods that if put together would be equal the *length* of the seven rod, the children can discover that it makes no difference which rod is placed first. The teacher should symbolize this for pupils as the children tell him what to write: 3 + 4 = 7 or 4 + 3 = 7. The teacher should say, "equal in length," or should use the word, "congruent."

The property of closure can be made more meaningful using rods. The child sees that when he places a units rod with the six rod, it is always congruent to the seven rod (Fig. 6.15). If the teacher symbolizes

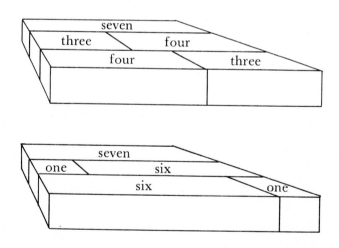

Figure 6.15

it in the manner shown in Figure 6.14, the child will see both closure and the commutative property. Each of the six combinations is equal to 7, thus illustrating the law of closure. It makes no difference in which order the rods are placed; thus, the child sees that the commutative property is true. Strips of paper of proportionate lengths and a number line may be used in the same manner as the rods.

As children progress (probably by second or third grade), the teacher can begin to ask questions such as, "Are the addends odd or even?" When the children discover that when the sum is odd, one addend is odd and one is even, the teacher can go on to question them about a sum that is an even number. Through working with many problems, the children can generalize that addends must be the same (two odd numbers or two even numbers) when the sum is an even number. Children can make use of this generalization when presented with a problem such as the following:

$$\begin{array}{ll} & \text{1. } 567 \\ \text{Given the sum } \begin{array}{r} 245 \\ +324 \\ \hline \end{array}, \text{ circle the correct answer: } & \text{2. } 568 \\ & \text{3. } 569 \end{array}$$

The child knows at once that answer number two is not correct. Since he sees that the answers are the same except for the units place, he will only have to add the units in order to know that answer number three is correct.

The teacher should spend more time in developing generalizations on the part of the children than in helping them memorize the addition facts. Children will remember combinations better if they use the concrete materials and talk about possible answers than if they are under pressure to memorize.

By the time the student has learned the addition combinations through the sum of ten, he will have some understanding of what addition means. He should have learned something of the qualitative meaning of addition so that he can use his quantitative knowledge in solving problems about his environment. He will have learned that you add like quantities, but that renaming is often possible so that seemingly unlike quantities may be put into the same category. Children who have had a background of experience with the manipulation of concrete materials will have some memory of sums and they will also have a way of finding answers in case memory fails them.

By the time a child learns the combinations for sums through ten (not all will reach this goal at the same time, probably not even in the same school year) he should understand:

1. If zero is added to a number, the result is the same number.
2. If one is added to a number, count up one to find the sum.
3. Only two numbers can be added at one time and it makes no difference which is placed first.
4. If two whole numbers are added, the sum will be a whole number.
5. If there are more than two numbers, any two of them can be added first. This is called the associative property:

$$1 + 2 + 4 = (1 + 2) + 4 = 3 + 4 = 7$$
$$(1 + 4) + 2 = 5 + 2 = 7$$
$$(2 + 4) + 1 = 6 + 1 = 7$$

When numerals are used, only two can be added at the same time, and the sum is the same no matter which two are associated (added together) first. This can be represented with rods, as shown in Figure 6.16.

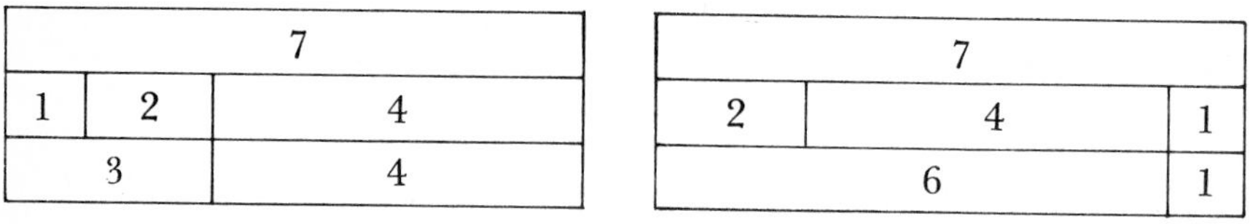

Figure 6.16

If blocks or cubes are used, the following order would be followed:

is the same as

If the blocks were rearranged to place the two first, it would look like this:

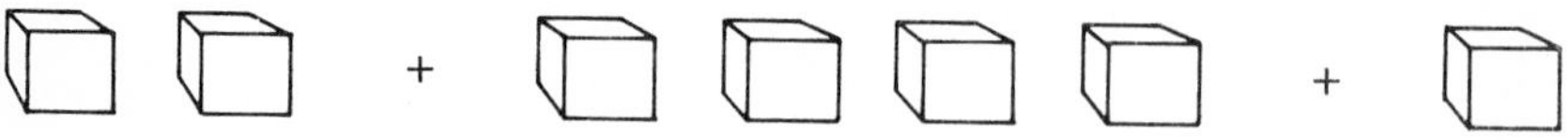

is the same as

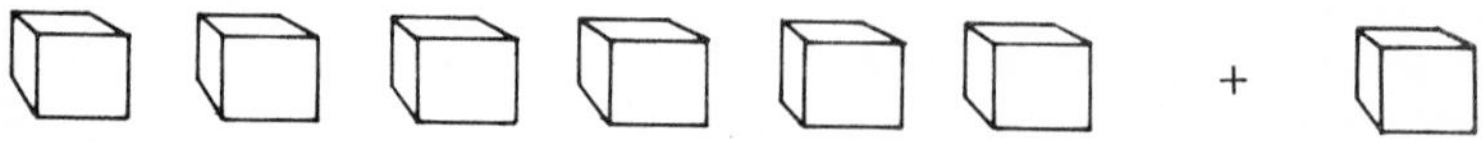

This would be written: $(2 + 4) + 1 = 6 + 1 = 7$

There are six combinations that could be made with these three rods, and each would equal 7 when added. Figure 6.17 shows the pattern of these combinations, with the written symbols for each.

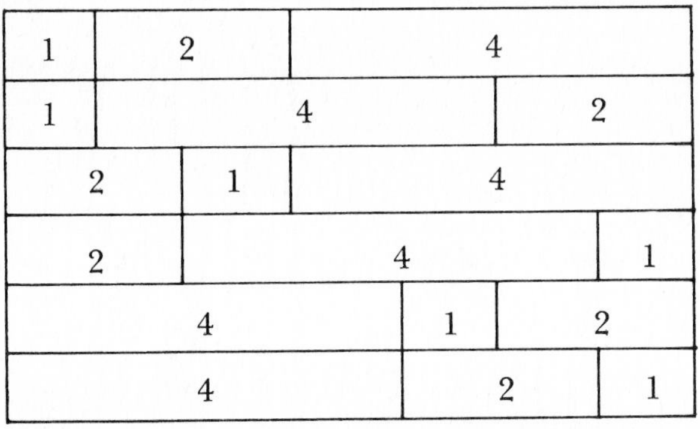

1	2	4		
1	4		2	
2	1	4		
2	4			1
4		1	2	
4		2		1

$(1 + 2) + 4 = 7$
$(1 + 4) + 2 = 7$
$(2 + 1) + 4 = 7$
$(2 + 4) + 1 = 7$
$(4 + 1) + 2 = 7$
$(4 + 2) + 1 = 7$

Figure 6.17

Each whole number has many names. The number nine can be represented as $(8 + 1)$, $(2 + 7)$, $(3 + 6)$, $(4 + 5)$ or the commutative for any of these. This is very convenient when the child has difficulty in adding certain addends as well as when the sum is more than ten. The addition with sums above ten should not be difficult, because the child learned the meaning of ten during the counting process and because he already knows the combinations to ten. For instance, if the problem is $8 + 7 + 4$, the child would know that if he adds 2 to 8, he would have ten. He also knows that another name for 7 is $(2 + 5)$. He uses this knowledge and writes $8 + (2 + 5) + 4 = (8 + 2) + 5 + 4 = 10 + 9$ or 19. In this way the child is relieved of the responsibility of memorizing combinations with sums above ten. He should be called upon to use the combinations with sums through ten often, and in this way will reinforce his knowledge. Many second-grade children are able to use this process.

Children often have great difficulty in adding columns of numbers that are symbolized vertically. For instance, with Figure 6.18,

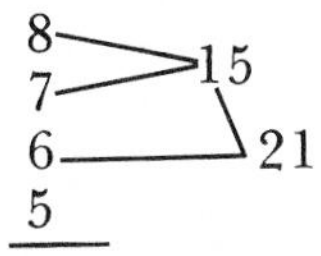

Figure 6.18

if a child can add eight and seven and get fifteen he would still have the problem of adding a number (6) that he can see to a number (15) that he cannot see. The sum goes into the next decade, making it difficult for him to hold all of the ideas in his head. If he gets the sum of 21, he has not finished, he must add the 5 to 21. It would probably be better to symbolize the problem horizontally so he could rename some of the addends:

$$(8 + 7) + (6 + 5) = 8 + (2 + 5) + 6 + (4 + 1) =$$
$$(8 + 2) + 5 + (6 + 4) + 1 = 10 + 10 + (5 + 1) = 20 + 6 = 26.$$

This may appear to take too much time, but this is a case of making haste slowly. The child who understands this process will often be able to do much of the work in his head once he has become familiar with the process. With $8 + 7 + 6 + 5$ vertically, he knows that $8 + 2 = 10$, and places a one in the ten's column. Since he has used a two out of the seven, he has five left. That five and the five in the problem can be combined to make another ten; therefore, he places another one in the ten's column. He has six units left, which will be brought down in the unit's place in the sum. One ten added to one ten would be two tens. The sum is 26. Each child will choose his own way of working. This method should not be used until after children are experienced in renaming numbers that are symbolized horizontally. We must remember that adults who add long columns of numbers use adding machines; therefore, the understanding of the process is the most important thing to the child.

The additive inverse, another property of addition, is explained in Chapter 13. This concept, however, would not be taught in the primary grades.

If the child understands that we add tens just as we add units and add hundreds just as we add tens and units, he can begin to add larger numbers as soon as he has an understanding of place value. Care should be taken at first to be sure that the sums in any column do not extend beyond ten. If the child adds 23 + 45, he might symbolize it vertically as in the example.

$$\begin{array}{r} 23 \\ 45 \\ \hline 68 \end{array}$$

He would add units to units and get eight units. He would add tens to tens and get six tens. However, he might symbolize it as

$$(20 + 3) + (40 + 5) = (20 + 40) + (3 + 5) = 60 + 8 = 68.$$

The addition of larger numbers can be understoood through expanded notation, as in the following example:

$$234 = 2 \text{ hundreds} + 3 \text{ tens} + 4 \text{ units}$$
$$+352 = 3 \text{ hundreds} + 5 \text{ tens} + 2 \text{ units}$$
$$5 \text{ hundreds} + 8 \text{ tens} + 6 \text{ units} = 586$$

This algorism would be used until the child understands that units are added to units, tens are added to tens, and hundreds are added to hundreds. Then it could be shortened to the following form:

$$234 = 200 + 30 + 4$$
$$+352 = 300 + 50 + 2$$
$$500 + 80 + 6 = 586$$

In this process the child not only employs the simple addition combinations that he knows, but develops a real knowledge of place value.

The next step would be to add numbers where the sums in the first two columns would be more than ten.

$$285 = 2 \text{ hundreds} + \qquad 8 \quad \text{tens} + \qquad 5 \text{ units}$$
$$+ 176 = 1 \text{ hundreds} + \qquad 7 \quad \text{tens} + \qquad 6 \text{ units}$$
$$3 \text{ hundreds} + (10 + 5) \text{ tens} + (10 + 1) \text{ units}$$
$$= \quad 300 \quad + (100 + 50) \quad + \quad (10 + 1)$$
$$= \quad (300 + 100) + \quad (50 + 10) \quad + 1$$
$$= \quad 400 \quad + \quad 60 \quad + 1 = 461$$

Teachers sometimes fear that children will continue using this longer form of addition. However, children who are successful with the process will soon begin to seek shorter ways of working. They will first proceed to the form shown below, recognizing that the one is symbolized in units' place, the one placed above the 8 represents one ten, and the one placed above the 2 represents one hundred. They will probably move on to addition without placing the one above the ten's column and the one above the hundred's column.

$$\begin{array}{r} 285 \\ +176 \\ \hline 461 \end{array}$$

After children have worked in this way, they can perform column addition more easily.

When adding, it is usually easier for children to add if numerals are placed in a horizontal position. Because there is still a demand for the skill, children will also need to be able to understand vertical numeration.

After the concept of addition is understood in its simplest form, a child should begin working problems using addition. As his grasp of the concept increases, the problems should be more complex, so that as he learns the process, he learns how to work more and more difficult problems using addition.

SUBTRACTION

The process of subtraction is often defined as the opposite of addition. Because this is true, many teachers start teaching subtraction as soon as children begin the process of putting sets together in addition. This practice often confuses the children and they learn neither process well. When two similar processes are taught at or near the same time, the learning of one process interferes with the learning of the other process. This psychological paradigm is known as *retroactive inhibition* and/or proactive inhibition. One of the ways of cutting down on such interference is to teach one process well before beginning the other. The child, then, should learn the sums through ten before he begins a formal study of subtraction.

Subtraction is not a simple concept. The questions of subtraction take many forms: "How many are left?" "What is the remainder?" "How much more is this one?" "How much less is this one?" "Which set is greater?" "Which set is least?" "How many more will you need?"

Two ways for a child to find the answer to 7 – 4 = _____ are shown in Figure 6.19. He can count blocks away from a group by moving four

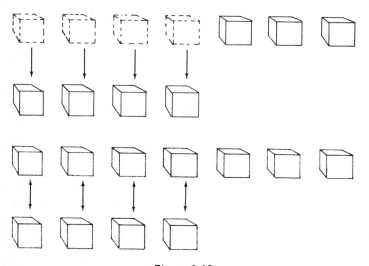

Figure 6.19

blocks and counting the blocks that remain: one, two, three. The remainder is three. Or he can take blocks to represent two sets and match them in one-to-one correspondence to find which set is greater, which set is less, how much greater, and how much less. Seven blocks would be three greater than four blocks. The child should practice this concept using different-sized sets of blocks before he goes to the concept of four is three less than seven.

The individualized approach is necessary here; few children will master the concept of *greater than* at the same time. Concept mastery is tested by moving among the children as they work and asking such questions as: "Would a set of eight blocks be greater than a set of ten blocks?" The statement of this question is more difficult for the child than a question such as: "Is five greater than three?" in which the larger set is named first.

The child needs concrete material to use when he is beginning to learn the concept of subtraction. If left with nothing except his fingers to count, he will use them, but gains an understanding of the process more quickly if he has objects to use that are not attached to his body. Cubes have the advantage of all having the same size and when the child compares two groups he is matching a block to a block of the same size. It is very difficult for a child to make a one-to-one comparison of four and six using his fingers, even though he has ten fingers; it is hard to compare a finger on one hand with another finger on the same hand.

Cuisenaire rods are also valuable. The blocks are used as a digital material and are counted away or compared one-to-one. The rods can be used as an analog material and differences measured. If at all possible, each child should have both experiences, thus using the counting process and the measuring process. The rods can be used as shown in Figure 6.20, and each teacher or child will find additional ways of using them.

Take a two rod (red) and place a units rod (white) *on top* of it. "Which is greater?" Find a rod that fills the space. Another white rod will fill the space. Lift the first white rod to show that you are taking it away; a white rod, or a one, remains. Placing the rods to be subtracted on top will help the child to differentiate between subtraction and the process of addition, in which he placed rods beside the other rods.

Take a light green rod (three) and place a white rod (one) on top of it. Find a rod that will fit the space that remains. The red rod (two) will fit the space. Lift the white rod to show that when you take the one away two remains.

Take a light green rod (three) and place a red rod (two) on top of it. Find a rod that will fit the space. The white rod will fit the space. Lift

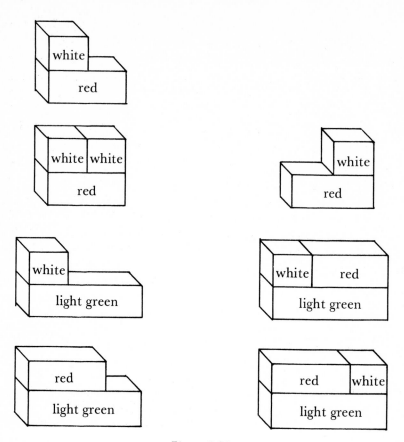

Figure 6.20

the red rod to show that you are taking it away. The white rod remains. If you take a two away from three, the remainder is one.

Only when the child understands the concept of subtraction from his experiences with cubes and/or rods is he ready for the symbolization: 3 − 2 = 1, 3 − 1 = 2, etc. This can then be related to what the child already knows about addition: (1 + 2 = 3), (2 + 1 = 3). If you subtract either addend from the sum, the other addend remains.

Continue the use of the rods as long as the child needs them in order to understand the process of subtraction. He should not need to go all the way through the use of the rods to ten. At some point he should be able to reason that since 5 + 3 = 8, you can take five away from eight and the remainder will be three, or you can take three away from eight and the remainder will be five.

A good practice exercise is for the teacher to place the diagram shown in Figure 6.21 on the board to be used by a small group of children. Ask the children to decide what they would subtract from eight in order to get the remainders that are represented by the numerals in the right- (or left) hand column. The question would be, "What would I subtract from eight in order to get a remainder of seven?" The children should all be allowed to answer at the same time, thus reinforcing the correct response. If there is a wrong answer from some member of the group, the teacher responds with the suggestion that they look at it again and places a marker under the (1 + 7) so that the children can see the numerals and not be confused by other pairs of numerals. The children do not write the numerals. This is an exercise in thinking and verbal expression of ideas gained from the stimulus of the diagram on the board. The children are not required to adjust their eyes from the far vision of reading from the board to the near vision required to write on their papers. They may need to write examples later, but they do not copy from the board.

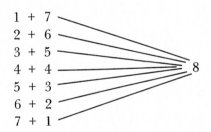

Figure 6.21

After this exercise, the children might demonstrate subtraction from eight by the use of the rods and might write what they have demonstrated and expressed verbally. Understanding is the important thing and it won't come for all children at the same time.

Once the child understands the relationship of addition to subtraction, and the relationship of subtraction to addition, he will not need to memorize answers for subtraction; he will know they are the reverse of addition.

The subtraction algorism most difficult for the child to understand is the one that asks the question, "How many more do I need?" Teachers often teach this as the missing addend with no explanation of how it is to be used. In a problem that states that John wants to buy a ball which costs seven dollars and he has only three dollars and asks how much more he needs, the child is often confused. He is even more confused if the problem is stated in such a way that John had three dollars and asks how much money his mother would need to give him so that he could buy a ball that costs seven dollars. The word *give* is a cue word for addition. If the child has been taught that if you subtract one addend from the sum the other addend remains, he will have no difficulty. The algorism could be simply written as 7 − 4 = 3. Later the child could write 4 + _____ = 7 and decide what he would need to add to 4 in order to get 7.

The inverse of addition concept of subtraction can be taught by the use of a number line and the idea of direction (Fig. 6.22).

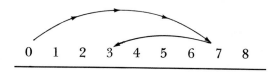

$$0 \quad 1 \quad 2 \quad 3 \quad 4 \quad 5 \quad 6 \quad 7 \quad 8$$

Figure 6.22

The child must go through all of the steps of subtraction for himself. He may need some direction, and he can probably profit from questions which lead him to generalize that if you know the addition combinations to ten, you already know the answers to subtraction problems.

The process of regrouping can be used to advantage for subtraction of larger numbers. A problem such as (12 − 8) may be rewritten as (10 + 2 − 8), which can then be regrouped as (10 − 8) + 2 = 2 + 2 = 4. A similar problem, (17 − 9) may be rewritten as (10 − 9 + 7) = 1 + 7 = 8.

The regrouping method may be used on larger problems to avoid the use of the term "borrowing," which has usually been hard for children to understand. The following problem using expanded notation where no regrouping is necessary would be excellent readiness for this concept:

$$
\begin{array}{r}
279 = 200 + 70 + 9 \\
-136 = -(100 + 30 + 6) \\
\hline
100 + 40 + 3 = 143
\end{array}
$$

The child should work many problems like the one above before he undertakes one in which regrouping must take place. A problem such as 453 – 136 may be written in expanded notation:

$$400 + 50 + 3$$
$$-(100 + 30 + 6)$$

Since six units cannot be subtracted from three units, it will be necessary to take one ten unit from 50 and add it to 3:

$$400 + 40 + (10+3)$$
$$-(100 + 30 + 6)$$

The child will recognize that the numerals in unit places may be rewritten as $10 - 6 + 3 = 4 + 3 = 7$. Since 30 can be subtracted from 40, no further regrouping will be necessary:

$$400 + 40 + (10+3)$$
$$-(100 + 30 + 6)$$
$$\overline{300 + 10 + 7 \qquad = 317}$$

A more difficult problem would be one in which regrouping would be necessary in the units' place and in the tens' place. A problem such as 632 – 248 could be regrouped first to take care of the units:

$$632 = \quad 600 + 30 + 2 = \quad 600 + 20 + 12$$
$$-248 = -(200 + 40 + 8) = -(200 + 40 + \quad 8)$$

Since 40 cannot be subtracted from 20, more regrouping will be necessary. The problem would be written:

$$632 = \quad 500 + 120 + 12$$
$$-248 = -(200 + \quad 40 + \quad 8)$$
$$\overline{300 + \quad 80 + \quad 4 = 384}$$

The child should understand the regrouping and renaming of numbers. A ten is taken from the group of three tens and is renamed as ten units and added to the two units. One hundred is taken from the group of six hundreds and is renamed as ten tens and added to the two tens to make 120.

The child should use this expanded notation and regrouping until he understands the process well. The teacher should probably not teach the shorter form, but students will go to it as soon as they can work it out for themselves.

Children should have much practice in working stated problems involving subtraction in many forms. The authors have been very successful with presenting the problem (involving situations that concern the child) orally and asking the child to tell what process he would use, not what answer he would get. This serves several purposes:

1. It takes the emphasis away from the answer and places it on the process.

2. The child can have success more quickly when he has less to think about.

3. The teacher leads children to make the algorisms gradually.

4. If the teacher is to complete the problem, children do the thinking, the teacher writes what the children tell him to write.

5. The child builds a backlog of success before he is left on his own to attack the stated problem, the number sentence, and correct answers.

(The process of subtraction where the remainder is a negative number or where a negative number is subtracted from another number is treated in Chap. 13.)

The child will not master all of the facets of subtraction at one time. If the teacher organizes the content so as to teach one concept at a time, teaches for the individual's way of learning, and paces the introduction of new concepts to correspond with the achievement of the child, subtraction should be practically painless for the child and he should be able to use the process in problem-solving with little difficulty.

MULTIPLICATION

Teachers often describe multiplication as a short way of adding. They often forget to mention that this definition is applicable only when the sets that are being added are equal sets. The process of multiplication resembles addition in two ways: (1) they are both ways of putting sets or groups together, and (2) a majority of the principles or laws of addition hold good for multiplication also.

One of the first steps in teaching multiplication is to demonstrate to the learner the patterns in which the digital and analog materials can be arranged to illustrate the multiplication process. The teacher illustrates the basic concept that the horizontal line in the array represents the number of elements in the set. Figure 6.23a shows one (1) set with four elements. Using numerals it would be symbolized $1 \times 4 = 4$. The second array, Figure 6.23b, represents two sets with four elements each and would be symbolized $2 \times 4 = 8$.

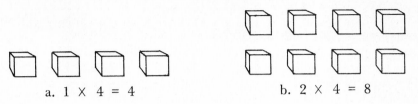

a. 1 X 4 = 4   b. 2 X 4 = 8

Figure 6.23

(Do not teach the commutative property at the same time that you are introducing the concept of multiple equal sets.) In this instance the elements of the set are equal units. The process of multiplying 2 X 4 can be represented accurately on a number line:

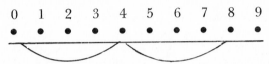

Multiplication may be introduced early in the second grade *for many children* when the children are able to count by twos. They can make the arrays with blocks (Fig. 6.24) to match the symbolizations 1 X, 2, 2 X 2, etc., made by the teacher. Later they will learn to write it for themselves.

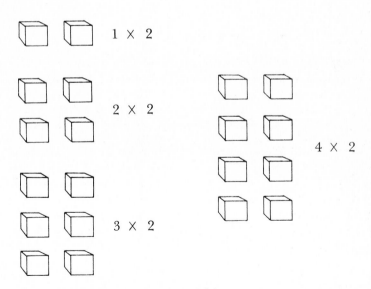

Figure 6.24

The number line is also a good material to use for teaching multiplication. Since the units are the same size on the number line, children can see that the unit is the important thing. It may be short on one number line and long on another number line, but 4 × 2 is 8 units on any number line:

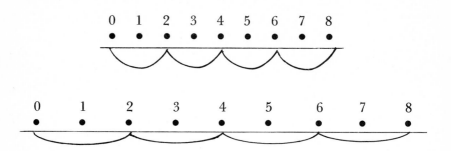

The rods as well as the blocks and number line serve as excellent materials to use in developing the concept of multiplication. Several rods of one kind can simulate equal sets. The child can arrange the desired number of rods either horizontally or vertically and can measure to find the product using the ten rod as a base.

A set of three red rods (3 × 2) can be measured by the dark green (6) rod. In this way the child can see the three sets of two (three red rods) and the measure. He can feel the three sets of two as he seeks to find the proper rod to use as a measure. He will find that the six rod will be equal in length to the three red (2) rods.

We sometimes place the child's hands under what we call a blind box. A small box (a shoe box is suitable) is placed on a table. A hole just large enough for the child's hands to fit into it has been cut into one end of the box. Several red rods, a yellow, dark green, black, and a brown rod are placed under the box. The problem for the child is to form a line of three red rods and find the correct measure. Children usually like this activity and are always anxious to lift the box to see the models they have made. The activity can be repeated many times using different sets. As the child becomes more adept, the number of rods may be increased. The measurement of sets of rods would become more difficult as the child begins to put sets together that have a product greater than ten. For instance, six red rods (6 X 2) would be measured by the orange rod and a red rod (10 + 2). This serves as an excellent way to practice a skill that the child has been able to see but under these conditions can only feel. The child should check each time to see the pattern and the measure. This makes an excellent activity for team learning; two children can work together and make any variations in the process that they would like to make.

The rods have been good materials for blind children to use in all four of the basic processes of addition, subtraction, multiplication, and division. The authors have been successful in using these rods with children from various backgrounds. The child who has a language difficulty seems to be able to learn readily using the rods. Many studies with rods have been made with children of different ethnic groups, and teachers have reported remarkable success with children from all groups.

As used by the authors the color of the rods is used only as a convenience in identifying a particular rod. In cases where similar, neutral rods have been used, children were able to work almost as fast and as accurately as with colored rods. The child learns the relative length of the rods both by sight and by feel. When the child is able to simulate an algorism with the rods, he is able to work with concepts at an earlier age and is able to work with more difficult concepts.

Children should continue making the arrays and working with the number line and the rods until they understand the process through (9 X 2 = 18). Though some will remember the products more readily than others, the important thing is understanding the process. Memory will come later as they use the products in problem-solving.

Many mathematics text authors and teachers go directly to multiplying sets of three as next in order. It would probably be better for the child if he could go to multiplying sets of five, since many children have already learned to count: five, ten, fifteen, twenty, and on. On the number line it looks like this:

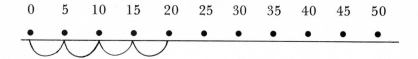

The child can see a pattern: 5, 10, 15, 20, ... He may be able to recognize that for the uneven number of sets the product ends in five, and for the even number of sets the product ends in zero:

$$1 \times 5 = 5, 2 \times 5 = 10, 3 \times 5 = 15, 4 \times 5 = 20, \text{etc.}$$

This will probably be the easiest one to remember. It may be difficult to make sure that he understands the process before he has it memorized.

The next concept to teach is that one multiplied by a set gives you that set, or one multiplied by a number gives that number. This is illustrated in Figure 6.25.

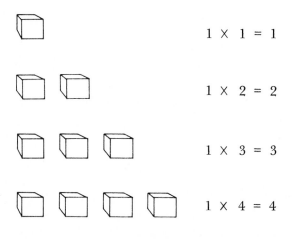

Figure 6.25

It is sometimes known as the law of one in multiplication or the identity law of multiplication. Once the child understands these concepts, he is ready to look at a matrix (Fig. 6.26) that is partially filled in.

X	0	1	2	3	4	5	6	7	8	9
0										
1		1	2	3	4	5	6	7	8	9
2		2	4	6	8	10	12	14	16	18
3		3	6			15				
4		4	8			20				
5		5	10	15	20	25	30	35	40	45
6		6	12			30				
7		7	14			35				
8		8	16			40				
9		9	18			45				

Figure 6.26

The child will probably recognize that the matrix in Figure 6.26 is much like number lines that have been drawn vertically and horizontally. Before the end of second grade, some children will be able to work with a number line and recognize that when you work with sets of four, you double the set of two:

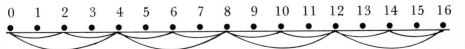

By finding the products (8 × 2 = 16) and (4 × 4 = 16) on the number line, he can fill in the four columns on the matrix or read it as the teacher fills it in. If children are not ready for this concept in second grade, it is, of course, better to wait until third grade. At any rate, children entering third grade will need to relearn the concept. The third-grade teacher would do well to reteach multiplication using blocks, rods, and number lines. Children should recall this readily if they understood the concept when it was taught in the second grade. If they did not understand it then, they now have another opportunity. The spaced learning time should permit children to get a deeper insight into the process. Where relationships such as between sets of two and sets of four are understood, the children will develop understanding more quickly.

At third-grade level, children are usually ready to begin counting by threes. They should begin as shown in Figure 6.27 by making the arrays with blocks and/or making the patterns with Cuisenaire rods. Number lines should also be used. In this way, the children will develop the meaning of equal sets of three in multiplication. Then they will be ready to move on to sets of fours. From the models and number lines, it can be seen that threes are doubled to get the products for sixes, and fours are doubled to get the products for eights. This double effect will show up again in the matrix (Fig. 6.28) when the children filled in the products they had learned.

The children will begin to understand that there is a structure to multiplication. The products are not just independent numbers to be remembered. By now they can fill in most of the matrix; Figure 6.29 shows on one matrix all the products illustrated in Figures 6.26 and 6.28. The nine pattern has been established and they will want to complete it using the pattern of increasing the tens' column by one and decreasing the units' column by one to fill the remaining spaces.

If the matrices can be made on an identical scale on transparencies for the overhead projector, they can be demonstrated with more clarity by using them singly at first and as overlays to demonstrate more complex patterns and/or concepts. It may take the better part of the year to develop the matrix as shown in Figure 6.30.

The teacher should space the work on multiplication with other things, coming back to it at intervals to develop concepts further and to

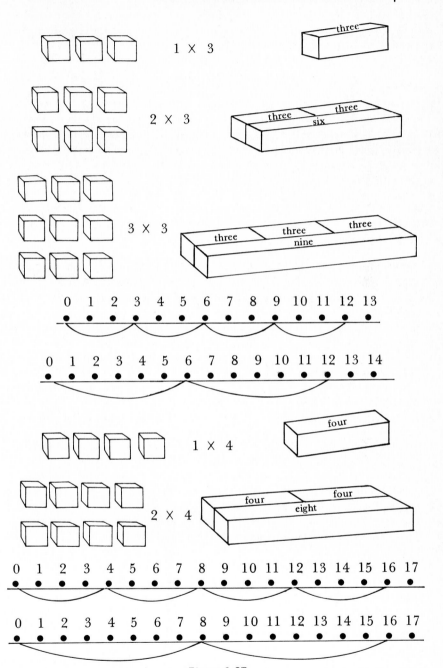

Figure 6.27

X	0	1	2	3	4	5	6	7	8	9
0										
1		1	2	3	4	5	6	7	8	9
2		2		6			12			
3		3	6	9	12	15	18	21	24	27
4		4		12			24			
5		5		15			30			
6		6	12	18	24	30	36	42	48	54
7		7		21			42			
8		8		24			48			
9		9		27			54			

Figure 6.28

×	0	1	2	3	4	5	6	7	8	9
0										
1		1	2	3	4	5	6	7	8	9
2		2	4	6	8	10	12	14	16	18
3		3	6	9	12	15	18	21	24	27
4		4	8	12	16	20	24	28	32	36
5		5	10	15	20	25	30	35	40	45
6		6	12	18	24	30	36	42	48	54
7		7	14	21	28	35	42		56	
8		8	16	24	32	40	48	56	64	72
9		9	18	27	36	45	54		72	

Figure 6.29

X	0	1	2	3	4	5	6	7	8	9
0	0	0	0	0	0	0	0	0	0	0
1	0	1	2	3	4	5	6	7	8	9
2	0	2	4	6	8	10	12	14	16	18
3	0	3	6	9	12	15	18	21	24	27
4	0	4	8	12	16	20	24	28	32	36
5	0	5	10	15	20	25	30	35	40	45
6	0	6	12	18	24	30	36	42	48	54
7	0	7	14	21	28	35	42		56	63
8	0	8	16	24	32	40	48	56	64	72
9	0	9	18	27	36	45	54	63	72	81

Figure 6.30

reinforce the insights gained. Children study *patterns* as they go, and individual children gain insights at their own rates.

Some of the patterns are:

1. You count by twos to find products when multiplying by two.

2. You double the products in the twos' column to find the products in the fours' column.

3. You double the products in the fours' column to find the products in the eights' column. The units go in a regular pattern in the eights' column: 8, 6, 4, 2, 0, 8, 6, 4, 2.

4. The units in the fives' column go 5, 0, 5, 0, 5, 0, 5, 0, 5.

5. The units in the nines' column go in a regular pattern: 9, 8, 7, 6, 5, 4, 3, 2, 1. The tens begin with $2 \times 9 = 18$ and continue 2, 3, 4, 5, 6, 7, 8.

6. The diagonal divides the matrix into two equal parts. Every product that is found on one side of the diagonal is also on the other side.

7. You count by threes to find the products in the threes' column, and you double these to find the products in the sixs' column.

8. The products in the nines' column are three times as large as those in the threes' column.

9. Seven times seven is the only product that is not filled in by filling in the other parts of the matrix. The product (7×7) could be written as $7 \times (3 + 4) = (7 \times 3) + (7 \times 4)$. By looking on the matrix, you can find that $(7 \times 3) = 21$ and $(7 \times 4) = 28; 21 + 28 = 49$, therefore, $(7 \times 7) = 49$.

The teacher will have begun teaching the principles or laws of multiplication as he goes along. The application of these properties to multiplication are presented next in summary.

The Commutative Property. Since the child already knows the word "commutative" and understands what it means for addition, he should have little trouble with the commutative property in multiplication. Figure 6. 31 shows that three times four is equivalent to four times three when counted by units or when measured on a number line. Children appreciate the commutative property when they are filling in the matrix. Once they have used the concrete materials to find products to place in the horizontal line, they can apply the commutative property and fill in the vertical column with the same products.

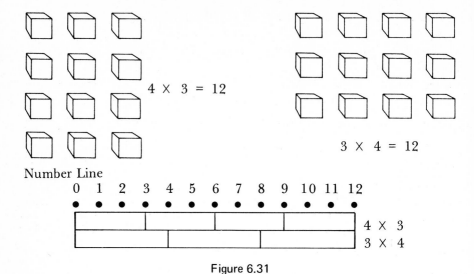

Figure 6.31

The Associative Property. Children who know the meaning of associative property in addition will readily understand that when you have three or more numbers to multiply, you may associate any two of them. (Multiplication is binary; you can only multiply *two* numbers at the same time.) Thus:

$$3 \times 2 \times 4 \text{ may become } (3 \times 2) \times 4 = 6 \times 4 = 24,$$
$$\text{or it may become } 3 \times (2 \times 4) = 3 \times 8 = 24.$$

The Distributive Property. Children know what it means to rename a number for addition. In multiplication, 3×9 may become:

$$3 \times (4 + 5) = (3 \times 4) + (3 \times 5)$$
$$= 12 + 15 = 27.$$

The matrix (Fig. 6.30) may be completed in this way: 7×7, which was left blank, could become:

$$7 \times (2 + 5) = (7 \times 2) + (7 \times 5) = 14 + 35 = 49$$

Another child might think it should be:

$$7 \times (3 + 4) = (7 \times 3) + (7 \times 4) = 21 + 28 = 49$$

Both children are correct. The distributive property would be applied in solving larger problems. For example:

$$(8 \times 200) + (8 \times 40) + (8 \times 8) = 1600 + 64 = 1984$$

Closure. As children measure equal sets on the number line, they will come to understand that the product of two natural numbers is always a natural number. They will also discover that the product of two even numbers is an even number (4 × 4 = 16). The product of an even number and an odd number is an even number (4 × 3 = 12). The product of two odd numbers is an odd number (3 × 5 = 15).

The Law of Zero. Any number multiplied by zero is zero.

Identity Element. Any number multiplied by one will give that number.

Multiplicative Inverse. When two numbers are multiplied together and the product is one, each is the multiplicative inverse of the other. Thus $\frac{4}{1}$ is the multiplicative inverse of $\frac{1}{4}$, and $\frac{2}{3}$ is the multiplicative inverse of $\frac{3}{2}$. (This is also called reciprocal.)

The teacher should use his discretion as to when to teach each property. Since many of the properties are so similar to those in addition, they can probably be learned by the end of the fourth grade.

The distributive property may be used when multiplying large numbers. 8 × 347 could be expressed

$$8 (300) + 8 (40) + (8 \times 7) =$$
$$2400 + 320 + 56 = 2776$$

When the child multiplies with this algorism, he must understand that he multiplies units times units to get units; the five that he must add to the second column is five tens; the three that he must add is 300. The expanded form should be used until the child understands the place value concept. If it helps the child to remember, he may place the numeral that represents the number that he will add above the place where he will be adding it:

$$\begin{array}{r} {\scriptstyle 3\ 5} \\ 347 \\ \times 8 \\ \hline 2776 \end{array}$$

This is usually called a crutch, but the understanding of the process is the important thing, since the adult usually has some kind of calculator that he uses for such problems once he is out of school and into the business world. Astute questioning on the part of the teacher will reveal what the child knows about the process. If the child does not understand, the teacher needs to reteach. The child probably needs to go back to the expanded notation process and work through it until he has a better understanding of place value. Continued practice on something that he does not understand may make him become mechanically accurate but will not add to his store of mathematically useful knowledge.

Too much emphasis cannot be placed upon understanding the concept of multiplication and how it is used in problem-solving. The teacher should make simple problems using examples from the child's environment until the process is thoroughly understood. The teacher can make use of the text as a test. The teacher teaches the concept using the digital and analog materials, makes simple problems from the child's environment using multiplication, and then goes to the text for other test situations.

The child usually works with the teacher for about one-half of the class period and works in a daily test situation where he and the teacher find how well he is able to work the examples and/or problems independently.

Multiplication of common fractions and decimal fractions will be studied in chapters 8 and 10 respectively. All of the laws except that of closure which hold good for whole numbers or natural numbers hold good for the multiplication of fractions.

DIVISION

Division is the opposite of multiplication. In the process of multiplication, equal sets are put together to form a whole; in the process of division, the total is parted or measured into equal sets. Division may involve the parting of many objects into equal sets or one object might be divided or measured into equal parts. The measurement concept of division is not limited to the above example. Both concepts, division as partition and division as measure, will be developed in the following discussion.

Although the concept of division is one that the child develops very early in his experience, the algorism is difficult. It probably would be impossible for the child to accomplish the division algorism until after he has made the algorisms for subtraction and multiplication.

When beginning the formal study (situations in which symbolization is made and algorisms set up) of division, the teacher should evaluate the information that children already have about division. The children will probably be able to demonstrate, using concrete materials, some of the most difficult concepts of division. They could divide 12 into equal groups of 3 by using the number line, cubes, or rods all of which are illustrated in Figure 6.32.

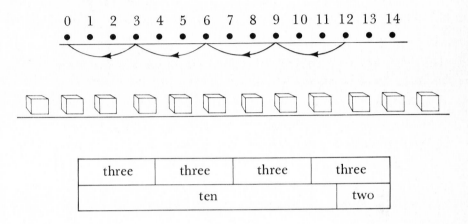

three	three	three	three
ten			two

Figure 6.32

Many children will be able to describe the meaning of division and should be given numerous opportunities to do so. Not all children will be ready to make the algorisms at the same time, and they should not be pushed into this activity until they are ready.

Making the algorisms for division requires a high degree of perception and knowledge of space relationships. All of the forms of division commonly used in the elementary school require some ability to determine which number is being divided, which number is the divisor, and where the quotient should be placed:

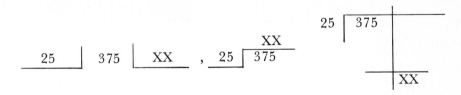

Probably the most effective form to use is the one shown in Figure 6.33 It is often called the Greenwood Method and can be found in books that were published about 1880. Some call it successive subtrac-

tion, although that term is applied when you make successive subtractions of the cardinal number of the division set. The authors find that
there is no need to teach another method once children have learned
the Greenwood Method well.

```
25 | 11,375  | 100          With experience, the child
     | 2,500  |             would shorten this to the
     |_____|             following steps:
     | 8,875  | 100
     | 2,500  |                  25 | 11,375 | 400
     |_____|                     | 10,000 |
     | 6,375  | 100                 |_____|
     | 2,500  |                     | 1,375  | 50
     |_____|                     | 1,250  |
     | 3,875  | 100                 |_____|
     | 2,500  |                     |  125   | 5
     |_____|                     |  125   |
     | 1,375  | 20                  |_____|
     |  500   |                     |        | 455
     |_____|
     |  875   | 30
     |  750   |
     |_____|
     |  125   | 5
     |  125   |
     |_____|
              | 455
```

Figure 6.33. An Example of the Greenwood Method of Division.

In this process the child had no occasion to use any number in the
partial quotient other than ten or a multiple of ten until the last step.
The child who has gained some maturity of thought in using the process
will probably use only a few steps in finding the quotient (as also
shown in Fig. 6.33).

This process usually seems more logical to a child for many reasons,
among which are the following:

1. The total dividend is used each time. In other methods, children
would have said "Twenty-five divided into one-hundred-thirteen is
four." There is no one-hundred-thirteen in this number.

2. The total remainder is used each time.

3. The child may use partial quotients, which are easier for him.

4. The child does not have to erase if he chooses a partial quotient
(such as the 100 in first part of Fig. 6.33) which is smaller than the
final quotient.

Although the following algorism is an old one it has been widely used of late. The values in this algorism are many. In the first place you are using the total number at first and the total remainder each succeeding time, thus it is mathematically accurate. Each child would be permitted to find as many partial quotients as he needed. There is less likelihood that children will make wrong estimates and have to erase.

```
10| 500 | 10
      100
     ─────
     400 | 10    59| 10738 | 100
     100             5900
     ─────          ──────
     300 | 30        4838 | 50
     300             2950
     ─────          ──────
         | 50        1888 | 30    165| 27680 | 100
                     1770             16500
                    ──────          ───────
                      118 | 2        11180 | 50
                      118            8250
                    ──────          ───────
                         | 182       2930 | 10
                                     1650
                                    ───────
                                     1280 | 5
                                      825
                                    ───────
                                      455 | 2
                                      330
                                    ───────
                                      125 | 167 remainder 125
```

The child may go to a more traditional form of division if he wishes, but the authors have found that children learn to make such mature estimates that they can work faster using this method.

As in multiplication, understanding the process of division is very important. The child needs to know what kinds of problems can be solved by the use of division. He needs to be able to answer questions about the problems and about division.

The child should recognize the symbols used for division:

$$(6 \div 2) \qquad \frac{6}{2} \qquad 2\overline{\smash{\big)}\,6} \qquad 2\,\underline{\big|\,6}$$

The Law of Zero. Any number divided by zero is indefinite and therefore it is impossible to obtain a quotient.

Identity Element. Any number divided by one is that same number. Four ÷ one is four; it would be symbolized $\frac{4}{1} = 4$.

Computation in Nondecimal Systems

Computation in nondecimal bases (since decimal means 10, these are bases other than 10) is not drastically different from the computation done in base 10. The greatest difference is that the grouping is by some other base than ten. One method of helping students compute in these nondecimal bases is to have them perform these operations on a number line. It will be noted that in using a number line it is numbered in the base being used. Adding 12_{five} and 11_{five} on the number line would be done like this:

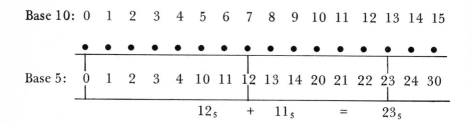

Another example of addition using the number line but using a different base is to find the sum of 6_7 and 13_7:

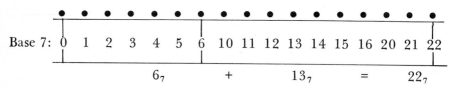

The number line is a most important and useful aid in helping elementary school pupils learn fundamental operations in any base. After achieving reasonable mastery of the operation on a number line, the pupil is guided into performing the same operation with the algorism for the process involved. If children are permitted to memorize sums in bases other than ten, they may become confused on combinations in base 10.

In making this transition from materials to the algorism, a useful aid is a place value chart (Fig. 6.34) for each pupil so that he can place counters in appropriate positional columns to represent the specified number and then perform the indicated operations with the counters. In performing the addition operation, the pupil is seeking to determine if there is one or more groups of the desired base contained in any of the positional columns. If the desired base is contained in a column, the counters are regrouped into one of the next larger groupings of the base. Any counters remaining in a column after the regrouping (or all the counters if there were not enough in the column to make a next larger grouping) are placed at the bottom of the chart in the appropriate place for the sum. In Figure 6.34, the place value chart will be utilized to find the sum of 244_7 and 354_7.

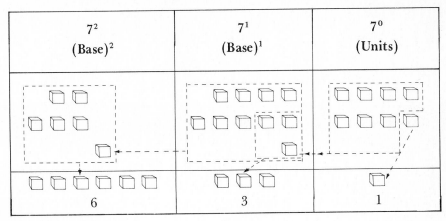

$$244_7 + 354_7 = 631_7$$

Figure 6.34

In the units' column, a group of seven with one left over was found. This group of 7 units was regrouped into one group of 7 and placed in the sevens' column. In the sevens' column, there was one group of 7 sevens with 3 sevens left. This group of 7 sevens was regrouped into one group of 49 and placed in the 7^2 column. In adding the 7^2 column, there were 6 groups of 7^2. The resulting sum was 631_7.

Another example in another base is shown in Figure 6.35. In this addition, there was a group of 5 units with one left in the units' column. The 5 units were regrouped into one group of five and placed in the fives' column. In the fives' column there were then 5 groups of five and these were regrouped into one group of twenty-five and placed in the twenty-fives' column, with no groups left over. The addition in the twenty-fives' column reveals there are 4 groups of twenty-five. Thus, $132_5 + 214_5 = 401_5$.

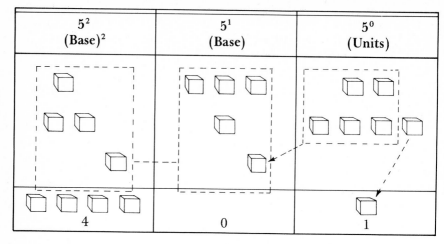

$$132_5 + 214_5 = \underline{\hphantom{xxx}}_5$$

Figure 6.35

Subtraction in nondecimal bases is not drastically different from subtraction in base 10. The major difference is that the grouping is in another base. The following illustration of subtraction in nondecimal bases will utilize the number line to show $14_{eight} - 7_{eight}$:

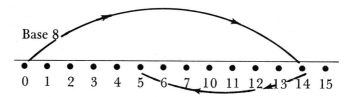

An example using the number line in subtraction in base 5 is the following; which shows that $31_5 - 14_5 = 12_5$:

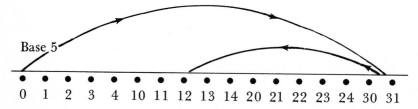

The use of the place value chart in subtraction is illustrated in Figure 6.36. In the subtraction ($573_8 - 262_8 = \underline{\hphantom{xxx}}$), there is a great deal of similarity with any base 10 problem.

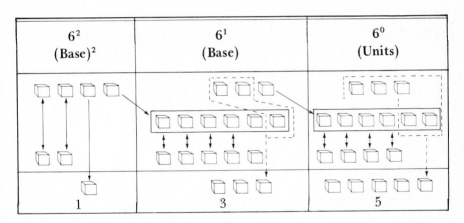

$$573_8 - 262_8 = 311_8$$

$$433_6 - 254_6 = 135_6$$

Figure 6.36

In the second example (Fig. 6.36), we are subtracting 254_6 from 433_6, and the difference in the method of grouping will become apparent. In the units' column, there are 3 units from which 4 units are to be subtracted; however neither this subtraction nor that in the sixes' column can be accomplished without regrouping. In order to do this, we will go to the Base² column and take one of these groups of thirty-six to be changed into 6 groups of six in the Base column. Then we will regroup once more, taking one group of six from the Base column and changing it into a group of 6 units. What we have done would look like this in expanded form:

$$433_6 = (400_6) + (30_6) + (3_6) = (300_6) + (120_6) + (13_6)$$
$$- 254_6 = - (200_6) + (50_6) + (4_6) = - (200_6) + (50_6) + (4_6)$$

After this regrouping, the subtraction can be done without having to "borrow."

As the transition is made from calculations using a place value chart to calculations involving an algorism, it is important to remember that in nondecimal systems you must think in terms of the base being used. It is much more difficult and less efficient to think in terms of base 10 and then convert back to the base being used. A most useful concept to use is that numbers have many names. For example, other names for 8 could be $(6 + 2)$, $(5 + 3)$, $(9 - 1)$, $(11 - 3)$, (4×2), $\frac{16}{2}$, or many, many other possibilities. In the following addition, the concept that numbers have many names is utilized: $(333 + 145)_6 = 522_6$.

36	6	6^0	36	6	6^0
300 +	30 +	3 =	300 +	$(20 + 10)$	+ $(1 + 2)$
100 +	40 +	5 =	100 +	40	+ 5
			400 +	$(20 + 40) + 10$	+ $(1 + 5) + 2$
			= $(400 + 100)$	$+ (10 + 10)$	$+ 2 = 522_6$

In the addition of the unit column, 3 was renamed $(2 + 1)$ because we were looking for groups of six and the 5 in the second addend with the one from $(2 + 1)$ gave a group of 6 units. This group of 6 units was then renamed one group of six (because 6 is the base used in this particular problem). When the one group of six was placed in the six column, that left two units remaining, so they were written in their proper place in the answer. The addition in the next column (the six column) was done in a similar manner. The 3 (representing 3 groups of six) was renamed $(2 + 1)$ so that the 2 from this group and the 4 of the second addend (representing 4 groups of six) could be combined into 6 groups of six and then renamed one group of thirty-six. When the one group of thirty-six was placed in its proper column, or place, two groups of six remained and they were written in their proper place in the answer. In adding the last column (the thirty-six column) there were 5 groups of thirty-six; this was not enough to make one of the next larger group, so the 5 was written in its proper place in the answer. It should be remembered that it is not always necessary to rename the number in the top or first addend. We could have renamed the numbers of the second addend just as easily. We have the freedom of choice to rename whichever number that will make our calculations easier.

The number line and cubes would be used for multiplying in other bases just as they are used in multiplication in base 10. Children should be led to see that the properties or laws are the same for multiplication in any other base as they are for base ten. Use should be made of the matrix (Fig. 6.37) so children can see the patterns, just as they could see patterns in base ten.

X	0	1	2	3	4	5	6	7
0	0	0	0	0	0	0	0	0
1	0	1	2	3	4	5	6	7
2	0	2	4	6	10	12	14	16
3	0	3	6	11	14	17	22	25
4	0	4	10	14	20	24	30	34
5	0	5	12	17	24	31	36	43
6	0	6	14	22	30	36	44	52
7	0	7	16	25	34	43	52	61

Figure 6.37

The child will be able to see commutative property. He will also be able to see patterns in the matrix. This process should not be continued beyond the time when the child can see the relationship to base ten. He should not be permitted to memorize products.

The child in the elementary school should not be required to work in division in bases other than ten beyond the stage where he divides a group of objects into equal sets representing any base other than ten, or does the same on a number line. As an adult he will use this process only when using a computer. Time should be spent on understanding the process, not on working problems using the process.

Related References

Dwight, Leslie A. *Modern Mathematics for the Elementary Teacher.* New York: Holt, Rinehart & Winston, 1966.

Lovell, K. *The Growth of Basic Mathematical and Scientific Concepts of Children.* London: University of London Press Ltd., 1960.

Piaget, Jean. *The Child's Concept of Number.* London: Routledge and Paul (International Library of Psychology, Philosophy, and Scientific Method), 1952.

———. *The Psychology of Intelligence.* Patterson, N.J.: Littlefield, Adams & Company, 1960.

School Mathematics Study Group. *Studies in Mathematics.* Vol. g. Board of Trustees of Leland Stanford Junior University, 1963.

Wheeler, Olive. *Cuisenaire Rods in the Elementary School.* Dallas: Hester and Associates (seven filmstrips with cassette tapes: Counting, Getting Acquainted with Rods, Addition: Sums to 10, Addition: Sums 11-18, Subtraction, Multiplication, Division), 1971.

———, et al. *Elementary School Mathematics, A Transitional Program.* Lubbock: Texas Tech Press, 1965.

CHAPTER 7

SOLVING STATED PROBLEMS

Stated problems are referred to in many ways. They are called written problems, story problems, word problems, verbal problems, and sometimes they are simply referred to as solving problems. Regardless of how they are labeled, probably no other area of arithmetic causes more concern to both teachers and students than solving stated or word-type problems. Students who normally perform computation with considerable skill may flounder and drop alarmingly below their usual standard of work when they encounter stated problems.

Students' difficulties with stated problems are usually complex and generally vary to some extent from student to student. There has been considerable research related to this topic, and several methods have been developed to help students who still have difficulty. Teachers are concerned because they may not know specifically how to help their students to be more successful in solving stated problems. Admittedly, this is sometimes a difficult area for teachers and students, but it can also be one of the most rewarding. The purpose of this section is to identify some of the sources of student difficulty, and offer suggestions for improving their ability to solve problems.

Rationale for Solving Stated Problems

Despite the implications given by some achievement tests and textbooks that solving stated problems is a separate topic for study, the opposite is true: solving stated problems should be an integral part of all phases of arithmetic. The initial phase in teaching any of the basic operations seeks to develop competency by guiding students in understanding and using mathematical concepts. After reasonable mastery of an operation has been achieved, students should then be guided into applying this knowledge to problem situations—not just any problem situation, but one that has meaning for the learner. A problem for which the students can see no need to find a solution will likely result in less than a half-hearted effort on their part. When teachers depend too heavily on word problems from a textbook, these problems tend to become a substitute for reality. Consequently, students see less and less relevance in the problems. The stated problems presented in most textbooks are usually intended to serve as a model which the teacher can follow in developing other problems that will be pertinent to and appropriate for his class.

Although there has been a considerable amount of research pertaining to solving stated problems, no one way has been shown to be the best method to teach solving problems. Solving stated problems is much more involved and complicated than computing, since computation is only one part of solving the problem. In computation, what to do has already been decided, and all that remains is the doing of it. On the other hand, solving stated problems requires the student to read, analyze, decide what is to be done (and sometimes the order in which it is to be done), and then perform the computation necessary to get the answer.

SOURCES OF STUDENT DIFFICULTY

One factor that most research in this area agrees upon is the importance of intelligence, or mental ability. Students with high mental ability usually have less difficulty in solving stated problems than students of low mental ability. A teacher who expects all of his students to exhibit the same ability in solving problems might as well expect all of his students to be exactly the same height, weight, or age. Regardless of how absurd this comparison may seem, many teachers still teach with the expectation that all students should master the same material in the same length of time. The implications of research is that the less capable students should work problems that are easier and less complex than the more capable students. A student who is successful in solving stated problems on his level builds confidence that he can solve other problems. As he builds this confidence, by being successful, he is also developing a problem-solving approach that may be one of his most useful skills in later life. Research indicates quite clearly that one of the major differences between successful and unsuccessful problem solvers is their *level of confidence.* (Probably we need to reevaluate the significance of the old cliché, "nothing succeeds like success.")

Students who have not achieved reasonable mastery of the basic operations involved will undoubtedly have difficulty. This would also include students who have learned the mechanical aspects of computation, but who have not developed an understanding of what they are doing. For example, many textbook authors emphasize that there is a great difference between knowing how to subtract and knowing when to subtract. A student who does not understand an operation will certainly encounter difficulty in solving word problems, because the student must determine which operation or process is needed to obtain the solution.

A major source of student difficulty in solving stated problems is that many students do not possess the reading skills necessary for solving problems at a certain grade level. Most authorities agree that approximately 60 percent of the errors made by students in solving stated problems result from reading difficulties. (Mathematical computation accounts for another 20 percent.)

The skills necessary for reading from a basal reader and the skills necessary for reading a problem with an understanding that results in a plan for a solution are sometimes quite different. Reading skills necessary in mathematics include not only the same skills as reading from a basal reader but also other skills, such as reading mathematical terms and symbols with understanding. Many students may know how to do the computation necessary to solve a problem, but they may be unable to get from their reading enough understanding to know what process or processes are required.

There is another source of difficulty that is also related to the previously mentioned difficulties: some students are unable to distinguish between information in the problem that is important and necessary for finding a solution, and information that is not vital. It would seem that this relates to a lack of reading ability and/or a lack of understanding of basic operations.

Another source of difficulty closely related to reading difficulty is that students often cannot translate verbal or written expressions into mathematical sentences. Lack of this essential skill can often prevent a student from achieving a mathematical solution. The student may comprehend what he reads, and he may have reasonable mastery of the basic operations; but if he is not able to translate what he has read into mathematical symbols, he likely will not reach a solution. The teacher must devote time, and guidance as well, in helping students develop the ability to translate story problems into the proper mathematical symbols and sentences.

Research on problem-solving has provided us with some interesting clues about the differences between fast and slow learners. Probably one of the most important differences between these two types of students is their confidence. The fast learner apparently has confidence that after reading and analyzing the problem, he can determine the first step necessary in the solution of the problem. He may not know exactly what his second or third steps will be, but he is confident that once he has determined the first step he can then determine the next step, and the next, until a solution is obtained.

In almost direct contrast to the fast learner, the slow learner seems hesitant and unsure about what his first step should be. He is almost as hesitant about and unsure of the succeeding steps leading to a solution. It probably should be noted that the student's confidence is also an important factor in situations where his attempt to find a solution is thwarted by an obviously wrong solution or a dead-end before the solution is reached. In this situation, the fast learner seems to be confident that he can retrace his steps and locate the point of error, or if necessary, he can start again at the beginning with another approach. On the other hand, the slow learner seems at a loss for an alternate plan and unable to retrace his steps. Usually after encountering an impasse and not knowing what else to do, the slow learner gives up.

The fast learner has more confidence in himself and his ability, and he is also more organized and systematic in his approach to the problem. He probably also organizes his thinking so that he can use the available information effectively, mentally arranges the parts, looking for patterns and relationships, compares what is known with past experiences, and tries out in his mind several approaches to the problem. The slow learner has access to exactly the same information as the fast learner, but he somehow fails to organize his information so that it can be useful.

FACTORS AFFECTING THE DIFFICULTY OF STATED PROBLEMS

Besides the sources of difficulty of individual students, there are other factors that also determine the degree of difficulty of a problem. The difficulty encountered in problem-solving depends not only on the individual student's ability, but also on the construction of the problem. For instance, there are basically two kinds of stated problems: one kind requires an answer only, the second kind requires the student to get an answer and to do something with the answer.

For example:

Example 1: All the money John has with him is a dime and a quarter. How much money does he have?

Example 2: All the money John has with him is a dime and a quarter. Can he give a friend the correct change for a half dollar?

It can be seen from these examples that the same addition problem ($10¢ + 25¢ = 35¢$) must be solved in both. The second example, however, requires the student to take his answer and make some type of decision or comparison to get a solution. Consequently, Example 2 is a more difficult problem than the first example.

Research has been done in this area by Leslie Dwight, Patrick Suppes, and others to determine which factors affect the difficulty of a stated problem and to what degree. Thus far, the research indicates the following factors are very influential in determining the degree of difficulty (they are not necessarily listed in order of importance or frequency):

1. Mathematical factors:
    a. The number of steps necessary to work the problem
    b. The presence or absence of cues (or key words) to indicate the operation to be used
    c. The presence or absence of division. (Division is the most difficult operation to learn. Some research indicates that many teachers teach only measurement division but test the student's understanding with problems that must be solved by partitioning division.)
    d. The number of different kinds of operations that must be used in reaching a solution

2. Language factors:
    a. The complexity of the grammar (or syntax) used in stating the problem
    b. The vocabulary used in stating the problem
    c. The total number of words, particularly the number of words in the longest sentence, used in stating the problem
    d. The use of number words and operation words instead of number symbols and operation symbols in stating the problem

3. Sequence factor:
    a. Whether the preceding problem required the same operation or a different one
    b. Whether or not the numbers mentioned in the problem are in the order they will be used in working the problem
    c. Whether the operations mentioned or called for in the problem are mentioned in the same sequence that they will be performed or used

There are many other sources of difficulty in solving stated problems. Those discussed have been the ones that most authorities recognize as being most troublesome.

Methods of Assisting Students in Improving Their Ability to Solve Stated Problems

One factor that seems important in aiding students to become more successful in their attempts to solve problems (although it apparently has not been considered in most research) is time—the amount of time that the pupil has to solve the problem, and the number of times that stated problems are studied or presented in class. Many teachers seemingly ignore the fact that solving stated problems is a more complex process than solving computation problems. As a result, students are often given insufficient time to consider and analyze a problem. Also related to the factor of insufficient time is the fact that many teachers do not systematically provide situations in which their students encounter stated problems. Some of the older traditional textbooks grouped all of the stated problems in one chapter, and they were usually studied as if they existed separately from the rest of mathematics. Most studies indicate that students who have frequent opportunities to solve stated problems seem to do better in problem-solving than those students who have infrequent opportunities.

The teacher can also help his students be more successful by introducing and developing the skills necessary for reading mathematical problems in much the same way that new words and skills are developed in the reading program. Research indicates that students having difficulty in comprehending the problems can be helped if someone reads the problem aloud. The students who become competent can be left on their own more and more, but those students whose progress is not as rapid will still need help and guidance from the teacher. The teacher can also help students get meaning from written words by guiding them to realize that it is usually necessary to read a problem several times before attempting a solution. The first time the problem is read, it will likely be read at the student's normal rate of reading in order to obtain an overview of the problem. After reading for an overview, the problem is then reread, but more slowly this time so that the component parts can be identified and placed in some perspective. It may be necessary to reread certain parts of the problem several times so that the proper perspective and arrangement of the component parts can be determined. Many students in the elementary school will need guidance in discovering the need for reading a problem several times and reading at different speeds.

Another factor that most research pinpoints as being important to successful problem-solving is the ability to estimate the answer mentally. This type of mental mathematics usually does not develop naturally, but it must be developed through sequentially planned activities that give the pupils a chance to practice and utilize mentally what they have learned.

There seems to be merit in attempting to reach a solution by using a systematic method of problem-solving. The *analysis method* is recommended by a number of textbook authors. This method involves using the following series of steps:

1. Read the problem to determine what is given and what is to be proved.
2. Determine what operation or operations will be required.
3. Estimate the answer.
4. Solve by performing the necessary operations.
5. Check the answer with the estimated answer and also in terms of the problem itself.

Another method is the *graphic method.* The graphic method utilizes a model, a diagram, or a graph so that relationships can be visualized. Probably a combination of the graphic and the analysis method would be more effective than either method alone. The teacher should not give either of these methods to the students, but should guide the pupils to develop them through inductive teaching.

Some of the newer elementary school mathematics textbooks have fewer stated type problems than the usual, traditional textbook contained. This does not mean that these newer programs are placing less emphasis on solving this type of problem; rather, it is intended that the teacher use the examples given in the textbook as a model and construct more problems, but using events and situations that will be interesting and meaningful to a particular group of pupils. This gives the teacher the freedom to construct different types and varieties of problems, ranging from problem situations that might arise in the classroom and daily life to problems bordering on the absurd or ridiculous (but constructed in such a way that they will capture the imagination and interest of the pupils).

There also seems to be merit in constructing problems in which the student has an interest and ones with which he can identify. Often the problems presented in elementary school mathematics books seem illogical and uninteresting to the students; problems that are more pertinent and interesting to a particular group of students can usually be constructed by their teacher.

Some authors recommend using stated-type problems to introduce a skill (or introduce a need for that skill). We believe that skills should be introduced first in a mathematical context. Then, after reasonable mastery of the skill is achieved, the pupil is shown social applications for his skills. Learning that follows the pattern of mastery of mathematical skills and then application in social situations will probably be less inhibiting to future learning.

Although there seems to be no one best method of helping all children learn how to solve stated problems, there are a number of things a teacher can do that will probably help most of the students. Research findings are substantiating the prognosis of Bloom's Taxonomy that there seems to be a sequence of subordinate skills that must be developed and blended together to be used in the complex process of problem-solving. Probably one of the most basic skills needed to solve a problem would be the ability to identify the correct operation(s) that must be used. There are indications that there is value in having children start by identifying only the process or operation that would be used to solve simple oral problems given by the teacher. The teacher encourages and guides students to explain how they know which process to use and what they might expect in terms of a solution. This discussion of expected answers is the initial development of estimating the answer in terms of what is presented in the problem. At a later time, the identification of the operation to be used can be approached from a slightly different direction by encouraging children to make up story problems suggested by a certain mathematical sentence or statement. For example, if the mathematical sentence $4 + 5 = 9$ were the equation being considered, the students would be asked to make up a story problem that this equation would solve. The student's story problem might be something like one of the following:

> "There are four boys and five girls in Susie's reading group."
> "There are four apples in the fruit bowl and Mother bought five more to put with them."

When reasonable skill has been developed by the students in stating story problems, they should be assisted in bringing in the "how many" question to the problem. One method some teachers have found particularly helpful in assisting children develop competency in relating mathematical thought to problem situations is an activity of headline story writing. This activity must be used at a time when the students are fairly proficient in writing; if they are not, it may be done orally with the teacher doing the writing. The key emphasis at this stage is the development of student awareness of the relationship between words, particularly mathematical words, and mathematical symbols arranged into sentences. When students have an awareness of this fundamental relationship, then emphasis should be focused on translating mathematical word sentences into mathematical sentences using symbols. Some children need more time and assistence in translating words into symbols than other children. This is particularly true of children still functioning at the concrete level of learning, because they have not yet reached the more abstract level of thought necessary to make translations of this kind.

As the children develop the skills of translating words into mathematical sentences, they must then unify and blend this skill with other skills into a more sophisticated and complex skill. Some mathematicians and educators call this higher skill "programing" and this term (borrowed from computer terminology) seems to describe quite accurately what must be done. Most people have some awareness of what a computer can and cannot do and also recognize that computers must be programed (or told what to do) before they can do it. Programing in this instance means analyzing the problem so that it can be broken down into and solved by a series of sequential steps. Apparently students must do almost exactly the same type of thing to solve problems. Some researchers report favorable results in developing problem-solving skills by having the teacher act as a computer and the students program what he must do to solve the problem. In this situation the teacher performs only what he is told to do; if a mistake appears in the program, the students must make the correction. Teacher guidance is given only when the students have seemingly exhausted all of their alternate plans. As the students develop their program for the computer, the teacher can guide them into an awareness of the desirability of building or sketching a model of the problem. Working with a model, the students will be more likely to see aspects of the problem that might have gone undetected otherwise. After the children develop proficiency in programing as a group, they are guided and encouraged to program individually. This sequential development of skills will probably occur over a period of years, not just a few short days or weeks. This means that students must encounter various problem situations on a regular and recurring basis if they are to develop the basic skills necessary for the formation of more complex skills.

Some teachers, when coming to the section on stated problems in their textbook, feel that they must stay with these problems until all or almost all of the children have mastered them. As a result, some children become bored, others become frustrated, and others become totally indifferent This reaction affects their attitude not only to stated problems, but possibly also to all of mathematics. About the only thing a teacher such as this accomplishes is reinforcing any dislike that the students might have for mathematics, and generating some dislike in those students who previously had none. It probably would be much more effective to work on stated problems until the students begin losing interest and then change to another topic. A short time later, stated problems can be reconsidered.

Extending Your Thinking

1. Using the following equations, write a different story problem for each equation.

a. $3 + 4 = \square$ c. $4 \times 3 = \square$

b. $9 - 6 = \square$ d. $8 - 2 = \square$

2. Using the equation, $5 + 8 = \square$, write a story problem that would require the student to solve this equation. Now modify your story problem so that the students would not only have to work this equation but also do something with their answer in order to solve the problem.

3. Using the subtraction fact, $12 - 4 = \square$, write a stated problem that would be solved by take-away subtraction. Now, write another stated problem based on the same fact that would be solved by comparison subtraction.

4. Using the division fact, $16 \div 2 = \square$, write a stated problem that would be solved by measurement division. Write another stated problem based on the same division fact that would be solved by partitioning division.

5. Identify at least five other school situations besides mathematics, in which elementary students would need to use their ability to solve stated problems.

6. Identify at least five everyday-life situations outside the classroom in which students would need to use their problem-solving ability.

7. Using the categories of the cognitive domain in Bloom's Taxonomy, write a separate stated problem for as many categories as you can that would require the use of the learning described in that category.

8. Briefly plan three different learning activities that would require elementary students to utilize their problem-solving skills.

Related References

Ashlock, Robert B., and Herman, Wayne L., Jr. *Current Research in Elementary School Mathematics*. New York: The Macmillan Co., 1970, Part 4, pp. 193-234.

Banks, J.H. *Learning and Teaching Arithmetic*. 2nd ed., Boston: Allyn & Bacon, Inc., 1964. Chap. 13.

Dwight, Leslie A. *Modern Mathematics for the Elementary Teacher*. New York: Holt, Rinehart, & Winston, Inc., 1966. Chap. 15.

Fehr, Howard F., and Phillips, Jo McKeeby. *Teaching Modern Mathematics in the Elementary School.* Reading, Mass.: Addison-Wesley Publishing Co., Inc. 1967. Chap. 14.

Kramer, Klaas. *The Teaching of Elementary School Mathematics.* Boston: Allyn & Bacon, Inc., 1966. Chap. 18.

Riedesel, C. Alan. *Guiding Discovery in Elementary School Mathematics.* New York: Appleton-Century-Crofts, 1967. Chap. 11.

Suppes, Patrick and Hill, Shirley. *First Course in Mathematical Logic.* Waltham, Mass.: Blaisdell Publishing Co., 1964.

Swenson, Esther J. *Teaching Arithmetic to Children.* New York: The Macmillan Co., 1964. pp. 9-11, 136-38.

Wheat, H.G. *How to Teach Arithmetic.* Evanston, Ill.: Row, Peterson and Company, 1956. Chap. 9.

CHAPTER 8

FRACTIONS

In the discussion of numeration systems, it was pointed out that as man developed a need for a more elaborate system of computation, he usually developed an extension of his number system that would meet this need. Early man's needs were largely concerned with counting and recording. As man developed ways of working with mathematical situations and became more proficient in his calculations, it became apparent that when dividing whole numbers, the division was not always exact, and the answer was not always a whole number. This inadequacy of the set of whole numbers existed and plagued man for quite some time before a solution in the form of common fractions was found. This chapter will be concerned with a brief history of the development of fractions; fundamental concepts of fractions, equivalent fractions, and kinds of fractions; prime numbers and prime factors; and the operations of adding, subtracting, multiplying, and dividing fractions.

History of the Development of Fractions

The word fraction is derived from the Latin word *fractio* (meaning "to break"). Fractions were first thought of as broken numbers. The Egyptians were among the first civilizations to recognize the concept of fraction; their concept was one of very limited scope, however, because for all practical purposes they only recognized reciprocals of whole numbers as fractions. That is, they worked with only *unit fractions* such as $\frac{1}{3}, \frac{1}{4}, \frac{1}{5}, \frac{1}{6}, \frac{1}{7}$, and so on. (A unit fraction is any fraction with a numerator of 1). Since the only fractions that they used had a numerator of one, any fractional part was expressed as the sum of unit fractions, for example, the fraction $\frac{29}{45}$ would have been expressed as the sum of $\frac{1}{3} + \frac{1}{5} + \frac{1}{9}$. Although the Egyptians were able to develop the concepts of reciprocals of whole numbers and adding unit fractions, they seemed to be unable to perceive a fraction as *a number.*

The Babylonians developed a scheme for working with fractions in such a way that any number could be used in the numerator, but because their number system was based on 60, only 60 or powers of 60, could be used as denominators. This idea was probably further refined into the concept used in what we now call decimal fractions. The Babylonians would express the fraction $\frac{13}{72}$ as $\frac{10}{60} + \frac{50}{60^2}$. Although they had a relatively sophisticated system, the Babylonians were also unable to perceive a fraction as *a number.* They thought of a fraction as resulting from two or more parts added together.

The Romans attempted to avoid fractions by creating new, smaller units of measure. For example, if a measurement of grain was $3\frac{1}{4}$ bushels, they introduced the smaller measure, peck, so that they would not have to refer to $3\frac{1}{4}$ bushels; instead they would refer to it as 3 bushels, 1 peck. It was not until the development of the Hindu-Arabic system that the concept of fractions, as we now know it, was possible. Not only is the Hindu-Arabic system functional and efficient for working with very large numbers, but it is also functional and efficient for working with very small numbers. Fractions evolved and were developed because of man's need for a more complete number system. In the early stages of development, fractions were considered as "broken numbers" or as the sum of two or more parts, but not as a number itself; until man could perceive fractions as numbers, however, they were of very little practical use to man.

Fractions

Since fractions are special kinds of numbers, children need to have readiness to develop an understanding of the meaning of fraction before beginning to work on the fundamental operations with fractions. Children in kindergarten and the primary grades usually have some knowledge about fractions because they have usually encountered situations involving fractions. For example, they have been given *half* of a glass of milk, told it was *half* an hour until bedtime, told that we are *half* way there while traveling, and so forth. But this knowledge of fractions is not always accurate; when something is divided between two children, one of them may complain, "His half is bigger than my half." Thus meanings and concepts of fractions are probably better developed using models than in social situations. Models can be chosen so that things can be divided into exactly the desired portion, while this is not always possible in social situations. For example, fruit does not make good illustrations of fractions because the objects themselves are not always symmetrical and consequently they are extremely difficult to divide exactly into halves, thirds, or fourths. Children are not as likely to be distracted from their learning when using models such as counting blocks and the Cuisenaire rods, as when using oranges, apples, or other such objects.

In developing readiness to work with fractions, there are many meanings of fractions which children must learn. These meanings will be listed in the approximate order that they need to be learned. It should be remembered that all children do not learn exactly alike, nor do they always learn in a prescribed order; also, some learnings seem to occur simultaneously. The meanings to be developed are:

1. The basic concept of a fraction implies dividing something into a specified number of *equal* parts. Thus, one-half implies dividing something into two equal parts; one-third implies dividing or separating into three equal parts; and so on.

2. A fractional part may be part of a unit or it may be part of a group. Figure 8.1 illustrates this concept:

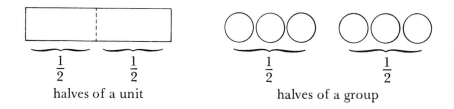

halves of a unit   halves of a group

Figure 8.1

3. The *namer* of a fraction (denominator) tells the number of equal *parts* into which a whole is separated or divided. Thus anything divided into two equal parts would be in halves, three equal parts would be in thirds, four equal parts would be in fourths, and so on.

4. The *numberer* of these equal parts (numerator) tells how many of the equal parts are being considered. If we were considering the fraction $\frac{1}{2}$, the child should be able to tell us in his terms that we have one portion of something which has been divided into two equal parts.

5. The greater the number of equal parts that we divide something into, the smaller each part becomes. The child can be guided to discover that $\frac{1}{2}$ of something is larger than (greater than) $\frac{1}{3}$ of the same thing; that $\frac{1}{3}$ of a thing is greater than $\frac{1}{4}$ of the same thing; and so on, as shown in Figure 8.2.

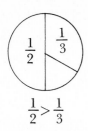

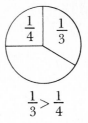

$$\frac{1}{2} > \frac{1}{3}$$

$$\frac{1}{3} > \frac{1}{4}$$

Figure 8.2

6. Two halves make a whole unit or group. Three thirds make a whole, and so on.

7. Fractional parts of the same thing are the same size but do not necessarily have the same shape. If you were asked to divide a sheet of paper into fourths, you could divide it any one of the ways shown in Figure 8.3 (and even some ways not shown) and be entirely correct.

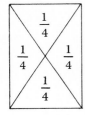

Figure 8.3

The children should be guided to generalize that there is no one definite shape for $\frac{1}{2}, \frac{1}{3}, \frac{1}{4}$ and so on.

8. During the time the meanings of fractions are being developed, the implication of division that is inherent in fractions should be stressed so that one-half of something is almost synonymous with dividing the same thing by two. Likewise, one-third becomes almost synonymous with dividing by three, and so on.

The child should be introduced to the concept of fractions through the use of concrete materials early in his school life. When he is developing the concept of sets, he can be led to understand that some groups can be divided into equal sets. If a group is divided into two equal parts, each part is one-half of the whole. The child can develop this concept even before he is able to count. He could place the objects into two sets one by one (Fig. 8.4), then he could match the objects in one-to-one correspondence to see if the sets were equivalent.

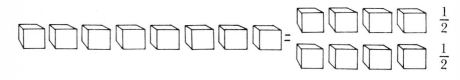

Figure 8.4

Each set would be one-half of the total group. In the same way, he could divide groups of objects into three equal parts, four equal parts and so on. The importance of equal parts should be stressed.

Twelve blocks (Fig. 8.5) should serve as a good model to illustrate the fact that if you divide a group of objects into more parts, each part will have fewer members.

As shown in Figure 8.6, the child could compare the blocks in $\frac{1}{2}$ of 12 with the blocks in $\frac{1}{3}$ of 12 and find that $\frac{1}{2}$ is greater than $\frac{1}{3}$ of the same group. He could compare the blocks in $\frac{1}{3}$ of 12 with the blocks in $\frac{1}{4}$ of 12. He would find that $\frac{1}{3}$ is greater than $\frac{1}{4}$ of the same group. He should be led to reason that if $\frac{1}{2} > \frac{1}{3}$ and $\frac{1}{3} > \frac{1}{4}$ then $\frac{1}{2} > \frac{1}{4}$. He should also be able to generalize that if you divide a group of objects into more parts, each part is smaller.

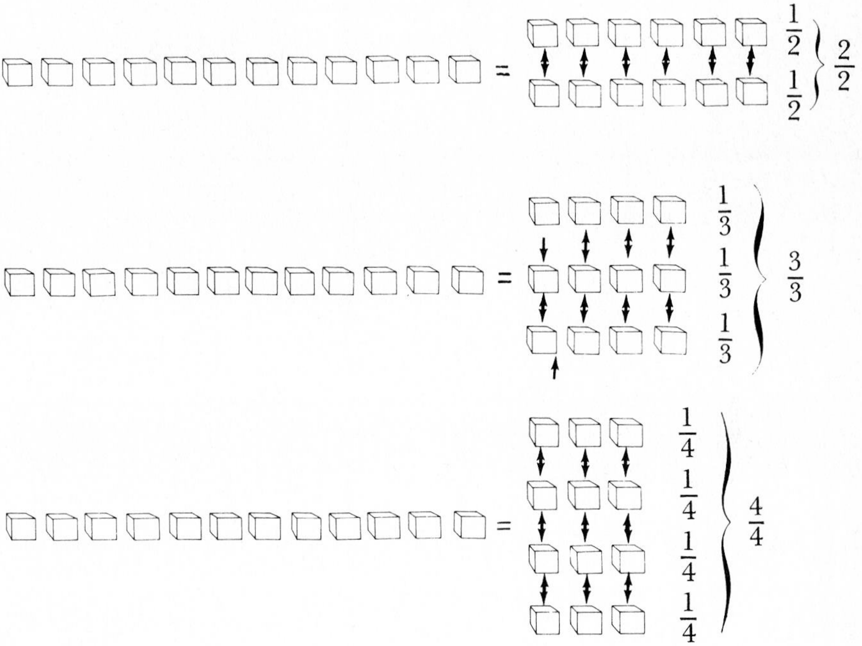

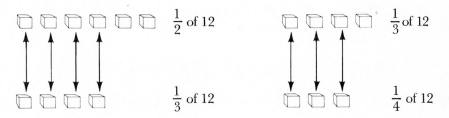

Figure 8.5

Figure 8.6

This same concept can be illustrated by the use of congruent geometric figures (Fig. 8.7). In this case one model would be divided into equal parts in different ways.

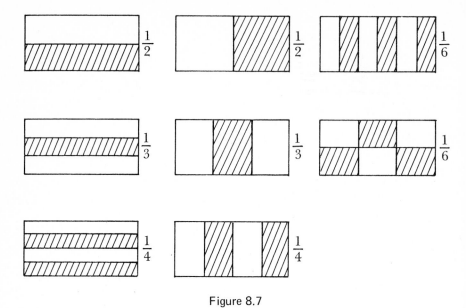

Figure 8.7

Equivalent Fractions

After reasonable mastery of the basic concepts of fractions is achieved, the pupils can be directed into developing the concept of equivalent fractions. This concept is very important because the operations of addition and subtraction of unlike fractions are dependent upon this concept. When you say that $\frac{2}{6}$ is the same as $\frac{1}{3}$, you are saying that $\frac{1}{3}$ is another name for $\frac{2}{6}$. These fractions are said to be equivalent. They stand for the same quantity.

The Cuisenaire rods can be used in teaching this concept. Figure 8.8 shows the purple rod used as a unit. A rod is sought such that two of them will fit the measure of the purple rod. The red rod would fit the space. Each of these rods would be $\frac{1}{2}$ of the purple rod. Each red rod would be equivalent to $\frac{1}{2}$ of the purple rod. Without removing this example, ask the children to see if they can find four rods of the same length that would measure exactly the same length as the purple rod. When the four rods are found by the children (in this case it will be four white rods) they would be led to recall that when anything is divided into four equal parts, each of the equal parts is one-fourth.

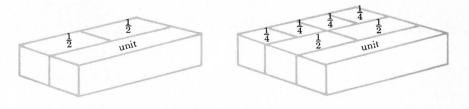

Figure 8.8

From this model, they can see that two of the $\frac{1}{4}$s are exactly the same as $\frac{1}{2}$. It can then be pointed out that $\frac{2}{4}$ is another name for $\frac{1}{2}$. When working with models and examples such as these, the children should be eventually guided to discover that when we divide something into smaller parts (as represented by the denominator of the fourths) it takes more of these smaller parts (as represented by the 2 in the numerator) to make it equivalent to a fraction that is not divided into so many parts.

This same concept can also be presented on the number line in at least two ways. One method illustrating the equivalence of halves and fourths is to make separate fractional lines of the halves and fourths, like this:

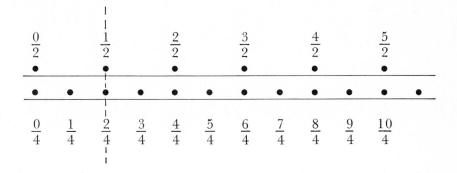

Another method would be to make a number line so that units of $\frac{1}{4}$ size are marked off on one side and units of $\frac{1}{2}$ size are marked off on the other side, such as:

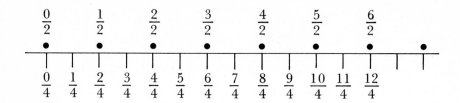

The concept of equivalence of fractions can also be shown with geometric figures, as shown in Figure 8.9.

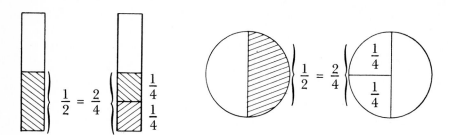

Figure 8.9

From this beginning, the children can then be guided into discovering other equivalences. These equivalences are usually expressed as follows:

$$\frac{1}{2} \equiv \frac{2}{4} \equiv \frac{3}{6} \equiv \frac{4}{8} \equiv \frac{5}{10} \equiv \frac{6}{12} \equiv \cdots$$

$$\frac{1}{3} \equiv \frac{2}{6} \equiv \frac{3}{9} \equiv \frac{4}{12} \equiv \frac{5}{15} \equiv \frac{6}{18} \equiv \cdots$$

As children discover these equivalent fractions, they also need to discover and be aware of the patterns that are present, and to be aware that all of these equivalent fractions are just other names for the same fraction.

The process of changing fractions to their lowest terms is often a problem to pupils because they forget to make the change, and it is a problem to teachers because they often count an answer which is not expressed in the lowest terms as incorrect. The point that should be remembered is that a fraction expressed in its lowest terms is easier and more convenient to visualize and understand. For example, $\frac{54}{81}$ is not very easy to visualize, but changed to $\frac{2}{3}$ it is much easier to understand and visualize. We usually change fractions to the most simple form as a matter of convenience. A method of changing fractions to a simplified form other than by knowing them as equivalent fractions will be discussed in a later part of this chapter.

Some concepts of equivalence that the child could develop would be:

1. When using groups of blocks with equal cardinal numbers: $\frac{1}{2}$ has the same number of blocks as $\frac{2}{4}$ or $\frac{3}{6}$ of that same group; $\frac{1}{2}$ does not have the same number of blocks as $\frac{1}{3}$ of the same group.

2. When using congruent rectangles $\frac{1}{2}$ is larger than $\frac{1}{3}$ or $\frac{1}{4}$ or $\frac{1}{6}$; $\frac{1}{3}$ is larger than $\frac{1}{4}$ or $\frac{1}{6}$; $\frac{1}{4}$ is larger than $\frac{1}{6}$.

Children should be given opportunities to divide groups of blocks to find which groups can be divided into equal sets. For instance, Figure 8.10 shows how 10 can be divided into two parts or into five parts.

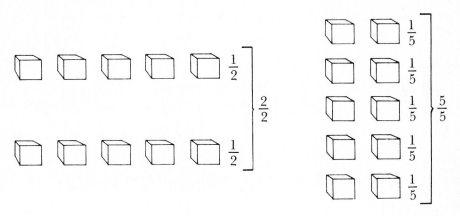

Figure 8.10

The children can see that $\frac{1}{2}$ of 10 is greater than $\frac{1}{5}$ of 10; but by matching 12 blocks and 10 blocks (Fig. 8.11), they could also learn that $\frac{1}{2}$ of 10 is *not* equivalent to $\frac{1}{2}$ of 12.

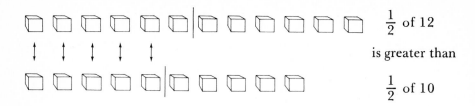

$\frac{1}{2}$ of 12

is greater than

$\frac{1}{2}$ of 10

Figure 8.11

By performing this exercise using many groups with different numbers of blocks, the child should be able to generalize that the number of elements in any fractional part of a group depends upon the original group for its cardinal number.

Children should work with squares and rectangles of different sizes, cutting them into different fractional parts. They would find that one-half of a rectangle that has sides equal to two inches and four inches respectively would not be congruent to or the same in area as one-half of a rectangle that has sides of four inches and eight inches respectively. The geometric figures must be congruent if halves of the figures are congruent.

The above is a necessary concept before the child can bridge the gap between using concrete materials and using fractions in an algebraic equation. He must recognize that the unit is important. When he compares two fractions he must assume that they are based on equal units:

1. One-half of 10 is not equal to one-half of 12.
2. One-half of a two-inch square is equivalent to two-fourths of a two-inch square.

Terminology of Fractions

Many terms are used in the study and description of fractions, some of the most common ones are explained below.

1. *Denominator:* the namer of the fraction, or the indicator of the number of equal parts into which something is divided.

2. *Numerator:* the numberer of the fraction, or how many of the equal parts are being considered.

3. *Common fractions:* fractions that are expressed in the form of $\frac{a}{b}$ (when b is not equal to zero). They are composed of an ordered pair of

numbers and they also express a ratio. A common fraction is composed of a numerator, denominator, and the line which separates the two parts. Examples of common fractions would be $\frac{1}{6}, \frac{3}{10}, \frac{47}{69}, \ldots$

4. *Proper fraction:* a common fraction that has a value less than one; or the denominator is greater than the numerator. For example $\frac{1}{2}, \frac{2}{3}, \frac{4}{5}, \frac{98}{101}, \ldots$

5. *Improper fraction:* a common fraction with a value greater than one; or the numerator is greater than the denominator. For example, $\frac{3}{2}, \frac{9}{7}, \frac{12}{10}, \frac{301}{100}, \ldots$

Note: The terms *proper fraction* and *improper fraction* are no longer recognized as being desirable terminology in fractions because the term improper fraction suggests that there is something wrong or undesirable, while proper fractions suggest desirability. Actually, both forms have their uses; we normally do not leave an answer as an improper fraction because it is more convenient to perceive as a mixed number. Thus both the proper and improper type fractions should be referred to as *fractions.*

6. *Mixed number:* an indicated sum of a whole number and a common fraction expressed as one number. It usually results from changing a fraction greater than one to a more convenient form. Examples of mixed numbers would be $3\frac{1}{5}$ or $\left(3 + \frac{1}{5}\right)$, $1\frac{6}{7}$ or $\left(1 + \frac{6}{7}\right)$, $14\frac{1}{2}$, or $\left(14 + \frac{1}{2}\right)$, $92\frac{1}{3}$ or $\left(92 + \frac{1}{3}\right), \ldots$

7. *Unit fraction:* any common fraction with a numerator of one. It is the basic unit of that particular fraction. For example, unit fractions would be $\frac{1}{3}, \frac{1}{11}, \frac{1}{18}, \frac{1}{26}, \frac{1}{113}, \ldots$

8. *Multiplicative inverse:* is the factor necessary to multiply another number by so that the product will be one. For example, the multiplicative inverse of 3 is $\frac{1}{3}$, the multiplicative inverse of $\frac{1}{5}$ is $\frac{5}{1}$ (or 5), the multiplicative inverse of $\frac{2}{7}$ is $\frac{7}{2} \ldots$ The multiplicative inverse is sometimes called a reciprocal.

9. *Decimal fractions:* a special group of common fractions in which the implied denominator is always 10 or a power of 10. Most important, these are positional fractions. Examples of decimal fractions, with the equivalent common fraction in parenthesis, are: $.7 = \left(\frac{7}{10}\right)$, $.03 = \left(\frac{3}{100}\right)$, $.001 = \left(\frac{1}{1000}\right), \ldots$

Basic Operations with Fractions

Basically there are three uses of fractions:

1. To make a comparison
2. To express division of one quantity by another.
3. To designate a certain quantity

Fractions may be added, subtracted, multiplied and divided. The concepts learned in working with whole numbers can be applied to fractions, but some of the properties that we found to be true in working with whole numbers do not hold true with fractions.

ADDITION

Addition is a putting-together process. When adding fractions that have the same denominator, such as: $\frac{1}{4} + \frac{1}{4}$, the student adds one and one and finds that he has two fourths. This concept is illustrated in Figure 8.12.

unity or whole

1 fourth + 1 fourth = 2 fourths

$$\frac{1}{4} \quad + \quad \frac{1}{4} \quad = \frac{2}{4}$$

unity or whole

1 third + 1 third = 2 thirds

$$\frac{1}{3} \quad + \quad \frac{1}{3} \quad = \frac{2}{3}$$

Figure 8.12

In introducing the algorism for adding fractions, the horizontal or equation form probably should be used at first, because the pupils will not be as likely to add the denominators as they would in the vertical algorism. As soon as the pupils begin understanding the addition of fractions, both the horizontal and vertical forms should be used.

The number line marked off in fractional parts is also useful in developing understanding of addition. The sum $\frac{1}{5} + \frac{2}{5} = \frac{3}{5}$ would be shown like this:

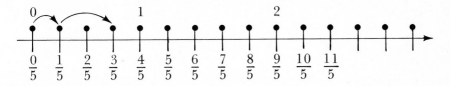

Similarly, the sum $\frac{1}{3} + \frac{1}{3} = \frac{2}{3}$ would be shown on a number line as follows:

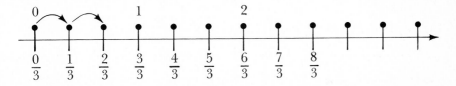

During the development of this skill, the teacher may need to emphasize the similarity of adding fractions to that of adding whole numbers, such as multiples of tens, like this:

$$
\begin{array}{ccc}
30 & & 3 \text{ tens} \\
40 & \equiv & 4 \text{ tens} \\
\hline
& & 7 \text{ tens} \quad \text{or} \quad 70
\end{array}
$$

In this addition, when we added three tens and four tens we got seven tens, not seven twenties (that is, we added only the cardinal numbers 3 and 4, but not the "tens" to the "tens"). In like fashion, in adding the fractions $\frac{1}{3}$ and $\frac{1}{3}$, we add only the numerators 1 and 1 and do not add the denominators; thus our answer is $\frac{2}{3}$. We could have counted our thirds to see how many we had, and we would have found that one third and one third would have given us two thirds. After the children have worked a number of similar problems, they should be led to make a generalization in their own terms concerning adding like fractions. This generalization would be phrased something like this: To add like fractions, add the numerators and place the sum over the same denominator.

After reasonable understanding of the addition of like fractions is achieved, the addition of like fractions whose sum would be a whole number may be introduced. For example, the number line could be used to show $\frac{3}{4} + \frac{1}{4} = \frac{4}{4} = 1$, like this:

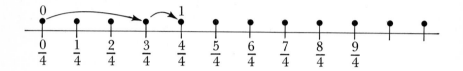

Or, geometric figures as shown in Figure 8.13 could be used.

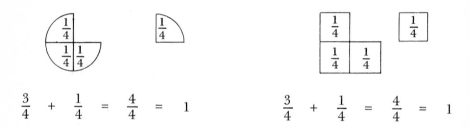

Figure 8.13

The children should be guided to realize that when the numerator and the denominator are the same, we rename the fraction as a whole number, for convenience. This can be related to grouping of whole numbers: when we get as many as ten ones, we regroup them into one group of ten. In fractions, for example, when we get four fourths, we regroup this into one group making a whole. Thus, if the teacher has postponed having fractional sums that are as large as one until reasonable mastery of the concept of adding fractions and its algorism is achieved, then the student will not be confronted with having to learn the algorism and the concept of grouping all at the same time.

The number line is useful in illustrating the concept of the adding of two common fractions whose sum is greater than one.

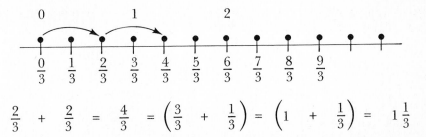

$$\frac{2}{3} + \frac{2}{3} = \frac{4}{3} = \left(\frac{3}{3} + \frac{1}{3}\right) = \left(1 + \frac{1}{3}\right) = 1\frac{1}{3}$$

In adding $\frac{2}{3}$ and $\frac{2}{3}$, the sum is $\frac{4}{3}$, but we rename it $1\frac{1}{3}$ for convenience and because of the previously mentioned aspect of grouping. Or this same addition can be illustrated with geometric figures, as shown both with circles and rectangles in Figure 8.14.

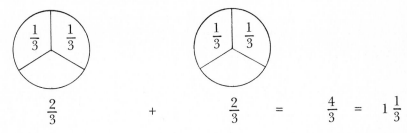

or like this:

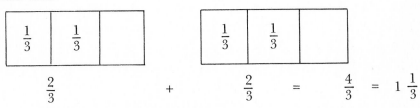

Figure 8.14

A mixed number represents the sum of a whole number and an additional fractional part. Following the addition of two fractions whose sum is greater than one, the adding of a mixed number and a fraction would be introduced. The sum $1\frac{1}{5} + \frac{3}{5} = 1\frac{4}{5}$ is illustrated in the number line below:

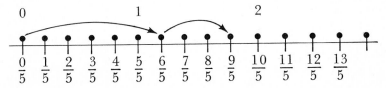

This sum could also be written as follows:

$$
\begin{array}{rll}
& 1 \text{ one} & + & 1 \text{ fifth} \\
+ & & & 3 \text{ fifths} \\
\hline
& 1 \text{ one} & + & 4 \text{ fifths}
\end{array}
$$

The introduction of two mixed numbers that have like fractions, but whose sum does not require carrying or regrouping, would be the next step. In this addition, we will utilize the expanded form in much the same manner as we did in adding a two-digit number to a two-digit number. Illustrating could be done like this:

$$1\frac{1}{3} \qquad + \qquad 2\frac{1}{3}$$

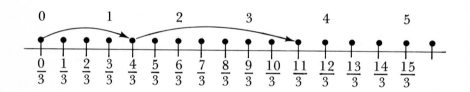

$$
\begin{array}{rcrcc}
& 1 \text{ one} & + & 1 \text{ third} & \quad 1 & + & \dfrac{1}{3} \\
+ & 2 \text{ ones} & + & 1 \text{ third} & \quad +2 & + & \dfrac{1}{3} \\
\hline
& 3 \text{ ones} & + & 2 \text{ thirds} & \quad 3 & + & \dfrac{2}{3}
\end{array}
$$

(with $\equiv$ between the two forms)

At this point, let's compare the algorism that we have just used with the algorism that we used in adding whole numbers. For example, let's compare the addition of 11 and 21 with the addition of $1\frac{1}{3}$ and $2\frac{1}{3}$.

1. Addition of whole numbers (11 + 21)

$$
\begin{array}{rlll}
 11 & \quad 1 \text{ ten} + 1 \text{ unit} & \quad 10 + 1 \\
+ 21 & \quad + 2 \text{ tens} + 1 \text{ unit} & \quad + 20 + 1 \\
\hline
32 & \quad 3 \text{ tens} + 2 \text{ units} & \quad 30 + 2 = 32
\end{array}
$$

2. Addition of fractions

$$1 \frac{1}{3}$$

$$+ \; 2 \frac{1}{3}$$

1 one + 1 third
+ 2 ones + 1 third
——————————
3 ones + 2 thirds

$$1 + \frac{1}{3}$$

$$+ \; 2 + \frac{1}{3}$$

——————

$$3 + \frac{2}{3}$$

The addition of two mixed numbers, with like fractions, whose sum involves regrouping should be introduced next. Once more it should be emphasized that we should utilize relatively the same method of teaching regrouping of fractions as we did in teaching regrouping of whole numbers. Thus, the addition of $3\frac{4}{5}$ and $5\frac{2}{5}$ would be as follows:

$$3 \frac{4}{5}$$

$$+ \; 5 \frac{2}{5}$$

3 ones + 4 fifths
+ 5 ones + 2 fifths
——————————
8 ones + 6 fifths

$$3 + \frac{4}{5}$$

$$+ \; 5 + \frac{2}{5}$$

————————

$$8 + \frac{6}{5}$$

8 units + 6 fifths	$= \; 8 + \frac{6}{5}$	
8 units + (1 unit + 1 fifth)	$= \; 8 + \left(\frac{5}{5} + \frac{1}{5}\right)$	
(8 units + 1 unit) + 1 fifth	$= \; (8 + \; 1) + \frac{1}{5}$	
9 units + 1 fifth	$= \; 9 + \frac{1}{5}$	$= 9\frac{1}{5}$

The addition of unlike fractions would be introduced following reasonable mastery of the adding of like fractions. If the rule of likeness has been stressed and understood while working with whole numbers, then the teaching of the addition of fractions should be easier. The rule of likeness tells us that we can only add like things. If things are not alike, they must be made alike before they can be added. A good way to illustrate the importance of the rule of likeness is to try to add three cats and four dogs. First-grade pupils will know you cannot do this because the things you are trying to add are not alike. In order to add these two things, we must first rename, or reclassify, them with a name that is common to both. In this case both the cats and dogs are animals, so now we can add three (cat) animals and four (dog) animals, and our answer will be in terminology common to both:

$$
\begin{array}{r}
3 \text{ (cat) animals} \\
+4 \text{ (dog) animals} \\
\hline
7 \text{ animals}
\end{array}
$$

In the beginning stages of teaching addition of unlike fractions, it would probably be best to teach the addition of unlike fractions in which one denominator is a multiple of the other, such as halves and fourths. In this way, knowledge of equivalent fractions can be utilized. For example $\frac{1}{2} + \frac{1}{4}$ could be illustrated:

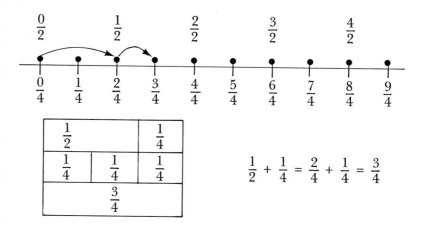

$$\frac{1}{2} + \frac{1}{4} = \frac{2}{4} + \frac{1}{4} = \frac{3}{4}$$

PRIME NUMBERS

Before proceeding further in the addition of unlike fractions (fractions that do not have the same denominator), we need to look at the meaning of prime numbers and the use of prime numbers in finding common denominators for fractions.

A prime number is a whole number larger than one which has only itself and one as factors. Other whole numbers are known as *composite numbers,* because they are a composite of factors other than themselves and one. Elementary school children can use a device known as the Sieve of Eratosthenes to find the prime numbers less than 100. To make this device, use either a number line to 100 or a table of numbers to 100, as shown in Figure 8.15.

1	(2)	(3)	~~4~~	(5)	~~6~~	(7)	~~8~~	~~9~~	~~10~~
(11)	~~12~~	(13)	~~14~~	~~15~~	~~16~~	(17)	~~18~~	(19)	~~20~~
~~21~~	~~22~~	(23)	~~24~~	~~25~~	~~26~~	~~27~~	~~28~~	(29)	~~30~~
(31)	~~32~~	~~33~~	~~34~~	~~35~~	~~36~~	(37)	~~38~~	~~39~~	~~40~~
(41)	~~42~~	(43)	~~44~~	~~45~~	~~46~~	(47)	~~48~~	~~49~~	~~50~~
~~51~~	~~52~~	(53)	~~54~~	~~55~~	~~56~~	~~57~~	~~58~~	(59)	~~60~~
(61)	~~62~~	~~63~~	~~64~~	~~65~~	~~66~~	(67)	~~68~~	~~69~~	~~70~~
(71)	~~72~~	(73)	~~74~~	~~75~~	~~76~~	~~77~~	~~78~~	(79)	~~80~~
~~81~~	~~82~~	(83)	~~84~~	~~85~~	~~86~~	~~87~~	~~88~~	(89)	~~90~~
~~91~~	~~92~~	~~93~~	~~94~~	~~95~~	~~96~~	(97)	~~98~~	~~99~~	~~100~~

Figure 8.15

Take the first prime, 2, and then cross out all other numbers which have 2 as a factor; these are composite numbers. Then progress through the set of counting numbers, dividing by the prime numbers 3, 5, 7, and others, and cross out the numbers that have these primes as factors. During the time the children are working with this array of numbers, the teacher should stress an awareness of the patterns and relationships that are present. On completion, the children should have found that the prime numbers less than 100 are 2, 3, 5, 7, 11, 13, 17, 19, 23, 29, 31, 37, 41, 43, 47, 53, 59, 61, 67, 71, 73, 79, 83, 89, and 97.

The number 1 is considered by some as a prime number, but generally it is considered as neither a prime nor a composite because it has the unique distinction of having every other whole number as a multiple of itself. The numbers that are not crossed out are prime numbers and the numbers crossed out are composite numbers. At this point, the children should be guided to make the generalization that *composite numbers are the product of two, or more, prime factors.* Thus any composite number can be written or expressed as a product of two or more prime factors. This process of expressing a composite number as a product of two or more factors is known as *factoring.*

Children should first learn to factor small numbers. Four has the factors of (2 × 2); another name for four is (2 × 2). It is usually symbolized in this way:

A number such as 12 has a more complicated form:

The child should begin factoring with the smallest prime number that he can use, trying the 2 first, then the 3, and so on until he finds a prime that will divide evenly into the composite number.

This process is used in finding the lowest common denominator for the addition or subtraction of fractions. Consider the sum $\frac{1}{2} + \frac{1}{4}$ and rewrite it $\frac{1}{2} + \frac{1}{(2 \times 2)}$ after factoring the 4. The union of the sets (2) and (2 × 2) would be (2 × 2). The first 2 is contained in (2 × 2) two times and (2 × 2) is contained in it one time. Thus:

$$\frac{1}{2} + \frac{1}{(2 \times 2)} = \frac{(2 \times 1) + (1 \times 1)}{(2 \times 2)} = \frac{2 + 1}{2 \times 2} = \frac{3}{4}.$$

A more complicated example would be when adding fractions where both denominators could be factored, as in the following:

$$\frac{5}{6} + \frac{7}{12} = \frac{5}{2 \times 3} + \frac{7}{2 \times 6} = \frac{5}{2 \times 3} + \frac{7}{2 \times 2 \times 3}$$

The new set for the denominator would be (2 × 3 × 2). Place the 2 × 3 × 2 in the position of the denominator. The 6, or (2 × 3), which is another name for 6, is contained in the new denominator two times. The 12 or (2 × 2 × 3) is contained in it one time. The symbolization would look like this:

$$\frac{5}{6} + \frac{7}{12} = \frac{5}{2 \times 3} + \frac{7}{2 \times 2 \times 3} = \frac{5(2) + 7(1)}{2 \times 2 \times 3}$$

$$= \frac{10 + 7}{2 \times 2 \times 3} = \frac{17}{12} \text{ or } 1\frac{5}{12}$$

If the child were adding such numbers as $\frac{5}{24} + \frac{7}{36}$, he would need to factor the 24 and 36 on paper to see where they intersect.

The factors of 24 are (2 × 2 × 2 × 3)

The factors of 36 are (2 × 2 × 3 × 3)

The set of factors of 24 or (2 × 2 × 2 × 3) intersects the set of factors of 36 (2 × 2 × 3 × 3) at (2 × 2 × 3). In other words the common factors are (2 × 2 × 3). The new set which would contain both sets would be (2 × 2 × 2 × 3 × 3). When you match the sets you find that 24 or (2 X 2 X 2 X 3) is contained in the new set 3 times; 36 or (2 X 2 X 3 X 3) is contained in the new set 2 times. The algorism is given below:

$$\frac{5}{24} + \frac{7}{36} = \frac{5}{2 \times 2 \times 2 \times 3} + \frac{7}{2 \times 2 \times 3 \times 3} = \frac{5(3) + 7(2)}{2 \times 2 \times 2 \times 3 \times 3}$$

$$= \frac{15 + 14}{72} = \frac{29}{72}$$

The child will not use the large numbers often in real life problems, but, the faster learners are challenged by the process and it gives them readiness for using the process in algebra. The difficulty of the examples given to the child should be determined by his ability to understand the process.

Another important use of prime factors is to use them to express fractions in their lowest terms. In this operation, both the numerator and denominator are expressed as the product of the prime factors. The prime factors common to both numerator and denominator are then divided out (not cancelled out) of both numerator and denominator. We can divide the same number out of both numerator and denominator, because we are, in effect, dividing the entire number by 1. Since one is the identity element of division, dividing a number by 1 does not change the value of the number. If we were simplifying the fraction $\frac{54}{81}$, we would proceed like this:

1. Determine prime factors in numerator and denominator

$$\frac{54}{81} = \frac{2 \times 3 \times 3 \times 3}{3 \times 3 \times 3 \times 3}$$

2. Divide common factors out of both numerator and denominator

$$= \frac{2 \times (\cancel{3}) \times (\cancel{3}) \times (\cancel{3})}{3 \times (\cancel{3}) \times (\cancel{3}) \times (\cancel{3})}$$

$$= \frac{2 \times 1 \times 1 \times 1}{3 \times 1 \times 1 \times 1} = \frac{2}{3}$$

More examples of the use of factoring in the addition of fractions with denominators that are not alike follow:

a. $\dfrac{3}{5} + \dfrac{3}{10} = \dfrac{3}{5} + \dfrac{3}{2 \times 5} = \dfrac{3(2) + 3(1)}{2 \times 5} = \dfrac{6 + 3}{10} = \dfrac{9}{10}$

b. $\dfrac{3}{10} + \dfrac{7}{15} = \dfrac{3}{2 \times 5} + \dfrac{7}{3 \times 5} = \dfrac{3(3) + 7(2)}{2 \times 3 \times 5} = \dfrac{9 + 14}{30} = \dfrac{23}{30}$.

The union of (2×5) and $(3 \times 5) = 2 \times 3 \times 5$; (2×5) is contained in the new set 3 times; (3×5) is contained in the new set 2 times. We then add $\dfrac{9}{30}$ to $\dfrac{14}{30}$.

c. $\dfrac{7}{12} + \dfrac{5}{18} = \dfrac{7}{2 \times 2 \times 3} + \dfrac{5}{2 \times 3 \times 3} = \dfrac{7(3) + 5(2)}{2 \times 2 \times 3 \times 3} = \dfrac{21 + 10}{36} = \dfrac{31}{36}$.

The union of $2 \times 2 \times 3$ and $2 \times 3 \times 3$ is $(2 \times 2 \times 3 \times 3)$
$2 \times 2 \times 3$ is contained in the new set 3 times
$2 \times 3 \times 3$ is contained in the new set 2 times

SUBTRACTION

Before we begin teaching the operation of subtraction of fractions, we must develop readiness for this skill. This readiness for subtraction of fractions would include a reasonable mastery and understanding of subtraction of whole numbers; the laws governing subtraction; and the concept of fractions. Also, if we think of addition as a putting-together process, then subtraction, the inverse of addition, would be thought of as a taking-apart process. Or, if we think of addition as a counting forward process, then subtraction is a counting backward process.

In beginning to teach the subtraction of fractions, we should follow the same general order that we did in teaching the addition of fractions. It is also well to remind the pupils of the similarity of operations with whole numbers and operations with fractions. It should be remembered that we taught addition of whole numbers well before introducing subtraction so that there would be less likelihood that the pupils would confuse these two operations with each other. This same timing should be applied to the teaching of fractions.

While there are three different meanings or interpretations of subtraction (the take-away idea, the comparison idea, and the missing additive), there is only one algorism. We should begin with taking away, or subtraction of like fractions, (fractions that have the same denominator). At first the children should take apart physical models and count the fractional parts remaining. Figure 8.16 shows how the teacher would symbolize on the chalkboard what they had done with concrete materials.

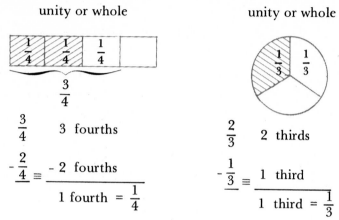

$$\frac{3}{4} \qquad 3 \text{ fourths}$$

$$-\frac{2}{4} \equiv \underline{\quad -2 \text{ fourths} \quad}$$

$$1 \text{ fourth} = \frac{1}{4}$$

$$\frac{2}{3} \qquad 2 \text{ thirds}$$

$$-\frac{1}{3} \equiv \underline{\quad 1 \text{ third} \quad}$$

$$1 \text{ third} = \frac{1}{3}$$

Figure 8.16

The same type of subtraction could be illustrated on the number line as shown below for $\frac{4}{5} - \frac{2}{5}$:

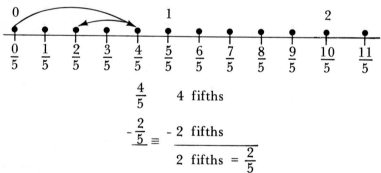

$$\frac{4}{5} \qquad 4 \text{ fifths}$$

$$-\frac{2}{5} \equiv \underline{\quad -2 \text{ fifths} \quad}$$

$$2 \text{ fifths} = \frac{2}{5}$$

During the development of this skill, the teacher will need to emphasize the similarity of subtracting fractions to that of subtracting whole numbers. For example, subtracting multiples of ten is shown like this:

$$\begin{array}{ll} 40 & 4 \text{ tens} \\ -20 \equiv & \underline{-2 \text{ tens}} \\ \overline{20} & 2 \text{ tens or } 20 \end{array}$$

In subtracting whole numbers, the position of the number tells the kind of number (for example the 4 in 40 signifies that it represents 4 tens), while in a fraction, the denominator tells the kind of number. Consequently, the children should be led to generalize that in subtracting like fractions, we only subtract the numerators (not numerators *and* denominators), and then place the remainder or difference over the given denominator.

After reasonable mastery of the subtraction of like fractions is achieved, the subtraction of a fraction from a whole number can be introduced. It will be remembered that in addition of like fractions when the numerator and the denominator were the same number, we renamed the fraction, one. In subtraction we will do the inverse of this by renaming one (or a whole number) to its equivalent fraction with a common denominator. To do this we must develop the concept that one (the unit) contains $\frac{3}{3}$, or $\frac{4}{4}$, or $\frac{7}{7}$, or $\frac{9}{9}$, or the same number of parts in the numerator as there are in the denominator. The number line is an excellent material to use in illustrating this. It can be seen below that 1 is equivalent to $\frac{4}{4}$, thus the subtraction $1 - \frac{3}{4}$ or $\frac{4}{4} - \frac{3}{4}$ is easily accomplished:

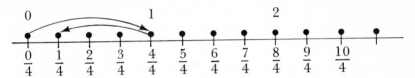

However, in working with the algorism, the solution is not that apparent. Since we cannot subtract $\frac{3}{4}$ from $\frac{0}{4}$, we must rename 1 as $\frac{4}{4}$ and regroup:

1	1 unit + 0 fourths	4 fourths + 0 fourths	4 fourths
$-\frac{3}{4} \equiv$	$-$ 3 fourths $\equiv$	$-$ 3 fourths $\equiv$	$-$ 3 fourths
			1 fourth $= \frac{1}{4}$

$$1\frac{0}{4} \qquad 1 + \frac{0}{4} \qquad \frac{4}{4} + \frac{0}{4} \qquad \frac{4}{4}$$
$$-\frac{3}{4} \equiv \qquad -\frac{3}{4} \equiv \qquad -\frac{3}{4} \equiv \qquad -\frac{3}{4}$$
$$\frac{1}{4}$$

The students should then progress to subtracting mixed numbers with like fractions involving regrouping. Figure 8.17 shows how they can make models with their concrete materials to perform the subtraction $\left(3\frac{1}{3} - 1\frac{2}{3}\right)$.

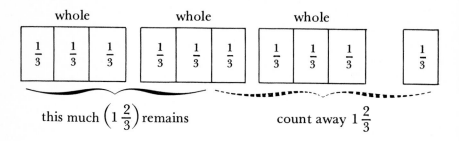

Figure 8.17

This same example could be worked with a number line like this:

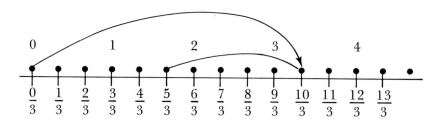

When the students begin making the transition from the materials to the algorism, they should be reminded of the method of regrouping used in subtracting whole numbers, for example, $(31 - 12)$:

$$\begin{array}{r} 31 \\ -\ 12 \end{array} \equiv \begin{array}{r} 3 \text{ tens } + \ 1 \text{ unit} \\ -\ (1 \text{ ten } + \ 2 \text{ units}) \end{array} \equiv \begin{array}{r} 2 \text{ tens } + \ 11 \text{ units} \\ -\ (1 \text{ ten } + \ \ 2 \text{ units}) \\ \hline 1 \text{ ten } + \ \ 9 \text{ units } = 19. \end{array}$$

This is written in a more concise form:

$$\begin{array}{r}
31 \\
- 12 \\
\hline
\end{array} \equiv \begin{array}{r}
30 + 1 \\
- (10 + 2) \\
\hline
\end{array} \equiv \begin{array}{r}
20 + 11 \\
- (10 + 2) \\
\hline
10 + 9 = 19.
\end{array}$$

In much the same manner, $3\frac{1}{3} - 1\frac{2}{3}$ would be subtracted like this:

$$\begin{array}{r}
3\frac{1}{3} \\
- 1\frac{2}{3} \\
\hline
\end{array} \equiv \begin{array}{r}
3 + \frac{1}{3} \\
- \left(1 + \frac{2}{3}\right) \\
\hline
\end{array} \equiv \begin{array}{r}
2 + \left(\frac{3}{3} + \frac{1}{3}\right) \\
- \left(1 + \frac{2}{3}\right) \\
\hline
\end{array} \equiv \begin{array}{r}
2 + \frac{4}{3} \\
- \left(1 + \frac{2}{3}\right) \\
\hline
1 + \frac{2}{3} = 1\frac{2}{3}
\end{array}$$

Progressing next to subtracting unlike fractions, the students should not encounter any unusual difficulty with this part of learning the operation if they have achieved reasonable mastery of determining prime factors and common denominators. Once more, pupils can be shown an application for a previously learned skill.

In the beginning stages of teaching subtraction of unlike fractions, it would probably be best to utilize problems like $\frac{3}{4} - \frac{1}{2}$ that have one fraction which is a multiple of the other, as shown in the number line below:

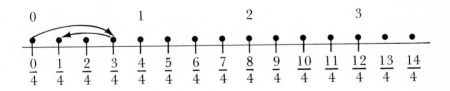

These are unlike fractions, but we can rename $\frac{1}{2}$ as $\frac{2}{4}$, and they are then like fractions:

$$\begin{array}{c} \dfrac{3}{4} \\ -\dfrac{1}{2} \end{array} \equiv \begin{array}{c} \dfrac{3}{4} \\ -\dfrac{2}{4} \\ \hline \dfrac{1}{4} \end{array} \quad \text{or} \quad \frac{3}{4} - \frac{1}{2} = \frac{3}{4} - \frac{2}{4} = \frac{1}{4}.$$

It will be recalled that in adding unlike fractions, there are limitations to this method of determining common denominators, because when fractions are not multiples of each other, the equivalent fractions with like denominators are not readily apparent. Consequently, we will need to use prime factorization and then determine the least common multiple of the two denominators involved. The rule of likeness (if things are not alike they must be made alike because only like things can be subtracted) needs to be reemphasized. It should be pointed out that we utilize the prime factor method of determining common denominators so that we can rename the original, unlike fractions to their equivalent fractions that have like denominators. If we were subtracting $\frac{7}{18} - \frac{5}{24}$, we could proceed like this:

$$\frac{7}{18} - \frac{5}{24} = \frac{7}{2 \times 3 \times 3} - \frac{5}{2 \times 2 \times 2 \times 3}$$

$$18 \begin{array}{l} \nearrow \searrow \\ 2 \times 9 \\ \nearrow \searrow \\ 2 \times (3 \times 3) \end{array} \qquad 24 \begin{array}{l} \nearrow \searrow \\ 2 \times 12 \\ \nearrow | \searrow \\ 2 \times 2 \times 2 \times 3 \end{array}$$

The union of these two sets of prime factors is made:

$$\{2 \times 3 \times 3\} \cup \{2 \times 2 \times 2 \times 3\} = \{2 \times 2 \times 2 \times 3 \times 3\}$$

Thus, the common denominator of 18 and 24 is the product of $(2 \times 2 \times 2 \times 3 \times 3)$ or 72. The quantity $(2 \times 3 \times 3)$ is contained in the new set 2×2 times; $(2 \times 2 \times 2 \times 3)$ is contained in the new set 3 times. The algorism would look like this:

$$\frac{7}{18} - \frac{5}{24} = \frac{7}{2\times3\times3} - \frac{5}{2\times2\times2\times3} = \frac{7(2\times2)}{2\times2\times2\times3\times3} - \frac{5(3)}{2\times2\times2\times3\times3} - \frac{7(2\times2)-5(3)}{2\times2\times2\times3\times3}$$

$$= \frac{28-15}{2\times2\times2\times3\times3} = \frac{13}{2\times2\times2\times3\times3} = \frac{13}{72}.$$

Subtraction of mixed numbers with unlike fractions could then be taught by utilizing the expanded form and determining the common denominator. For example, $2\frac{7}{18} - 1\frac{5}{12}$ has the common denominator $(2 \times 2 \times 3 \times 3)$ or 36, so the subtraction algorism would be as follows:

$$\frac{2 + \dfrac{7\,(2)}{2 \times 2 \times 3 \times 3}}{-\left(1 + \dfrac{5\,(3)}{2 \times 2 \times 3 \times 3}\right)} \equiv \frac{2 + \dfrac{14}{36}}{-\left(1 + \dfrac{15}{36}\right)} \equiv \frac{1 + \dfrac{36}{36} + \dfrac{14}{36}}{-\left(1 + \dfrac{15}{36}\right)} \equiv \frac{1 + \dfrac{50}{36}}{-\left(1 + \dfrac{15}{36}\right).}{\dfrac{35}{36}}$$

MULTIPLICATION

Before beginning teaching multiplication of fractions, there are some readiness activities from which children could profit. Figure 8.18 shows such activities as putting together equal-size fraction parts, counting in equal-size fractions on a number line and performing addition algorisms for equal-size fractions.

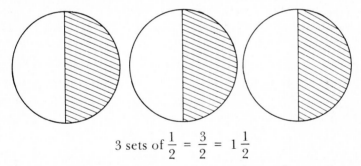

$$\text{3 sets of } \frac{1}{2} = \frac{3}{2} = 1\frac{1}{2}$$

Counting 4 sets of $\frac{2}{5}$ on the number line gives $\frac{8}{5}$ or $1\frac{3}{5}$:

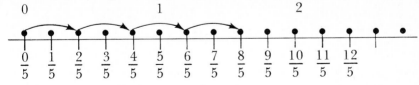

The algorism for adding 5 sets of $\frac{3}{4}$:

$$\frac{3}{4} + \frac{3}{4} + \frac{3}{4} + \frac{3}{4} + \frac{3}{4} = \text{5 sets of } \frac{3}{4} = \frac{15}{4} = 3\frac{3}{4}$$

Figure 8.18

In the beginning phase of teaching multiplication of fractions, the teacher should relate this process as much as possible to that of multiplying whole numbers. The previously described readiness activities are designed to lead into multiplication of fractions. In multiplying fractions, the first method to be developed should be the multiplication of a whole number times a fraction, because it more readily relates to the previously learned concept of multiplication of whole numbers. Using the example of 4 groups or sets of $\frac{3}{4}$, we could illustrate it as shown in Figure 8.19.

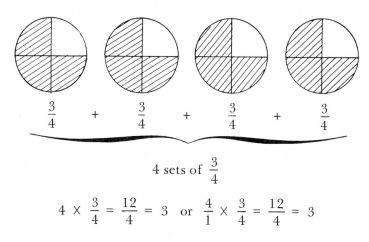

$$4 \times \frac{3}{4} = \frac{12}{4} = 3 \quad \text{or} \quad \frac{4}{1} \times \frac{3}{4} = \frac{12}{4} = 3$$

Figure 8.19

The number line used like this shows the same process:

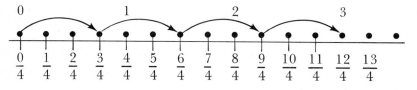

We can see that $\frac{3}{4} + \frac{3}{4} + \frac{3}{4} + \frac{3}{4}$ equals four sets of $\frac{3}{4}$. Thus, $4 \times \frac{3}{4} = \frac{12}{4} = 3$, or we can write $\frac{4}{1} \times \frac{3}{4} = \frac{12}{4} = 3$.

After using several examples in which a whole number is multiplied by a fraction, the teacher should guide the pupils to generalize and make a rule for multiplying a whole number and a fraction. the generalization, in the pupil's terms, should be something like this: to multiply a whole number times a fraction, multiply the whole number times the numerator of the fraction, and divide by (or place the product over) the denominator of the fraction.

A word of caution is in order at this point: *Do not guide the pupils too quickly into the commutative property of multiplication.* The reason for this word of caution is that we can interpret $4 \times \frac{3}{4}$ to be taking $\frac{3}{4}$ as an addend 4 times $\left(\frac{3}{4} + \frac{3}{4} + \frac{3}{4} + \frac{3}{4} \right)$, but when we turn it around to $\frac{3}{4} \times 4$, this would have to be interpreted as taking 4 as an addend $\frac{3}{4}$ of a time. Symbolizing 4 as an addend $\frac{3}{4}$ of a time would be rather difficult; however, concrete materials, geometric figures and the number line can be used (Fig. 8.20) to symbolize the product $\frac{3}{4} \times 4$.

It may have become apparent from the examples illustrated in Figure 8.20 that this problem was solved by using partitioning division. If you will go back and check the examples of multiplying a whole number times a fraction, you will find that those examples were solved by measurement division. After several opportunities to work with similar examples, the children should attempt, with teacher guidance, to generalize a rule for multiplying a fraction times a whole number. The generalization, in pupil terms, should be something like this: To multiply a fraction by a whole number, multiply the numerator by the whole number and divide this product by (or place this product over) the denominator. If we compare the rule previously developed for multiplying a whole number by a fraction with the one just developed, we can note that for all practical purposes they are the same. Now it should not be too difficult to develop an understanding of the commutative property of multiplying a fraction times a whole number or a whole number times a fraction.

After formulating the rule for multiplying fractions and whole numbers, the pupils will be guided into determining a method for multiplying a fraction by a fraction. Once more it is emphasized that the multiplication of fractions should be related to the multiplication of whole numbers. If 4×3 is interpreted to mean "4 sets of 3," then $\frac{1}{2} \times \frac{1}{3}$ should be interpreted to mean $\frac{1}{2}$ of a set of $\frac{1}{3}$. The importance of using geometric figures in helping children develop understanding must not be overlooked, especially in learning to multiply fractions. It would be difficult for the students to perceive the multiplication of $\frac{1}{2} \times \frac{1}{3}$ as

Concrete Materials

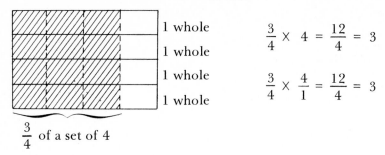

1 whole

1 whole

1 whole

1 whole

$$\frac{3}{4} \times 4 = \frac{12}{4} = 3$$

$$\frac{3}{4} \times \frac{4}{1} = \frac{12}{4} = 3$$

$\frac{3}{4}$ of a set of 4

Geometric Figures

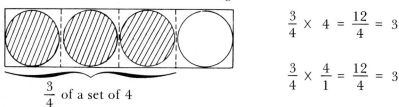

$\frac{3}{4}$ of a set of 4

$$\frac{3}{4} \times 4 = \frac{12}{4} = 3$$

$$\frac{3}{4} \times \frac{4}{1} = \frac{12}{4} = 3$$

Number Line

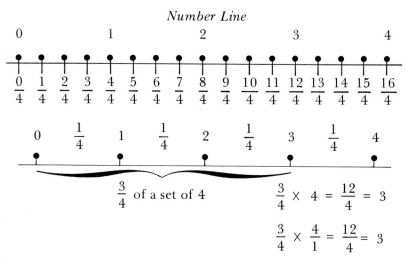

$\frac{3}{4}$ of a set of 4

$$\frac{3}{4} \times 4 = \frac{12}{4} = 3$$

$$\frac{3}{4} \times \frac{4}{1} = \frac{12}{4} = 3$$

Figure 8.20

meaning $\frac{1}{3}$ taken as an addend $\frac{1}{2}$ of one time, but with geometric figures the children can see for themselves the relations necessary to development of understanding.

Geometric figures can be used as shown in Figure 8.21 to illustrate the multiplication $\frac{1}{2} \times \frac{1}{3}$. Observing these illustrations, the pupils can see

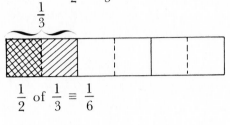

$$\frac{1}{2} \text{ of } \frac{1}{3} \equiv \frac{1}{6}$$

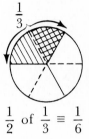

$$\frac{1}{2} \text{ of } \frac{1}{3} \equiv \frac{1}{6}$$

Figure 8.21

that we subdivided the set of $\frac{1}{3}$ into 2 equal parts (or we divided it into halves). The pupils will probably need help in naming the new part that resulted from this operation. We use the entire unit, divided into thirds. If each of these thirds is halved, then there are 6 equal parts, or each part would be a sixth. Also it can be recalled from equivalent fractions that $\frac{1}{3}$ can be renamed $\frac{2}{6}$. Now if we take $\frac{1}{2}$ of $\frac{2}{6}$, we would again have $\frac{1}{6}$. The following number line shows thirds renamed as sixths:

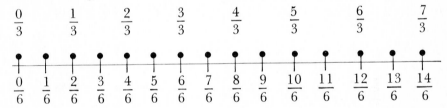

It could be used as shown below to illustrate the multiplication $\frac{1}{2} \times \frac{1}{3}$.

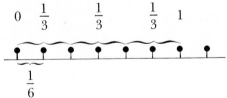

Both the geometric figures (Fig. 8.21) and the number line illustration show that by halving one-third we have created two new, smaller units called sixths. Thus, $\frac{1}{2}$ of a set of $\frac{1}{3}$ would be $\frac{1}{6}$.

Consider the example: $\frac{3}{4} \times \frac{2}{3} \equiv \frac{3}{4}$ of a set of $\frac{2}{3}$. In this example the pupil begins by dividing a whole into thirds (Fig. 8.22), and then designates 2 of the thirds. Since he is seeking $\frac{3}{4}$ of $\frac{2}{3}$, he would then divide the whole into fourths (in the other direction, making 12 parts in the whole) and use 3 of the 4 sections within the designated 2 thirds part, as shown in Figure 8.22.

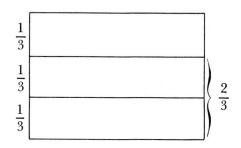

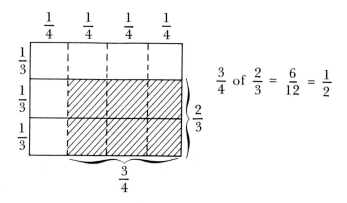

$$\frac{3}{4} \text{ of } \frac{2}{3} = \frac{6}{12} = \frac{1}{2}$$

Figure 8.22

Thus, in finding $\frac{3}{4}$ of $\frac{2}{3}$, he has involved 6 of the 12 parts.

Figure 8.23 illustrates another example: $\frac{2}{3} \times \frac{5}{6}$. This time $\frac{2}{3}$ of a set of $\frac{5}{6}$ is sought, and it is shown that 10 of the 18 parts are involved.

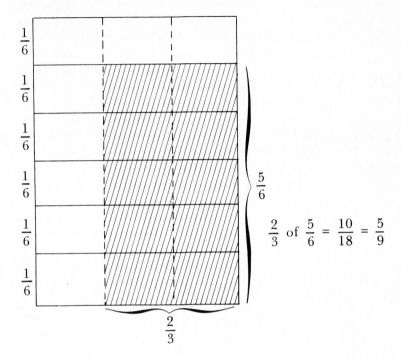

Figure 8.23

After numerous opportunities to work problems similar to these, pupils should be guided to develop a rule for multiplying a fraction times a fraction. Probably some of the faster pupils will have already discovered the rule. In general, the pupil's rule should be something like this, (in their own terminology): To multiply a fraction by a fraction, multiply the numerator of one fraction by the numerator of the other fraction and place this product over the product of one denominator multiplied by the other denominator.

We can now finish developing an understanding of the commutative property of multiplication of fractions. We can take $\frac{1}{2} \times \frac{1}{3}$ and $\frac{1}{3} \times \frac{1}{2}$ and illustrate these two operations with the geometric figures shown in Figure 8.24.

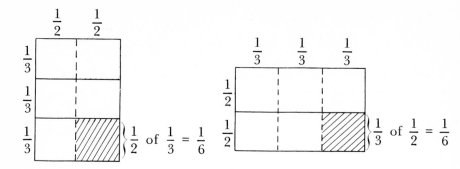

Figure 8.24

It can be seen that these two illustrations are not exactly alike, but the product of each is same. After numerous other examples similar to this one, the pupils, with teacher guidance, can probably generalize that although the two examples are not exactly the same, when we are seeking only the product, we can multiply the first number by the second or the second number by the first and get the same product.

The next phase of teaching multiplication of fractions is multiplying fractions and mixed numbers. In this multiplication we will utilize two previously learned skills, the distributive property of multiplication and renaming a number to its equivalent fraction. Two different methods of multiplying fractions and mixed numbers will be discussed. The first method will utilize the distributive property of multiplication. It will be recalled that a mixed number was described as an indicated sum of a fraction and a whole number. To multiply $\frac{2}{3} \times 4\frac{1}{3}$, we could proceed like this:

1. Rename the multiplicand as an indicated sum.

$$\frac{2}{3} \times \left(4 + \frac{1}{3}\right)$$

2. Distribute multiplication—by doing this we have broken the problem into two parts that we already know how to work: multiplying a fraction times a whole number and multiplying a fraction times a fraction.

$$\left(\frac{2}{3} \times 4\right) + \left(\frac{2}{3} \times \frac{1}{3}\right)$$
$$= \frac{8}{3} + \frac{2}{9}$$

3. Now we need a common denominator, so rename $\frac{8}{3}$ as its equivalent fraction in ninths, $\frac{24}{9}$

$$\frac{8}{3} + \frac{2}{9} = \frac{24}{9} + \frac{2}{9}$$

4. Complete the indicated process.

$$\frac{24}{9} + \frac{2}{9} = \frac{26}{9} = 2\frac{8}{9}$$

This same process is illustrated by the example, $\frac{1}{4} \times 3\frac{1}{2}$:

Rename the multiplicand.

$$\frac{1}{4} \times \left(3 + \frac{1}{2} \right)$$

Distribute multiplication.

$$= \left(\frac{1}{4} \times 3 \right) + \left(\frac{1}{4} \times \frac{1}{2} \right)$$

Rename $\frac{3}{4}$ to its equivalent fraction in eighths, $\frac{6}{8}$.

$$= \frac{3}{4} + \frac{1}{8}$$

$$= \frac{6}{8} + \frac{1}{8} = \frac{7}{8}$$

Using the distributive property when multiplying a whole number times a mixed number is even more efficient. Consider the example, $3 \times 4\frac{1}{2}$:

Rename the multiplicand.

$$3 \times \left(4 + \frac{1}{2} \right)$$

Distribute multiplication.

$$= (3 \times 4) + \left(3 \times \frac{1}{2} \right)$$

$$= 12 + \frac{3}{2}$$

$$= 12 + 1\frac{1}{2} = 13\frac{1}{2}$$

Another example of a whole number times a mixed number, using the distributive property is the product $3 \times 2\frac{3}{4}$:

Rename multiplicand.
$$3 \times \left(2 + \frac{3}{4}\right)$$

Distribute multiplication.
$$= (3 \times 2) + \left(3 \times \frac{3}{4}\right)$$

Rename $\frac{9}{4}$ to $2\frac{1}{4}$.
$$= 6 + \frac{9}{4}$$

$$= 6 + 2\frac{1}{4} = 8\frac{1}{4}$$

By extending this method, we can develop a method for multiplying a mixed number times a mixed number, for example $4\frac{1}{3} \times 3\frac{1}{4}$:

Rename both multiplier and multiplicand.
$$\left(4 + \frac{1}{3}\right) \times \left(3 + \frac{1}{4}\right)$$

Distribute multiplication.
$$= (4 \times 3) + \left(4 \times \frac{1}{4}\right) +$$
$$\left(\frac{1}{3} \times 3\right) + \left(\frac{1}{3} \times \frac{1}{4}\right)$$

Rename $\frac{4}{4}$ and $\frac{3}{3}$ each to 1.
$$= 12 + \frac{4}{4} + \frac{3}{3} + \frac{1}{12}$$

$$= 12 + 1 + 1 + \frac{1}{2} = 14\frac{1}{12}.$$

It can be seen in the above example that by renaming both the multiplier and the multiplicand and then applying the distributive property of multiplication, we have reduced the solution of this problem to the sum of four products, all of which we have previously learned. Another example using a mixed number would be the product $2\frac{1}{5} \times 5\frac{1}{7}$:

Rename multiplier and multiplicand. $\left(2 + \dfrac{1}{5}\right) \times \left(5 + \dfrac{1}{7}\right)$

Distribute multiplication. $= (2 \times 5) + \left(2 \times \dfrac{1}{7}\right) + \left(\dfrac{1}{5} \times 5\right) + \left(\dfrac{1}{5} \times \dfrac{1}{7}\right)$

Rename $\dfrac{2}{7}$ to $\dfrac{10}{35}$. $= 10 + \dfrac{2}{7} + 1 + \dfrac{1}{35}$

$= 10 + \dfrac{10}{35} + 1 + \dfrac{1}{35}$

$= (10 + 1) + \left(\dfrac{10}{35} + \dfrac{1}{35}\right) = 11\dfrac{11}{35}$

The second method of multiplying a fraction by a mixed number involves renaming the mixed number into its equivalent fraction, and then proceeding by multiplying a fraction by a fraction. Consider, for example, the product $\dfrac{2}{3} \times 3\dfrac{3}{4}$:

Rename the multiplicand. $\dfrac{2}{3} \times \left(3 + \dfrac{3}{4}\right)$

Rename 3 to its equivalent fraction in fourths, $\dfrac{12}{4}$. $= \dfrac{2}{3} \times \left(\dfrac{12}{4} + \dfrac{3}{4}\right) =$

Combine multiplicand, and then proceed to multiply a fraction times a fraction. $= \dfrac{2}{3} \times \dfrac{15}{4}$

$= \dfrac{30}{12} = 2\dfrac{6}{12} = 2\dfrac{1}{2}$

Another example of multiplying a fraction by a mixed number by renaming the mixed number to its equivalent fraction would be the product $\dfrac{4}{7} \times 5\dfrac{1}{3}$:

Rename the multiplicand.

$$\frac{4}{7} \times \left(5 + \frac{1}{3}\right)$$

Rename 5 to its equivalent fraction in thirds, $\frac{15}{3}$.

$$= \frac{4}{7} \times \left(\frac{15}{3} + \frac{1}{3}\right)$$

Combine multiplicand, and then proceed to multiply a fraction times a fraction.

$$= \frac{4}{7} \times \frac{16}{3}$$

$$= \frac{4 \times 16}{7 \times 3} = \frac{64}{21} = 3\frac{1}{21}$$

To use this same method to multiply a mixed number times a mixed number, we must rename both multiplier and multiplicand to their equivalent fractions and then multiply as we did in multiplying a fraction times a fraction. This is done in the following example, $1\frac{2}{9} \times 2\frac{3}{7}$:

Expressing problem in expanded form.

$$\left(1 + \frac{2}{9}\right) \times \left(2 + \frac{3}{7}\right)$$

Rename 1 in multiplier to its equivalent fraction in ninths, $\frac{9}{9}$; and rename the 2 in the multiplicand to its equivalent fraction in sevenths, $\frac{14}{7}$.

$$= \left(\frac{9}{9} + \frac{2}{9}\right) \times \left(\frac{14}{7} + \frac{3}{7}\right)$$

Combine terms in multiplier and in multiplicand.

$$= \frac{11}{9} \times \frac{17}{7}$$

Multiply numerator times numerator and denominator times denominator.

$$= \frac{11 \times 17}{9 \times 7} = \frac{187}{63} = 2\frac{61}{63}$$

Another example of a mixed number times a mixed number would be the product $3\frac{2}{3} \times 4\frac{3}{4}$:

Express problem in expanded form.

$$\left(3 + \frac{2}{3}\right) \times \left(4 + \frac{3}{4}\right)$$

Rename multiplier and multiplicand to their
equivalent fractions.

$$= \left(\frac{9}{3} + \frac{2}{3}\right) \times \left(\frac{16}{4} + \frac{3}{4}\right)$$

Combine terms.

$$= \frac{11}{3} \times \frac{19}{4}$$

Multiply.

$$= \frac{11 \times 19}{3 \times 4} = \frac{209}{12} = 17\frac{5}{12}$$

MULTIPLICATIVE INVERSE

The identity element of multiplication is one. There are times when we need to multiply a quantity by something which will make it equal to identity, or one. This can be done with a fraction by multiplying it times its multiplicative inverse. The multiplicative inverse is a fraction that is the inverse or opposite of a given fraction. For instance, the multiplicative inverse of $\frac{2}{3}$ would be $\frac{3}{2}$. The new fraction has as its numerator the denominator of the first fraction, and as its denominator it has the numerator of the first fraction. The multiplicative inverse may also be called the reciprocal, but the former term is used more often in elementary mathematics, because it is a more descriptive term and its name suggests how it is to be used. A symbolization of using the multiplicative inverse of $\frac{2}{3}$ to obtain identity, or one, is as follows:

$$\frac{2}{3} \times \frac{3}{2} = \frac{6}{6} \text{ or } 1.$$

DIVISION

The division of fractions is a process which requires a great deal of abstract thought and is often not applicable to the everyday life of the child. For these reasons, many children should not attempt to learn the process while in elementary school, but should wait until they have attained more maturity. On the other hand, many children would be challenged by the concept and could profit by it since this knowledge would enable them to go on to more complex tasks and thought.

In the multiplication of fractions, we thought of multiplication as the putting together of equal-size sets. Since division is the inverse of multiplication, division will be thought of as a parting or measuring away of equal-size groups. Readiness would also include reasonable mastery and understanding of division of whole numbers, the laws governing division of whole numbers, and the concept of fractions.

When teaching division of fractions to elementary school children, the students should be provided with many opportunities to work with concrete materials for as long a period of time as they feel the need. As concepts and understandings are developed, children will progress at their own rate from the concrete to the more abstract. Since division is probably the most difficult of the four basic operations, time spent by the children with concrete materials developing concepts and understandings must not be slighted or hurried.

To introduce division of fractions, the teacher can guide the students to recall that in dividing whole numbers they either measured (or parted away) equal size groups from a total group. Division of fractions is similar in that we are going to measure (or part away) equal-size fractional parts from a whole. This whole may be a unit (one), or it may be a group (more than one). Probably the best place to begin teaching division of fractions is the division of a fraction by a whole number in which the number in the numerator and the whole number divisor are the same. In this way we will not have to further subdivide the fractional parts. This particular division will be solved by using partition division; for example, $\frac{3}{4}$ divided by 3 is illustrated in Figure 8.25.

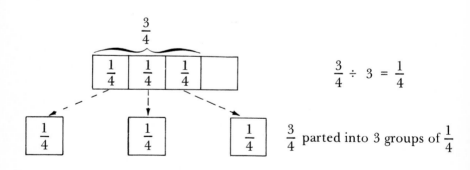

$$\frac{3}{4} \div 3 = \frac{1}{4}$$

$\frac{3}{4}$ parted into 3 groups of $\frac{1}{4}$

Figure 8.25

It can be seen that the total group, $\frac{3}{4}$, was separated into 3 equal groups, with $\frac{1}{4}$ in each equal group. It will be recalled from the fundamental concepts of fractions, that fractions are implied division. Thus, dividing by 3 should be synonymous with taking $\frac{1}{3}$ of a quantity. Conversely, $\frac{1}{3}$ of a quantity should be synonymous with dividing by 3.

After working with a number of examples of a fraction divided by a whole number, in which there can be an exact division of the fractional parts $\left(\text{the whole number divisor is the same number as the numerator of the fraction, such as } \frac{4}{5} \div 4, \frac{3}{8} \div 3, \frac{6}{7} \div 6, \ldots\right)$, the pupils are then guided into dividing a fraction by a whole number that is not the same as the numerator of the fraction, such as $\frac{3}{5} \div 4$, or $\frac{4}{5} \div 2$. In this division, partitioning division will again be used; however, since we cannot partition the indicated fraction as we did in $\frac{3}{4} \div 3$, we must now partition each of the individual fractional parts, as shown in Figure 8.26 for the division $\frac{1}{3} \div 4$.

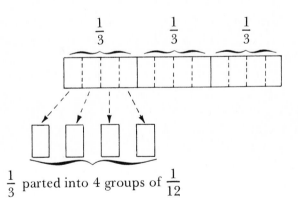

$\frac{1}{3}$ parted into 4 groups of $\frac{1}{12}$

Figure 8.26

When we separated the $\frac{1}{3}$ into 4 equal parts, we in effect subdivided the whole into 12 equal parts; thus, we partitioned the $\frac{1}{3}$ into 4 groups with $\frac{1}{12}$ in each group.

Next, we would proceed to a slightly more involved process. Figure 8.27 illustrates the process involved for the division $\frac{2}{5} \div 3$.

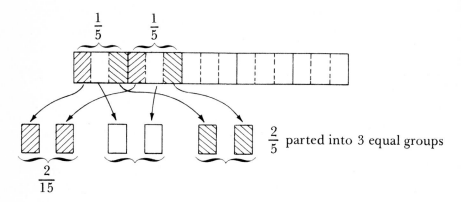

$\frac{2}{5}$ parted into 3 equal groups

Figure 8.27

It will be recalled that in partitioning division we know the total group $\left(\frac{2}{5}\right)$ and the number of groups (3), but we do not know how many will be in each equal group. Thus we subdivide each of the $\frac{2}{5}$ parts into 3 equal parts. Then we take the first of the 3 equal parts from each of the two $\frac{1}{5}$'s and place them in a group; next we take the second of the 3 equal parts from each of the two $\frac{1}{5}$'s and place them in another group; and then we take the third of the 3 equal parts of the two $\frac{1}{5}$'s and place them in still another group. We have now parted the $\frac{2}{5}$ into 3 groups with $\frac{2}{15}$ in each equal group.

After working several such problems, the students should be guided into formulating a rule for dividing a fraction by a whole number. The rule, in student terminology, would be something like this: To divide a fraction by a whole number, multiply the whole number by the denominator and place the numerator of the original fraction over this product. If we compare this rule with the rule we developed for multiplying a fraction by a whole number, we find that in multiplying fractions we multiply the numerator times the whole number, but in dividing fractions we multiply the denominator times the whole number. This should be just about what we expected, since division is the inverse of multiplication. Using the preceding example of $\frac{2}{3} \div 3$, we can begin establishing the rule of the multiplicative inverse (reciprocal) in the division of fractions. We also know that dividing by 3 is the same as finding $\frac{1}{3}$ of a quantity. Consequently, $\frac{2}{5} \div 3$ should give the same results as $\frac{2}{5} \times \frac{1}{3}$. Multiplying by $\frac{1}{3}$ (the multiplicative inverse) gives exactly the same answer as dividing by 3 (the whole number).

It will be recalled that division of a fraction by a whole number is about the only type of division involving fractions that can be solved by partitioning division. Thus, almost every other type of division involving fractions is solved by measurement division.

The next step in teaching division of fractions would be to introduce the division of a whole number by a fraction. Measurement division is used to illustrate this division. In measurement division, we know the size of the total group and the number in each equal group, but we do not know how many equal groups we will have. To illustrate this process, the number line is very useful.

This shows 3 measured by $\frac{1}{2}$ into 6 equal groups, which can also be written: $3 \div \frac{1}{2} = 6$ groups of $\frac{1}{2}$. Although the quotient, 6, appears to be larger than either of the other terms, it represents the number of equal groups of $\frac{1}{2}$ that was measured in 3. In effect, we renamed 3 to $\frac{6}{2}$ so we could measure the number of $\frac{1}{2}$'s. Thus, we actually divided $\frac{6}{2}$ by $\frac{1}{2}$, like this:

$$6 \text{ halves} \div 1 \text{ half} = 6 \text{ groups of } \frac{1}{2} \text{ or } \frac{6}{2} \div \frac{1}{2} = 6 \text{ groups}$$

A little later, we can draw an interesting parallel between the algorisms for multiplying fractions and dividing fractions.

Next we would want to progress to the division of a whole number by a fraction that is not a unit fraction, like this:

To divide 4 by $\frac{2}{3}$, 4 is measured by $\frac{2}{3}$'s into 6 equal groups. This may be written: $4 \div \frac{2}{3} = 6$ groups of $\frac{2}{3}$.

In this division, the answer is apparently larger than either the dividend or divisor. However, when we consider that the answer represents 6 groups, not 6 units, this is a reasonable answer. We have in effect renamed 4 to $\frac{12}{3}$ so that we could measure the number of $\frac{2}{3}$'s it contained, and then divided like this:

$$\frac{12}{3} \div \frac{2}{3} = 6 \text{ groups of } \frac{2}{3}.$$

or to show measurement division more clearly, like this:

$$12 \text{ thirds} \div 2 \text{ thirds} = 6 \text{ groups of } \frac{2}{3}.$$

After working several such problems in which there was an exact division when the fractional part was measured, the pupils should be guided into problems in which a whole number would be divided by a fraction and the resulting quotient would be a mixed number. For example, $3 \div \frac{2}{5}$ could be illustrated on the following number line:

In this case, 3 is measured by $\frac{2}{5}$ into 7 equal groups of $\frac{2}{5}$ with a remainder of $\frac{1}{5}\left(\text{which is } \frac{1}{2} \text{ of a set of } \frac{2}{5}\right)$, thus our answer is $7\frac{1}{2}$. Again in this example the answer is apparently larger than either the divisor or dividend, but the quotient of $7\frac{1}{2}$ represents $7\frac{1}{2}$ equal groups of $\frac{2}{5}$ each. In this division $\left(3 \div \frac{2}{5}\right)$, we renamed 3 to $\frac{15}{5}$ so that we could measure the number of $\frac{2}{5}$'s contained in 3. The algorism is written like this:

$$3 \div \frac{2}{5} = \frac{15}{5} \div \frac{2}{5} = \frac{15}{2} = 7\frac{1}{2}$$

or, to show measurement more clearly, like this:

$$15 \text{ fifths} \div 2 \text{ fifths} = \frac{15}{2} \text{ or } 7\frac{1}{2}.$$

At about this point, pupils should be ready, with teacher guidance, to formulate a rule for dividing a whole number by a fraction. The rule would be something like this: To divide a whole number by a fraction, rename the whole number to its equivalent fraction with the same denominator as the fraction in the divisor and then you have common denominators, simply divide the numerator of the dividend by the numerator of the divisor.

After the child understands the concept of division of fractions he is ready for making algorisms and analyzing problems on his own. In an example such as $\frac{2}{3} \div \frac{4}{5}$ we have one fraction divided by another fraction. The child could estimate that the quotient would be a fraction, since $\frac{4}{5}$ is greater than $\frac{2}{3}$. He could also rewrite the problem in another form. It could be written as $\dfrac{\frac{2}{3}}{\frac{4}{5}}$.

In this case the fraction needs to be simplified. If the denominator could be multiplied by something so that it would be a unit, or one, the fraction would be simplified. When a fraction is multiplied by the multiplicative inverse, the product is one. The $\frac{4}{5}$ can be multiplied by $\frac{5}{4}$ and the denominator would be one; however, if you multiply the denominator by a number, you must multiply the numerator by the same number. The algorism would look like the following example:

$$\dfrac{\frac{2}{3} \times \frac{5}{4}}{\frac{4}{5} \times \frac{5}{4}} = \dfrac{\frac{10}{12}}{\frac{20}{20}} = \dfrac{\frac{10}{12}}{1} = \frac{5}{6}$$

The denominator is one, therefore, the quotient is $\frac{10}{12}$ or $\frac{5}{6}$. Another example of the division of one fraction by another would be one in which the dividend is larger than the divisor:

$$\frac{3}{4} \div \frac{2}{3} \quad \text{may be written as} \quad \dfrac{\frac{3}{4}}{\frac{2}{3}}$$

This is often called a complex fraction. It may be simplified by multiplying the denominator by its multiplicative inverse, but the numerator must also be multiplied by the same number:

$$\frac{\frac{3}{4} \times \frac{3}{2}}{\frac{2}{3} \times \frac{3}{2}} = \frac{\frac{9}{8}}{1} = 1\frac{1}{8}$$

Many children will see that you have inverted the divisor and multiplied and will take this short cut. This process should not be taught. The child should use the long process until he sees a way of shortening the process for himself.

A fraction can be divided by a whole number in the same way.

$\frac{2}{3} \div 4$ may be written in the form of a complex fraction: $\frac{\frac{2}{3}}{\frac{4}{1}}$.

This may be simplified by multiplying both the numerator and the denominator by the multiplicative inverse of $\frac{4}{1}$:

$$\frac{\frac{2}{3} \times \frac{1}{4}}{\frac{4}{1} \times \frac{1}{4}} = \frac{\frac{2}{12}}{1} = \frac{1}{6}$$

A fraction may be divided by a mixed number. An example of this would be $\frac{3}{4} \div 1\frac{2}{3}$. The divisor must be expressed in a fraction form. The problem would become $\frac{3}{4} \div \frac{5}{3}$ and may be written as a complex fraction, $\frac{\frac{3}{4}}{\frac{5}{3}}$.

Multiply the numerator and denominator by the multiplicative inverse of $\frac{5}{3}$, and solve as in the previous examples:

$$\frac{\frac{3}{4} \times \frac{3}{5}}{\frac{5}{3} \times \frac{3}{5}} = \frac{\frac{9}{20}}{1} = \frac{9}{20} .$$

It will be difficult to find applications for the division of fractions that will be meaningful to the child. Many children will accept the process as readiness for algebra and can profit from working this concept. No child should be forced to divide fractions who is not mature enough in mathematics to understand what is done and why.

Extending Your Thinking

1. Work the following problems by the *common denominator* method of division, then work the same problems by the *multiplicative inverse* method of division.

a. $\frac{1}{3} \div 4$ c. $5 \div \frac{3}{8}$ e. Show how these two methods are related.

b. $\frac{2}{3} \div \frac{4}{7}$ d. $4\frac{1}{4} \div \frac{7}{16}$

2. Show how you would illustrate:

a. $\frac{2}{3} \times 4$ c. $\frac{1}{4} \times \frac{3}{7}$ e. $3 \div \frac{5}{8}$

b. $5 \times \frac{3}{8}$ d. $\frac{1}{5} \div 2$ f. $\frac{3}{4} \div \frac{3}{8}$

3. Work the following problems using prime factorization to find the common denominator.

a. $\frac{7}{16} - \frac{3}{12}$ c. $3\frac{1}{4} + \frac{3}{24}$

b. $\frac{5}{7} + \frac{3}{35}$ d. $5\frac{5}{6} - 3\frac{2}{9}$

4. Show how you would illustrate $\frac{3}{4} \times \frac{5}{6}$. Now show how you would illustrate $\frac{5}{6} \times \frac{3}{4}$. Are these two illustrations exactly the same? How do the two illustrations compare? What can you conclude from these two illustrations?

5. Work the following problems by using the distributive property

of multiplication, then work these same problems by changing the mixed number and whole number to fractional form.

a. $\frac{2}{5} \times 4\frac{1}{6}$ c. $5\frac{1}{4} \times 3$

b. $2 \times 3\frac{2}{7}$ d. $1\frac{2}{7} \times 2\frac{3}{16}$

6. Show how you would work the following without bridging or carrying.

a. $\frac{7}{8} + \frac{11}{12}$ c. $2\frac{1}{3} + 1\frac{7}{10}$

b. $1\frac{1}{3} + \frac{7}{8}$ d. $3\frac{4}{5} + 6\frac{1}{2}$

7. Show how you would work the following without borrowing.

a. $1\frac{1}{8} - \frac{6}{7}$ c. $2\frac{1}{3} - 1\frac{6}{10}$

b. $3\frac{1}{2} - 1\frac{4}{5}$ d. $4\frac{2}{5} - 2\frac{8}{9}$

8. How would you show (illustrate) that $12 \times \frac{1}{3}$ is the same as $12 \div 3$?

9. How would you guide children to generalize that the larger the number is in the denominator, the smaller each part of the fraction becomes?

10. Using prime factors, reduce the following fractions to their lowest form.

a. $\frac{24}{36}$ c. $\frac{27}{81}$ e. $\frac{96}{36}$

b. $\frac{45}{63}$ d. $\frac{78}{132}$

ANSWERS TO SELECTED QUESTIONS

1a. Common denominator method

$$\frac{1}{3} \div 4$$

$$= \frac{1}{3} \div \frac{12}{3}$$

$$= \frac{1 \div 12}{3 \div 3}$$

$$= \frac{1 \div 12}{1}$$

$$= 1 \div 12 = \frac{1}{12}$$

Multiplicative inverse method

$$\frac{1}{3} \div 4$$

$$= \frac{\frac{1}{3}}{\frac{4}{1}}$$

$$= \frac{\frac{1}{3} \times \frac{1}{4}}{\frac{4}{1} \times \frac{1}{4}}$$

$$= \frac{\frac{1}{3} \times \frac{1}{4}}{1} = \frac{1}{3} \times \frac{1}{4} = \frac{1}{12}$$

2a. $\frac{2}{3} \times 4$

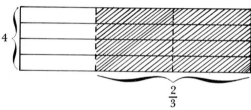

3a.

$$\frac{7}{16} \qquad \frac{7}{2 \times 2 \times 2 \times 2} \qquad \frac{7 \times 3}{2 \times 2 \times 2 \times 2 \times 3} \qquad \frac{21}{48}$$

$$-\frac{3}{12} \equiv -\left(\frac{3}{2 \times 2 \times 3}\right) \equiv \frac{3 \times 2 \times 2}{-2 \times 2 \times 2 \times 2 \times 3} \equiv -\frac{12}{48}$$

$$\frac{9}{48} \quad \text{or} \quad \frac{3}{16}.$$

5a. Distributive method

$$\frac{2}{5} \times 4\frac{1}{6}$$

$$= \frac{2}{5} \times \left(4 + \frac{1}{6}\right)$$

$$= \left(\frac{2}{5} \times 4\right) + \left(\frac{2}{5} \times \frac{1}{6}\right)$$

$$= \frac{8}{5} + \frac{2}{30} = \frac{48}{30} + \frac{2}{30} = \frac{50}{30} = 1\frac{2}{3}$$

Changing to fractional form

$$\frac{2}{5} \times 4\frac{1}{6}$$

$$= \frac{2}{5} \times \frac{25}{6} = \frac{50}{30} = 1\frac{2}{3}$$

6a.

$$\frac{7}{8} \qquad \frac{21}{24}$$

$$+\frac{11}{12} \equiv +\frac{22}{24}$$

$$\frac{43}{24} = \left(\frac{24}{24} + \frac{19}{24}\right) = 1 + \frac{19}{24} = 1\frac{19}{24}$$

7a.
$$1\frac{1}{8} \qquad \frac{9}{8} \qquad \frac{63}{56} = \frac{15}{16}$$
$$\frac{6}{-7} = \frac{6}{-7} = \frac{48}{-56}$$

10.
$$\frac{24}{36} = \frac{2 \times 2 \times 2 \times 3}{2 \times 2 \times 3 \times 3} = \frac{2}{3}$$

Related References

Banks, J. Houston. *Learning and Teaching Arithmetic.* 2nd ed. Boston: Allyn and Bacon, Inc., 1964. pp. 291-319.

Dwight, Leslie A. *Modern Mathematics for the Elementary Teacher.* New York: Holt, Rinehart, and Winston, Inc. 1966. pp. 362-425.

Grossnickle, Foster E., and Brueckner, Leo J. *Discovering Meanings in Elementary School Mathematics.* 4th ed. New York: Holt, Rinehart, and Winston, Inc. 1963. Chaps. 10 and 11.

The National Council of Teachers of Mathematics, *Topics in Mathematics for Elementary School Teachers.* 29th Yearbook Washington, D.C.: 1964. pp. 215-308.

School Mathematics Study Group *Studies in Mathematics.* vol. 9, rev. ed., Palo Alto, Calif.: ,Stanford University, 1963. pp. 219-90.

Swenson, Esther J. *Teaching Arithmetic to Children.* New York: The Macmillan Company., 1964. pp. 302-82.

CHAPTER 9

GEOMETRY

The teaching of geometry has earned a place in the elementary school mathematics program. Research has provided much evidence that children who have studied the ideas of point, line, curves, planes and space have a better perception of their physical environment than children who have not had this opportunity. Children are often highly motivated by the study of geometry. This is especially true of children who have been somewhat handicapped in the study of school subjects by having spoken English as a second language. The vocabulary of geometry is usually as strange to the child who speaks English as a native language is to the child who speaks English as a second language; thus, children approach this subject without the feeling that some children have an advantage.

Units of science have been built around the geometric shapes. In this study children learn such concepts as classification or codification. They come to understand differences in color, shape and size. The geometric shapes have been used as a basis for language development programs for children who are learning English as a second language. The children appear to be interested in the study of geometric shapes and the subject lends itself to the construction of language patterns that children can repeat.

Definitions, axioms, and proof should be used sparingly with elementary school children; the inductive method should be used instead. Besides the practical values of developing readiness for future study, the study of geometry can help a child to interpret his environment, can help him to develop logical thinking, and can possibly help him to be more creative.

In the following sections on geometric models, the information is presented as information for teachers on some of the subject matter which has been adapted to the elementary school program. The method of teaching should be a combination of identification and discovery. Questions would be asked that will help children to express ideas, opinions, and known facts. When necessary the teacher should furnish the name for a model. Where possible, the teacher should use models that will help children make their own definitions. For instance, the teacher might draw several lines intersecting at one spot (representation of a point) on the chalkboard. Children would be asked how many lines could be drawn through a point. After many lines had been drawn through the point, and after many demonstrations, children would discover that many lines could be drawn through a point. If the children's maturity of thought permits, they may express the idea that an infinite number of lines could be drawn. Less mature children would express the idea that you can't count the number of lines, still others might say that many lines could be drawn.

After this concept has been explored, the teacher might present two dots as representations of two points. Children would discover that many curved and broken lines can be drawn between two points, but only one straight line can be drawn between two points. By measuring the curves, broken lines, and straight lines, the children would discover that a straight line is the shortest distance between two points.

Each new concept must be approached from the reference point of what the children already know, what they can learn at their present maturity level, and how appropriate a concept is in relation to the total mathematics program. Children learn simple concepts such as classification of different figures at first. This is begun in the first grade. The child first learns what a triangle is and later looks for uses of the triangle in his environment. He is not concerned with such topics as area and perimeter until much later in the program. Each time a topic is introduced it should involve a higher level of conceptualization. If the child learns through this spaced presentation, he will be able to make more discoveries and generalizations for himself. His interest will increase if he is involved in experimentation using materials. This subject offers an excellent opportunity for some team learning. Four or five children can be placed in a group. If each has a geometric figure, they can have as their goal the finding of the likenesses and differences of the figures. If each has a triangle, but none of the triangles are the same size or shape, they can begin with a comparison of color of triangles, number of sides, and number of angles. Differences would include such things as smaller, larger, and other comparisons.

If a child examines a figure carefully enough to discuss it with classmates, he will very likely be able to identify and describe the figure in the future. One of the skills that a child needs to learn is how to obtain information from other students and how to have information that he gives accepted by other students. Geometry provides an excellent opportunity to develop these skills. Learning usually runs over into home or other out-of-school situations. As children find evidences of the geometric shapes in their homes and all around them, they become more perceptive about their environment. They find squares in the floor covering, triangles used to brace new houses, fence posts, and many other things. Illustrations are available on every hand.

Materials and Geometric Models

The materials that are probably most helpful in teaching the concepts of the different polygons would be strips of cardboard or lightweight wood such as balsa wood. These strips should have a small hole near each end so that a brad can be inserted.

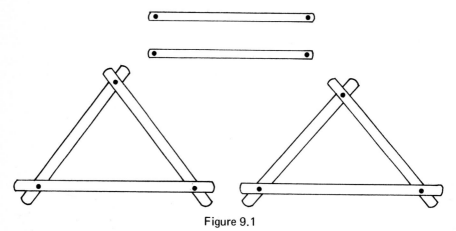

Figure 9.1

Children can make the different polygons by putting the pieces together with brads, as shown in Figure 9.1. They can be led to observe the different shapes of triangles as they use different lengths of strips. An equilateral triangle could be formed by taking three strips of equal length. Children could prove that the angles (or openings between the strips) are equal by drawing along the two sides of one angle on a piece of transparent material and then using this as a measure for the other two angles. They can observe that the triangle changes shape (Fig. 9.1) when one strip is traded for a longer strip: The angle at the top would no longer be the same as (congruent to) the copy that he had made on the transparent material; it would be larger. He might be led to generalize that when one angle is made larger, at least one of the other angles will be smaller and usually both of them will be smaller. From this beginning, he might learn to copy the three angles on a line made

on a transparent sheet (Fig. 9.2). He could learn that the sum of the
angles of a triangle are always the same as a straight line or a straight
angle of 180°. These are progressive concepts and a child needs to have
a great deal of coordination in order to do the measuring himself. The
child would observe that if he replaced the strip opposite angle C (Fig.
9.2) with a strip shorter than the original one, his triangle will be taller.
A measure of the angles with the copy of the original one would reveal
that angle C is smaller and that angle A and angle B are larger. He could
be led to understand that the size of the angle depends upon the relative lengths of the sides of the triangle.

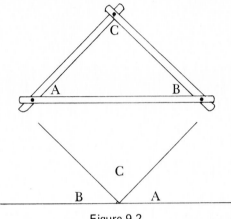

Figure 9.2

The child would find that when a right triangle (a triangle with one
90° angle) is formed, there must be a certain ratio between the length
of the sides. A convenient ratio to use would be 3, 4, and 5 units. The
child could enlarge the triangle and keep the same ratio. If the short
side is 6, then the other two sides would be 8 and 10. Children could
draw a right angle by using a book or the corner of a tablet. Or they
could fold a piece of paper twice, as shown in Figure 9.3. The folded
edge could serve as a model for a right angle. After the right angle is
drawn, the child could experiment by placing a piece of wire or one of
the strips across the angle to form right triangles of different sizes.

Children are able to discover many things about triangles through the
use of materials in answer to astute questioning on the part of the
teacher and other students. With the assurance that the inductive
method will be used, that children will study geometry for short spaces
of time (probably about two weeks at one time), that they will be
taught concepts which are suitable to their maturity (physical as well as

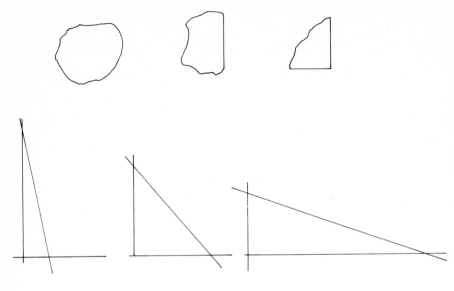

Figure 9.3

mental), and that suitable materials will be furnished, we shall proceed to describe some of the subject matter that is being used in the elementary school program. By the time children are in the upper grades they will probably be able to use a compass and straight edge to great advantage.

THE POINT

The idea of a point is suggested by the tip of a pencil or a dot on a piece of paper. A point cannot be defined or accurately described. We have no way of representing a point in space that can be minute enough to represent the point and at the same time be large enough to be observed. Even in first grade, and probably in kindergarten, children are taught that a dot is not a point, but *represents* a point. First grade children are usually ready to study models and representations of geometric ideas. These models are being used in mathematics as readiness for further study and to help the child interpret his environment; they are being used in science to teach a scientific way of expressing ideas and to help the child understand the structure and unifying forces in nature; they are being used in experimental programs in teaching English as a second language. Research in the use of geometric models in teaching English has revealed that great motivation is often gained from the use of models, and has provided opportunity for exact practice of English without the stigma of using subject matter that English-speaking children already know well. The English-speaking children and non-English speaking children both need practice in naming and describing the geometric models.

A point is usually represented by a dot. It is customary to designate a certain point by a letter and refer to a point as point A or point B. A small dot (·) is a better representation of a point than a large dot (●). A point has a fixed location, it does not move. If we erased the dot, the point that it represented would remain. The dot can be erased, but the point remains where it was.

Once the representation of a point is understood, the idea of space as the set of all points can be presented. Most children will have gained some idea of space from the space program, but they may need more orientation about the top of a desk or table as space or of an object occupying space, than they do for outer space as it is described to the television viewer. Space may be thought of as represented by all possible locations of points (the set of all points).

A *curve* might be represented by taking two points A and B as they are represented in space and representing one path from A to B by small dots (Fig. 9.4). As the dots decrease in size and increase in number, the path comes to look more like a solid line. Thus the idea of a line as a *set of all the points* in a certain path is called a curve or a curved segment. Figure 9.4 also shows that when the curve is represented by a string tightly strung between two points, it is called a *straight line segment* or, by some textbook authors, a straight *curve*

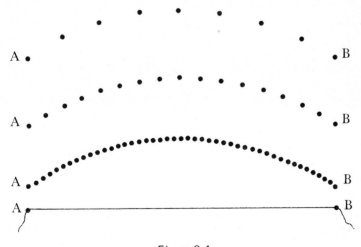

Figure 9.4

segment. The line or curve includes the points A and B. The symbol for the segment is $\overline{AB}$. If $\overline{AB}$ is extended in both directions along the same line so that it does not stop at any point, the result is a straight line; the symbol is $\overleftrightarrow{AB}$. A straight line is usually called a line. It is indefinite in length and is made up of an infinite number of points.

Exercises.

1. Represent the points x and y. How many lines are determined by (end with) these two points?

2. Represent the points x, y, and z. How many lines are determined by these points?

3. Represent the points w, x, y, z. How many lines are determined by these points?

4. Represent the points v, w, x, y, z. How many lines are determined by these points?

PROPERTIES OF A LINE OR LINES

Figure 9.5 illustrates some properties of lines: through any point A, many lines can be drawn. So many lines could be drawn that you could not count them. An infinite number of lines can be drawn through one point.

If you add a second point B, only one straight line can be drawn through both points.

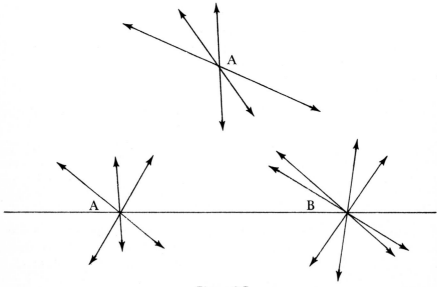

Figure 9.5

Two straight lines (a and b) can intersect in only one point (Fig. 9.6). The lines consist of the sets of all the points that belong to both lines, and the sets intersect on *one* point only. The line determined by two points such as x and y in Figure 9.6 is called the line xy and the symbol is $\overline{xy}$; the line segment determined by $\overline{xy}$ is that portion of the line between x and y including points x and y. The symbolization for a line segment may be complete. The symbolization for a line is, of necessity, incomplete $\overset{\longleftarrow}{\underset{x}{\rule{0pt}{0pt}}} \rule{5cm}{0.4pt} \overset{\longrightarrow}{\underset{y}{\rule{0pt}{0pt}}}$. It goes on and on and could not be represented on one small piece of paper.

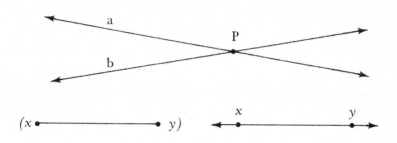

Figure 9.6

Exercises.

1. Draw lines through one point.
2. Locate three (3) points on one line.
3. Place any three (3) points on your paper; see if you can draw a straight line through the three points.
4. Draw a line and see if you can measure it.
5. Cut off a line segment on the line and measure it.
6. Draw several line segments. Make a copy of one line segment by drawing it on a transparent sheet that is placed over the line. Use an A.V. pencil, a nylon tip pencil, or a crayon. Place this copy over other line segments that you have drawn on your paper. Check it with each line segment to see if it is greater, less than, or equal to each segment.

THE RAY

The two points x and y determine another particular set of points called the ray $\overrightarrow{xy}$. The symbol for this ray would be $\overrightarrow{xy}$. The ray begins at point x, passes through the point y and extends in one direction indefinitely. The ray could be represented as a pinpoint beam of light with source x that extends through y and on to an indefinite distance.

If the ray begins at x and extends in a straight line, many names for the ray ($\overrightarrow{xy}$, $\overrightarrow{xz}$, $\overrightarrow{xw}$, $\overrightarrow{xv}$) can be represented on one line:

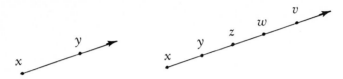

The number of rays that could be represented is infinite. The source of the ray is x, hence every representation must begin with x. An angle (X in Fig. 9.7) is the union of two rays which have the same end point.

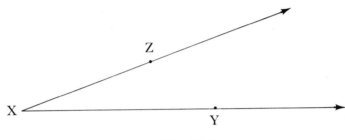

Figure 9.7

The two rays are called the sides of the angle and their common end point is called the vertex. The angle represented is formed by the union of rays $\overrightarrow{XY}$ and $\overrightarrow{XZ}$. The sides of the angle are the rays $\overrightarrow{XY}$ and $\overrightarrow{XZ}$. The angle could be symbolized ∢ YXZ or ∢ ZXY. The letter at the vertex is always placed in the center of the symbolization. Sometimes for the sake of brevity a number (Fig. 9.8a and b) is placed inside the angle to designate which angle is being discussed. When there is no danger of confusion, a single letter as shown in Figure 9.8c, may be used to designate an angle. This practice would be confusing in the situation pictured in Figure 9.8d.

Exercises.

1. Draw several angles on your paper.
2. Copy an angle on a transparent sheet.
3. Check the copy with each angle on your paper. Find whether it is greater than, less than, or equal to each angle.
4. Make a measure for a right angle by folding a piece of paper twice. Measure each angle to see if any are right angles.

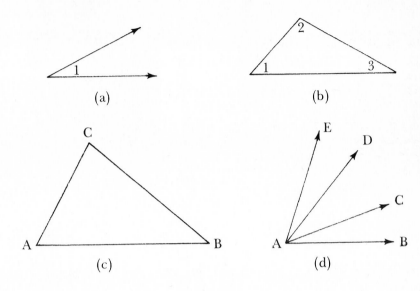

(a) (b)

(c) (d)

Figure 9.8

5. Take two strips of heavy paper. Put them together at one end with a brad. Move the strips to make:

    a. acute angles
    b. right angles
    c. obtuse angles

DEFINITIONS BASIC TO RAY, ANGLES, AND TRIANGLES

An *angle* is the union of two rays which have the same end-point but do not lie in the same line. The two rays are called the *sides* of the angle, and their common end-point is called the *vertex*.

The angle in Figure 9.9 which is the union of $\overrightarrow{AB}$ and $\overrightarrow{AC}$ is denoted by ⊰ BAC, or by ⊰ CAB, or simply by ⊰ A if it is clear which rays are

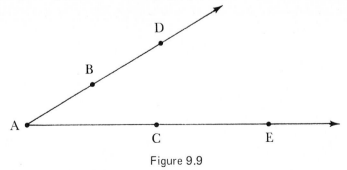

Figure 9.9

meant. Notice that ⊰ BAC can be equally well described by means of A and any two points on different sides of the angle. In Figure 9.9, ⊰DAE is the same as ⊰BAC, because $\overrightarrow{AD}$ is the same as $\overrightarrow{AB}$ and $\overrightarrow{AE}$ is the same as $\overrightarrow{AC}$.

Notice that an angle goes out infinitely far in two directions because its sides are rays, rather than segments. Angle BAC in Figure 9.10a is a specific angle, but it is not all of the angle; to get all of the angle, we have to extend the segments $\overline{AB}$ and $\overline{AC}$ getting rays $\overrightarrow{AB}$ and $\overrightarrow{AC}$, as shown in Figure 9.10b.

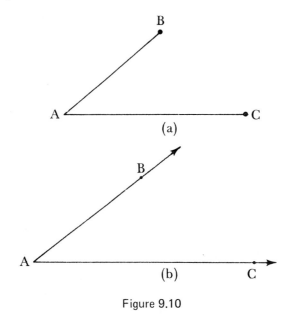

(a)

(b)

Figure 9.10

The *interior of an angle* consists of all points that lie inside the angle; the *exterior* consists of all the points that lie outside. In Figure 9.11, all points in area (P) make up the interior of ⊰ BAC; all points in areas (Q), (R), and (S) are exterior.

The *interior of a triangle* consists of the points that lie inside it, as illustrated in triangle ABC, Figure 9.11. More precisely, a point lies in the *interior* of a triangle if it lies in the interior of each of the angles of the triangle. A point lies in the *exterior* of a triangle if it lies in the plane of the triangle but is not a point of the triangle or of its interior.

A *right angle* is an angle of 90°. Two intersecting sets, each of which is a line, a ray, or a segment, are *perpendicular* if the two lines which contain them determine a right angle.

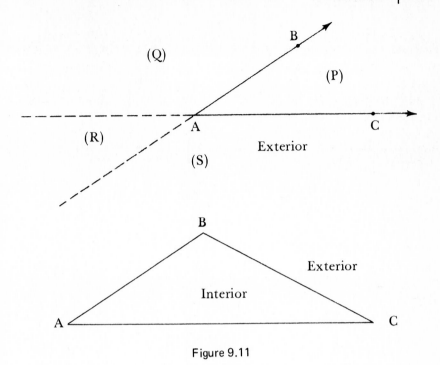

Figure 9.11

If the sum of the measures of two angles is 90°, then the angles are called *complementary*, and each of them is called a *complement* of the other.

Angle 1 in Figure 9.12 measures less than 90° and is called *acute*, and angle 2, which is greater than 90°, is called *obtuse*.

Angles with the same measure are called *congruent angles*.

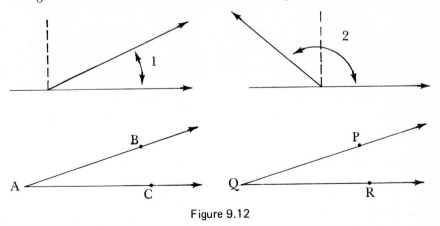

Figure 9.12

That is, ∡BAC and ∡PQR in Figure 9.12 are congruent if m∡BAC = m∡PQR (m∡BAC is read: measure of ∡BAC). In this case we write: ∡BAC ≅ ∡PQR. Notice that the equation m∡BAC = m∡PQR and the congruency ∡BAC ≅ ∡PQR are completely equivalent; we can replace one by the other any time we want to.

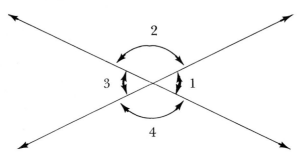

Figure 9.13

When two lines intersect, they form four angles as shown in Figure 9.13. ∡1 and ∡3 are called vertical angles, and ∡2 and ∡4 are also called vertical angles. More precisely, two angles are *vertical angles* if their sides form two pairs of opposite rays. It looks as if these pairs of vertical angles ought to be congruent, and in fact this is what always happens: vertical angles are congruent.

Exercises.

1. Draw two lines that meet.
2. Measure the angle which they form with the folded paper.
3. See if you can draw a line which is perpendicular to a second line.
4. Make a copy on a transparency of the angles made by two intersecting rays; number the angles.
5. Compare the size of each angle with every other angle.
6. Which angles are congruent?
7. On your paper, draw a number of intersecting lines. Copy each on a transparency. Check to see if each pair of opposite angles is congruent. Make a generalization about vertical angles made by intersecting lines.

PLANES

A plane is thought of as any flat surface such as a page in a book, a wall, a ceiling, or a door of a room. The items listed indicate that a plane may assume many positions. It may be horizontal, it may be vertical, or it may be situated in any of the positions in between the horizontal and vertical.

If we think of a chalkboard in a classroom as a plane, we can easily understand that it could be extended in all directions. Figure 9.14 shows some facts about planes.

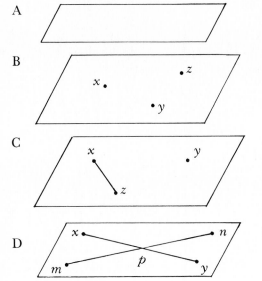

A. A plane can be extended in all directions.

B. Three points may be placed on a plane, but if we had a fourth point, we could not be sure it would be on the plane.

C. One line (determined by two points) and a point can be placed on a plane.

D. Two lines xy and nm intersecting at p may be placed on a plane.

Figure 9.14

They may be summarized:

  a. A plane is usually represented by a drawing of a flat surface.
  b. Three points determine a plane. (While a plane contains many points, you can be sure of placing a plane through three points in space, when the points are chosen at random.)
  c. A plane is determined by a line (two points) and a point.
  d. Two intersecting lines determine a plane (if part of a line is in a plane, the whole line is in the plane). In Figure 9.14D, lines mn and xy intersecting at p are represented by points x, p, and m, or x, p, and n; or n, p, and y; or y, p, and m. No matter which symbol we use, it represents three points and confirms the statement made in section B that three points determine a plane.
  Through two points in space, or through a line in space, many planes may pass. If the pages of a book are thought of as being bound in one line, the pages would represent planes through that line. This is illustrated in Figure 9.15.

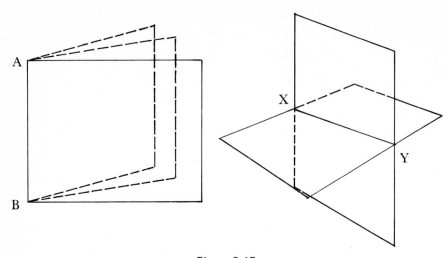

Figure 9.15

Exercises.

1. Stand a book on end on your desk (preferably a paper back) slightly open.

2. How many planes (pages) do you find that meet in a line (the binding of the book?

3. Does each plane touch one plane (the desk)?

4. Close the book and lay it on your desk.

5. Is the first page of the book parallel to the last page in the book?

6. In the above position, would the front cover and the back cover be parallel planes?

Consider points, rays and lines which are located in one plane. Any plane is made up of an infinite number of points; any line is made up of an infinite number of points. Any point divides a line into two half lines. This does not indicate that the two parts of a line are always equal. It does indicate that you could not draw a straight line from A to B or from B to A in Figure 9.16 without passing the pencil through point C. A line divides a plane into two half planes. This does not indicate that the parts of the plane are equal, it does indicate (Fig. 9.16) that one could not draw a line or a curve from P to Q or from Q to P without crossing the line *l*. Since line *l* in infinite in length, the pencil would have to cross it.

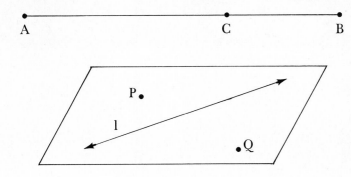

Figure 9.16

SIMPLE CURVES

Curves that can be represented by placing a pencil point on a plane and moving it without lifting it are called plane curves. In Figure 9.17, (a) is a simple plane curve; (b) represents an intersecting curve, it intersects itself, therefore, it is not a simple curve. A straight curve or a straight line is shown by (c). The straight portion of a curve is represented by line segment AB in (d). Two points may be connected by many curves, only one of which can be a straight curve, *or* a straight line, AB in (e), Figure 9.17.

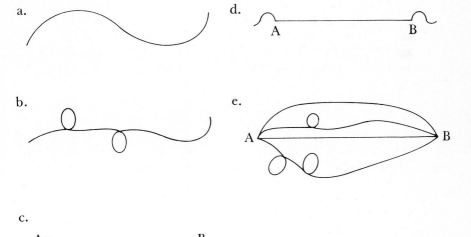

Figure 9.17

Curves may be simple closed curves. This means that if the pencil traces the curve, the line represented by the moving pencil point would not cross itself. Figure 9.18 shows several examples of simple closed curves. One important type of simple closed curve is the one made up of a curve called the broken line, as shown in (3) and (4), Figure 9.18. In these examples the broken line (or curve) does not intercept itself. It can be drawn without lifting the pencil.

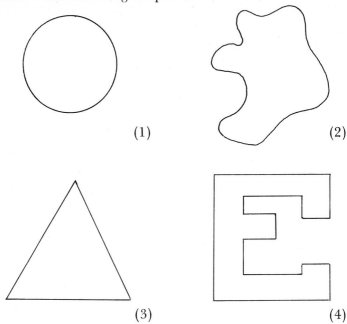

(1)   (2)

(3)   (4)

Figure 9.18

The interior of any closed curve, together with the curve, is called a *region*. The curve is the boundary of the region. Not all closed curves are simple closed curves. If the curve intersects itself (Fig. 9.19), it is not a simple closed curve.

(1)   (2)   (3)

Figure 9.19

Exercises.

1. Draw curves on your paper.
2. Ask other members of the class to decide whether a curve is:
    a. a simple curve
    b. a closed curve
    c. a simple closed curve

POLYGONS

If a simple closed curve is the union of three or more line segments (Fig. 9.20), it is called a polygon.

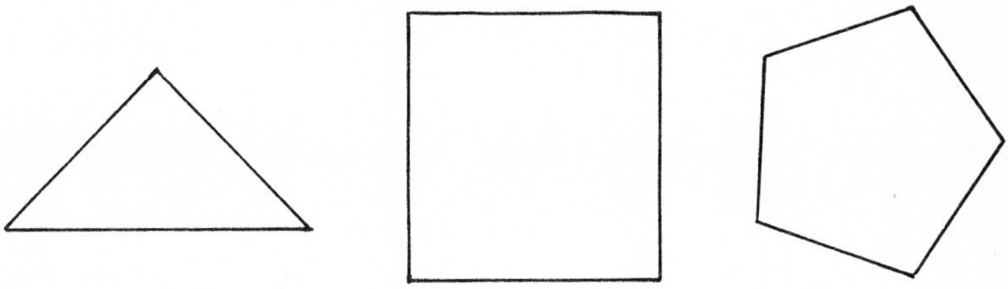

Figure 9.20

Polygons are of many shapes and sizes. Polygons that have all sides congruent are called *regular polygons*. Some of them have special names; for example, the triangle with all sides congruent is called an *equilateral triangle*. The table in Figure 9.21 designates polygons by the number of sides. The boundary of the polygon, together with the interior, is known as a *region*.

Three sides ....triangle △
Four sides .... quadrilateral ☐
Five sides .... pentagon ⬠
Six sides .... hexagon ⬡
Seven sides ....septagon ◯
Eight sides .... octagon ◯
Ten sides .... decagon ◯
Twelve sides ....duo-decagon ◯

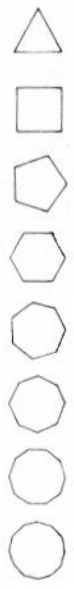

Figure 9.21

TRIANGLES

Triangles may be described by the relative lengths of the sides or by the relative size of the angles. By definition, a triangle has three sides. The sum of the degrees of the angles of a triangle is equal to 180° or, stated in another way, if you copied all of the angles side by side (Fig. 9.22), they would make a straight line. In Figure 9.22, the sum of the angles in triangle (a) is 180° as shown in (b).

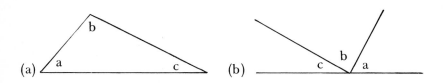

Figure 9.22

The three line segments and the interior of the three lines is called a triangular region. The three line segments form the perimeter of (or the distance around) the triangle. The different types of triangles are shown and described in Figure 9.23.

Exercises.

1. Give strips of tagboard and brads to pupils.

2. Ask class members to make triangles with the strips of tagboard.

3. Is the figure rigid? That is, can you change its shape?

4. Work in teams to see what kinds of triangles you have made.

5. See if you can make a right triangle.

6. What condition would be necessary to make an angle of 90°?

1.

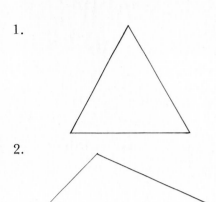

1. The triangle with all sides congruent is called an *equilateral* triangle. The equilateral triangle also has equal angles and can be called equiangular. (Each angle equals 60°).

2.

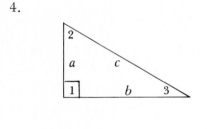

2. A triangle which has no sides congruent is called a *scalene* triangle. None of the angles are equal.

3.

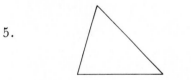

3. A triangle that has two sides congruent is called an *isosceles* triangle. It also has two equal angles.

4.

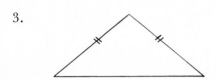

4. A triangle that contains one 90° angle is called a *right* triangle; a and b are called sides or legs; a is perpendicular to b; c is the hypotenuse. Angle 1 contains 90°. Angles 2 and 3 are each less than 90° and are called acute angles.

5.

5. A triangle that contains no angle as large as 90° is called an *acute* triangle.

6.

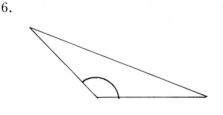

6. A triangle that contains one angle that is larger than 90° is called an *obtuse* triangle. (An angle larger than 90° but less than 180° is an obtuse angle.)

Figure 9.23

QUADRILATERALS

Quadrilaterals are polygons with four sides. Different types of quadrilaterals are named according to the relative lengths of the sides. Some have special angles. Figure 9.24 summarizes types of quadrilaterals and their properties.

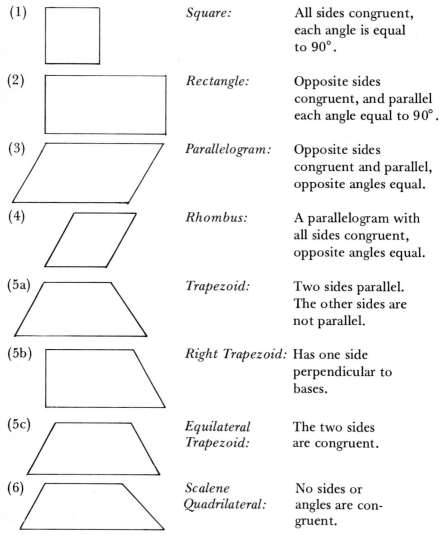

(1) *Square:* All sides congruent, each angle is equal to 90°.

(2) *Rectangle:* Opposite sides congruent, and parallel each angle equal to 90°.

(3) *Parallelogram:* Opposite sides congruent and parallel, opposite angles equal.

(4) *Rhombus:* A parallelogram with all sides congruent, opposite angles equal.

(5a) *Trapezoid:* Two sides parallel. The other sides are not parallel.

(5b) *Right Trapezoid:* Has one side perpendicular to bases.

(5c) *Equilateral Trapezoid:* The two sides are congruent.

(6) *Scalene Quadrilateral:* No sides or angles are congruent.

Figure 9.24

Exercises.

1. Take strips of tagboard and brads. Make quadrilaterals of many shapes and sizes.
2. Are the figures rigid (will they hold one shape)?
3. What would you have to do to the quadrilateral to make it rigid?
4. Measure the angles. Are any angles 90°?
5. If the angles are not equal, make an hypothesis about the length of the sides and the size of the angles.
6. Test the hypothesis by measuring.

Relationships Between Plane Figures

Elementary school children can find relationships between two plane figures if they can cut one of them out and place it on the other figure. This can also be accomplished by copying one figure on a transparent sheet and then measuring the other figures by placing this copy on it.

CONGRUENCY

The idea of the congruence of two or more figures is one that can be taught in the elementary school. Two geometric figures are congruent if they have exactly the same size and shape. For example, in Figure 9.25, all three triangles are congruent.

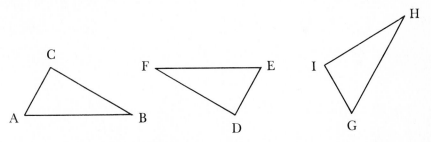

Figure 9.25

One way of describing the situation is to say that any one of these triangles can be moved onto any other one, in such a way that it fits exactly. Thus, to show what we mean by saying that two triangles are congruent, we have to explain what points are supposed to go where. For example, to move △ ABC onto △ DFE, we would put A on E, B on F, and C on D. We can write down the pairs of corresponding vertices like this:

$$A \leftrightarrow E$$
$$B \leftrightarrow F$$
$$C \leftrightarrow D$$

To describe the congruence of the first triangle and the third, we should match up the vertices like this:

$$A \leftrightarrow G$$
$$B \leftrightarrow H$$
$$C \leftrightarrow I$$

How would you match up the vertices to describe the congruence of the second triangle with the third?

A matching-up scheme of this kind is called a *one-to-one correspondence* between the vertices of the two triangles. If the triangles can be made to fit when the vertices are matched up in the prescribed way, then the one-to-one correspondence is called a *congruence* between the two triangles. For example, the correspondences that we have just given are congruences. Sometimes congruencies are found within one figure; for instance, if two sides of a triangle (Fig. 9.26) are congruent ($PQ \cong RQ$), then the angles opposite these sides are congruent. Children can prove this by copying one angle on transparent paper and then measuring the other angle with this copy.

In the quadrilaterals pictured in Figure 9.26, $\overline{AD} \cong \overline{BC}$; $\overline{AB} \cong \overline{DC}$; $\overline{LA} \cong \overline{LB} \cong \overline{LC} \cong \overline{LD}$. Congruence can be shown with many figures.

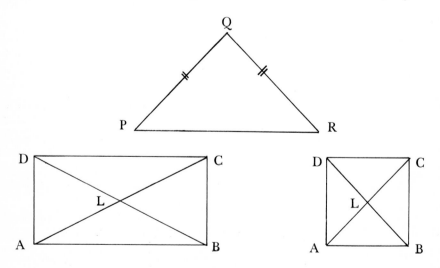

Figure 9.26

MODELS WITH CURVED PERIMETERS

The circle is probably the curved line figure that children know best. They would probably be able to identify a circle. If they should call it a ball or some other name, show them a ball and a sphere that has been cut through the center so they can recognize the difference between the ball (a sphere) and the circle. They may be able to give their own definition of a circle if the teacher draws a model as shown in Figure 9.27. The dots represent points. Each point is what distance from center 0? The children can discover that each point is the same distance from center 0 as every other point.

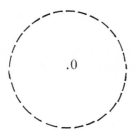

Figure 9.27

When the perimeter is drawn as a solid line (Fig. 9.28), children should be reminded that a line is made up of the set of all the points between two points, or in the case of a closed curve it is made up of the set of all points from the beginning of the curve to the stopping point. (The beginning and stopping points coincide or form the same point.)

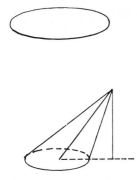

The ellipse is a closed curve figure that children have become familiar with through watching telecasts of the orbiting of the earth by space ships while commentators described the path which the ship took as an ellipse. It is difficult to construct an accurate ellipse, since the curve must have a definite form. Models may be purchased from school supply houses. One may be made by cutting a right cone. The cross-section will be in the shape of an ellipse.

The distance (AB in Fig. 9.28) across a circle, through the center is called a *diameter.* The distance from the center to the circumference (OA, OB or OC) is called a *radius.* The diameter is equal to two radii. The part of the circle cut off by two radii is called a *sector.* The angle made by the radii (∢BOA) is called a *central angle.* A *chord* is a line (XY) whose end points are on the circumference of a circle. The part cut off by a chord is called a *segment;* it is bounded by the chord and the arc that it cuts off. Figure 9.28 illustrates both a sector and a segment.

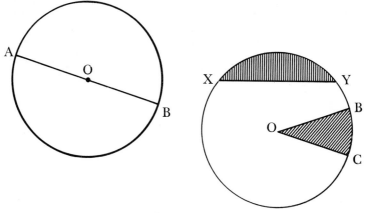

Figure 9.28

Exercises.

1. With a compass, draw a circle. Mark the center.
2. Draw one radius and make a copy of it on the transparent sheet.
3. Measure with the line on the transparent sheet to see if the center is the same distance from the center to the perimeter at every place on the circle.
4. Draw two diameters that are perpendicular to one another.
5. What part of the circle does each angle cut off?

MEASUREMENT OF PLANE FIGURES

Children need to find ways of measuring the different types of figures. A copy may be made of one side of a figure and this can be compared with other sides. Figure 9.29 shows a rectangle with copies of sides $\overline{AD}$ and $\overline{AB}$. The child will find that when the copy of AD is compared with side $\overline{BC}$, $\overline{AD}$ is congruent to $\overline{BC}$ (they are the same in length). When the copy of $\overline{AB}$ is compared with side $\overline{CD}$, the child finds that they are congruent, or equal in length. The teacher should not be

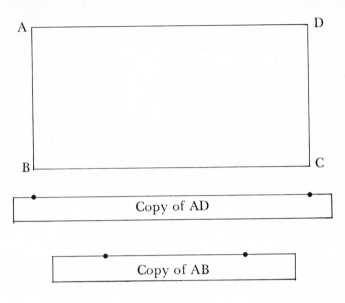

Figure 9.29

concerned about teaching the child the word, "congruent." If the teacher uses the correct word, the child will eventually learn the term and will use it when he feels that he will not make a mistake. The symbol for congruent (≅) will soon be recognized by children. Other concepts of measure should include such ideas as greater than (>), less than (<) and not equal (≠).

Copies may be made of any figure on transparent sheets. These may be compared with other figures to see if a figure is congruent to a second one. If figures have been cut from construction paper or tag board, children can compare them by placing one on top of the other to see if they are congruent.

An approximate measure for any plane figure is the number of square units that are included inside the boundary lines of the figure. One of the ways to measure is by the use of a grid. If the grid has been made on transparent material, the grid may be placed over the figure. Figures like the square and the rectangle can often be measured exactly by the use of a grid. By counting squares in the rectangle in Figure 9.30, the child can discover that the rectangle covers 15 square units. Many figures do not fit the grid exactly, but an approximate measure can be found by the use of the grid. The child can find the total number of squares and parts of squares covered by the triangle in Figure 9.30. On grid B, the number is 35. He can then find the number

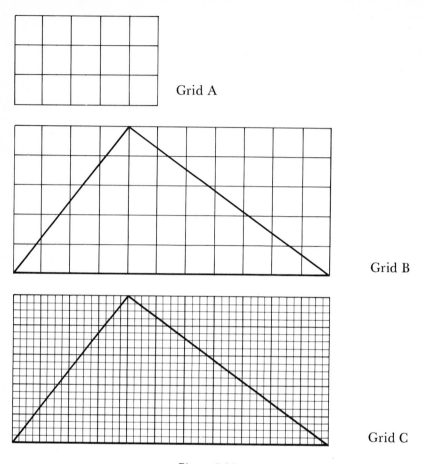

Grid A

Grid B

Grid C

Figure 9.30

of squares that are totally covered by the triangle. This number is 18 and is the minimum area. The real area is somewhere between 18 and 35, or _____ . He could probably find a more accurate measure if he reduced the size of the squares as shown in grid C. In grid C, the size of each square is 1/4 the size of those in grid B. We find there is a maximum number of 120 parts of squares covered. The minimum number (squares totally covered) is 90. The difference between the two is 30. The difference is larger than in the first problem, but since each square of grid is only 1/4 the size of those in grid B, the difference is only 7 1/2 as measured by grid B.

The same process may be used to measure the area of circles, ellipsis, and many irregular figures (Fig. 9.31).

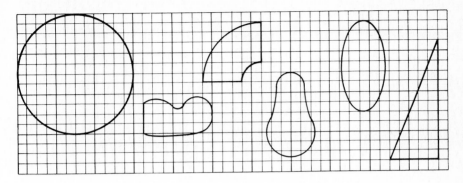

Figure 9.31

CONSTRUCTION OF PLANE FIGURES

Small children can learn to make different plane figures by drawing around different shapes. The older child (4th, 5th, 6th grade) can use a compass and construct different figures. One basic skill is that of constructing a 90° angle, or constructing one line perpendicular ($\perp$) to another line. Figure 9.32 shows the construction of a line perpendicular to a line segment $\overline{AB}$. This is done as follows: place the point of the compass on A and draw one arc above the line and one below. Place the point of the compass on B and, with the same radius, draw one arc above the line cutting the first arc. Draw an arc below the line, cutting the other arc (point Y). Draw $\overline{XY}$. The line $\overline{XY}$ is perpendicular to $\overline{AB}$, and $\overline{AP} \cong \overline{PB}$. Angles BPX, APX, APY, and BPY are each equal to 90°.

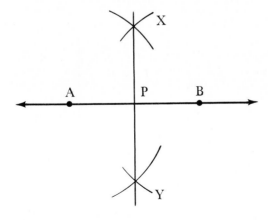

Figure 9.32

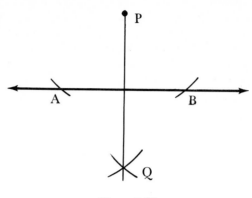

Figure 9.33

Figure 9.33 shows the construction of a perpendicular from a point, P, to a line AB. Place the compass on point P. Make an arc that cuts the line at two points. Call them A and B. Place the point of the compass on A and, with a radius of $\overline{AP}$, draw an arc below the line. Do the same with the point of the compass on B. Call the intersection of these two arcs, point Q. Draw $\overline{PQ}$; then $\overline{PQ}$ is ⊥ to $\overline{AB}$. With this as a basis, the child can construct squares and rectangles.

One method of constructing equilateral triangles is shown in Figure 9.34. Draw a line called a base line. Cut off segment $\overline{AB}$. This will be

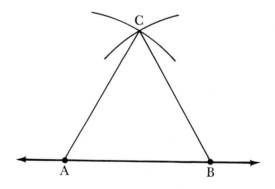

Figure 9.34

the length of the side of the equilateral triangle. Place the point of the compass on A, with the length of $\overline{AB}$ as the radius; draw an arc above the line. With the point of the compass on B, using the same radius, cut the first arc and call this point C. Draw $\overline{AC}$ and $\overline{BC}$. $\overline{AB} \cong \overline{AC} \cong \overline{BC}$. The child can discover that ∡ A ≅ ∡ B ≅ ∡ C by making a copy of ∡ A on a transparent sheet and measuring ∡ B and ∡ C.

A second way of constructing an equilateral triangle (Fig. 9.35) would be to draw a circle and measure the radius around the circle. It will measure exactly six times. Connect every other point. This forms an equilateral triangle. A child will soon find that he has also learned to construct a hexagon. By connecting each successive point, he can draw a regular (all sides equal) hexagon.

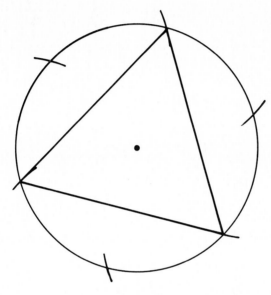

Figure 9.35

Bisect an Angle. The method for bisecting an angle is shown in Figure 9.36. Draw an angle of any size. Place the point of the compass on point A. Using a convenient radius, draw arcs cutting the rays that form the angle at B and C. Place the point of the compass on B, draw an arc in the interior of the angle. Place the point of the compass on C, cut the first arc, determining point P. Draw $\overline{AP}$. Since $\overline{AP}$ bisects ⊀CAB, ⊀1 ≅ ⊀2.

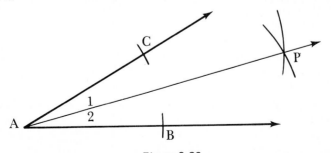

Figure 9.36

Some special cases of bisecting angles would be:

a. By bisecting a 90° angle, you could form two angles each equal to 45°.
b. By bisecting a 60° angle (angle of an equilateral triangle), you could form two angles each equal to 30°.
c. By bisecting one of the 30° angles formed above, you could form two 15° angles.

Copy of Angle. A small child can copy an angle by drawing around a model. On some occasions this would not be satisfactory, however, for the needs of a child who can solve more difficult problems. He should copy the angle by using a compass and straightedge. Draw an angle such as ∡ A in Figure 9.37. Select a point such as point X on a workline. Place the point of the compass on vertex A of the given angle and cut the sides of the angle, determining B and C. Place the compass on X and make an arc with radius ≅ AB ≅ AC cutting the ray at Y. Measure the distance between B and C using a compass. With this distance as a radius, place the point of the compass on Y and draw an arc cutting the first arc to determine Z. Draw $\overline{XZ}$. ∡ X ≅ ∡ A.

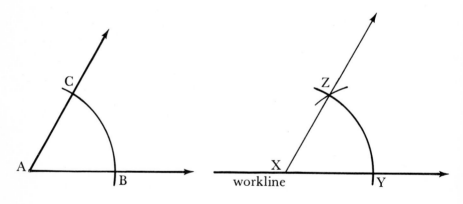

Figure 9.37

The above skill may be used in constructing parallel (∥) lines (Fig. 9.38). Take a workline with segment AB. Draw an angle with A as the vertex. Take point C on this ray. At point C, construct an angle ≅ ∡ A. Draw $\overleftrightarrow{CD}$. $\overline{CD}$ is parallel to $\overline{AB}$. The child should be able to discover much about the congruency of angles made by cutting two parallel lines by a transversal.

The teacher must be careful not to push children who are not ready physically as well as mentally for the tasks of construction. Many children will not be able to handle such tasks during the years in elementary school; however, children who are ready for the development

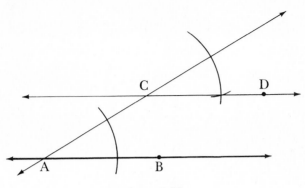

Figure 9.38

of the skill should not be kept from going forward. If children are properly motivated, they will accept their capabilities and will move forward at their own rates. One of the elements of proper motivation is to have the child accept himself as he is and thus form a good basis for progress.

The Geo Plane. One of the most important readiness exercises for working with, or constructing plane figures is the use of the geometry plane. The geometry plane, or geo plane as it is sometimes called, is an excellent material to use to help children discover many ideas about geometry. The plane (Fig. 9.39) is made by placing nails in a board in patterns making squares. It can be made by placing pegs in a peg board. The idea is that the board is a plane and, by using rubber bands, different kinds of figures can be outlined on the plane. Children need to learn early that plane figures are constructed on a plane.

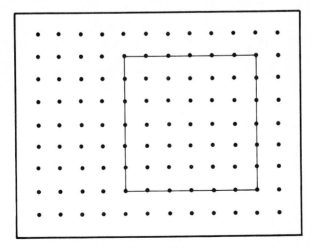

Figure 9.39

Some suggestions for ways in which small children could use the geo plane are to:

1. Construct a square.
2. See if you can construct a square that is twice as big as the one that you just constructed.
3. Construct a triangle.
4. Construct a triangle different from your first one.
5. See how many different-shaped triangles you can make.
6. Construct a rectangle.

    a. Construct a rectangle that has one unit on one side and two units on the other side.
    b. How many squares are in this rectangle?
    c. Count the units around the rectangle.

7. Construct a rectangle that has twelve square units inside it.

Children in third and fourth grade could construct more difficult kinds of figures as suggested in the following:

1. Construct a pentagon. What is its area?
2. Construct a hexagon.
3. Divide the hexagon into as many triangles as possible.
4. Construct an octagon.
5. See how many different figures you can construct that have equal areas.
6. Construct a trapezoid.
7. Construct as many different-shaped trapezoids as you can.
8. Construct a parallelogram.
9. Construct a rectangle that has the same length as the parallelogram and the same height.
10. Prove that the parallelogram and the rectangle have the same area. (This may be done by using different-colored rubber bands.)
11. Construct a rhombus.
12. See how many different figures you can make on the plane board.

Fifth and sixth grade children may be more precise in their construction. They should be able to carry out the following suggestions:

1. Construct a rectangle—two units on one side, three units on the other.

    a. Divide the area into two parts.
    b. Are the areas of the parts equal?

   c. Divide the area into equal thirds by means of another color rubber band.

   d. Can you find one-sixth of the total area?

   e. Can you illustrate on the plane board that $\frac{1}{2} \times \frac{1}{3} = \frac{1}{6}$?

2. Construct a triangle with area equal to three square units.

3. Construct a parallelogram with area equal to three square units.

4. Construct a trapezoid with area equal to three square units.

5. Construct a triangle and a rectangle so that they both have equal areas.

   a. Which has the smallest perimeter?

   b. Could you make another shaped triangle that would have the same area as the rectangle?

6. Construct a rectangle and a square so that they both have equal areas. Which of these has the smallest perimeter?

By definition, two plane figures are *similar* if their sides have proportional lengths and their angles are equal. A square two inches on one side is similar to a square three inches on a side. Two plane figures are congruent if you can place one on top of the other and they fit in all of their parts. A square two inches on one side is congruent only to another square two inches on a side. Children can gain understanding of similarity and congruency by constructing and comparing many figures on the geo plane.

Some relationships of squares and triangles can be illustrated by the following activities.

1. Construct a square. Make a diagonal of the square. Answer these questions:

   a. What kind of triangles are included in the square?

   b. Are the triangles congruent?

2. Construct a right triangle.

3. Construct a square on each side of the right triangle. Divide the squares into square units.

   a. Count the units in the large square.

   b. Count the units in the two small squares.

   c. How do the number of units in (a) and (b) compare?

After children have worked with the geo plane or the peg board making the different types of figures and seeing the relationships of the figures, you will find that they have learned a great deal about discovery. They will have found that discovering new ideas is fun. Children will have learned that they have ability to discover relationships among figures. They probably will want to use the plane board when they come back to study other figures and their relationships. This work will help them to be more receptive. When they are working with pencil and straightedge, they will have a memory of having looped the rubber bands to make certain forms and shapes and they will be able to visualize this before they draw. Children should be permitted to go back and work with the plane board at any time they desire, particularly at times when they are constructing figures or trying to see whether or not figures are equal in area, equal in perimeter, and so forth.

The suggestions given above do not exhaust the possible list of exercises and examples that could be performed on the geo plane. Other ideas will come to children as they are working with the board. Also, the teacher will find as he teaches that he needs to make illustrations; later in the mathematics program, when children are studying such things as projective geometry or topology or set theory, many of the ideas can be illustrated on the geo plane.

If colored yarn or other colored string is used, the children are able to make very attractive bulletin boards on the peg board. This would indicate to any who see it what they are studying; the more intricate the designs, the more learning has probably taken place. This type of work is an opportunity for children to work together.

Three-dimensional Models

In traditional programs, plane geometry was taught in one grade, usually the tenth, and solid geometry was usually taught as an elective course in the twelfth grade. Today we recognize that children in all elementary grades can learn a great deal about objects that extend into space in three dimensions. They build with blocks as soon as they begin to play, they feel the roundness of a cup or glass, and they fill cups and boxes of all kinds with sand when they begin to play in the sandpile. In order to help a child understand spatial relationships and to interpret his environment, the elementary school mathematics program has been extended to include an inductive study of three-dimensional models.

THE CYLINDER

A cylinder is made by two congruent, simple closed curves that lie in parallel planes and the curved surface which connects the two closed curves. The can that we see in the home each day is an example of such a cylinder. Children can make a cylinder by taking two congruent circles and a rectangular piece of heavy paper (Fig. 9.40) that is equal in length to the circumference of the circle. The paper is rolled into the shape of a tube and put together with tape. The circles are taped to the ends of the tube.

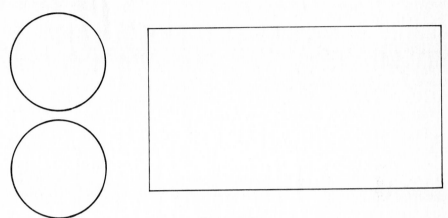

Figure 9.40

We usually think of the cylinder as having round bases, but this is not always true. The base might be in the form of an ellipse. The things to remember are that (1) the bases are congruent, (2) the bases lie in parallel planes, (3) the bases are enclosed by a simple closed curve. With these conditions in mind, we must recognize that the bases might take any curved shape, such as model A illustrated in Figure 9.41. In this case, the bases are congruent, the bases are parallel, and the bases are enclosed in a simple curve. It is a cylinder.

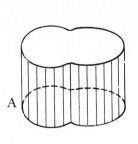
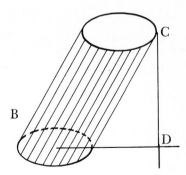

Figure 9.41

Cylinders are called right cylinders if the lateral sides are perpendicular to the bases. Other cylinders, such as model B in Figure 9.41, might take a different form. The bases are still congruent, they are parallel, and they are bounded by a simple closed curve. The height of the cylinder would be measured by the line CD, which is the perpendicular distance from the top circle to the bottom one.

A prism is a very special kind of cylinder. The bases are congruent and parallel, but the bases are polygons of different shapes. The rectangular prism is often spoken of as a box by children. the top and bottom are made up of congruent rectangles that are parallel, but the sides are made up of polygons that are not in the same plane. Examples of different types of prisms are shown in Figure 9.42.

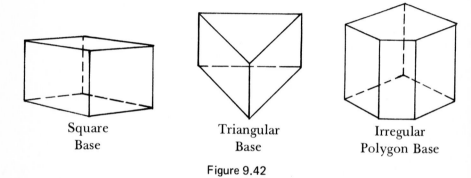

| Square
Base | Triangular
Base | Irregular
Polygon Base |

Figure 9.42

It is relatively easy for a child to make a grid of blocks to find the volumes of a square- or rectangle-based prism. He stacks blocks for

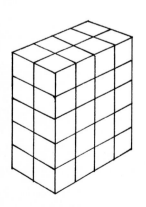

Figure 9.43

width, length, and height (Fig. 9.43) and then counts the units that are in the model. He finds that if he multiplies the width times the length, he has the area of the base (2 X 4 = 8). He then multiplies this area by the height (8 X 5 = 40). These are cubic units, as he finds when he unstacks the blocks. This will be used later in finding volume.

The prisms which we have discussed have been right prisms. The volume is found in the same way whether the prism is a right prism or an oblique one, but the height must always be measured on a line perpendicular to the plane of the base. The generalization can be made that the volume of a cylinder or a prism is the area of the base multiplied by the height.

Exercises.

1. Take inch blocks, make them into a square five (5) to each side. Count the number of blocks.

2. Place on the above square a second square with four (4) to each side.
   a. Count the number of blocks.
   b. Count the difference between $(5)^2$ and $(4)^2$.

3. Place on the above square a square with three (3) to each side.
   a. Count the number of blocks.
   b. Count the difference between $(4)^2$ and $(3)^2$.

4. Place on the above square a square with two (2) to each side.
   a. Count the number of blocks.
   b. Count the difference between $(3)^2$ and $(2)^2$.

5. Place one block on the above square. Count the difference between $(2)^2$ and $(1)^2$.

			Difference
5^2	=	25	
4^2	=	16	9
3^2	=	9	7
2^2	=	4	5
1^2	=	1	3

6. Make cubes of blocks (up to five to each side):
   a. 3 per side, 9 blocks square for base, 3×9 or 27 blocks in the cube.
      (1) How many blocks are hidden?
      (2) How many blocks do you see?
      (3) How could you prove this?
   b. Use four (4) blocks to each side so that there are 4×4 or 16 blocks in the square base. Make the model four blocks high and fill in all four layers with blocks so there are 16 blocks in each layer.
      (1) How many blocks are there altogether?
      (2) How many can you see (include the ones on the bottom as if the model could be turned over)?
      (3) How many are hidden?
   c. Repeat the same activity using five (5) blocks to each side: 5×5 or 25 blocks in the base, 5 layers of blocks.

(1) How many blocks are there this time?
(2) How many blocks can you see?
(3) How many blocks are hidden?
    d. How many cubic units will each of the above models contain?

7. Make a rectangular prism three (3) units wide, six (6) units long and two (2) units high. How many unit blocks will it hold?

8. Make rectangular prisms with the following dimensions and show how many cubic units each would hold:
    a. 4 X 4 X 6 units
    b. 3 X 3 X 6 units
    c. 3 X 5 X 6 units
    d. 3 X 3 X 5 units

9. Measure a milk carton and tell how many cubic inches it holds.

10. Measure many boxes that are in the shape of rectangular prisms. Give the volume of each.

PYRAMIDS AND CONES

A pyramid (Fig. 9.44) is a surface which is made up of a base in the shape of any polygon and has triangular faces, one for each side of the base. The intersection of any two faces is an *edge* and the intersection of three or more edges is a point called a *vertex*. This vertex is not in the same plane with the base.

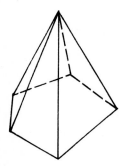 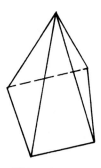 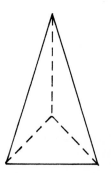

Figure 9.44

If you had a prism with square base, and a pyramid with a base congruent to base of prism, and the two heights were the same, the child could find that if he filled the pyramid with sand and emptied it into the prism it would take three pyramids full of sand to fill the prism. The volume of the pyramid would be 1/3 the volume of the prism with an equal base. Thus, the volume of any pyramid is 1/3 ✕ area of base ✕ height.

The cone has the same relationship to the cylinder as the pyramid has to the prism (Fig. 9.45). The base may be a circle, but it has to be a simple closed curve. The most familiar cone is the one with circular base. If the line from the vertex to the center of the circle makes a 90°

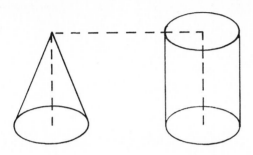

Figure 9.45

angle with the base, the cone is a *right cone*. Some circular base cones are not right cones. They are *oblique*. The cone has a base, a lateral area, and a vertex. A cone may be made from heavy paper. If we had a cylinder and a cone with congruent bases and equal heights, it would take three cones full of sand to fill the cylinder. The volume of the cone would be 1/3 ✕ area of the base ✕ the height.

Some experience with prisms, pyramids, cylinders, and cones will help children to understand their environment better. Learning to verbalize (not say from memory) what they have learned will be a great advance in learning how to learn.

Exercises.

1. Find cylinders (cans) of different sizes and estimate the volume of each.

2. Fill each with sand and pour sand into a prism that you have measured previously. Check your estimate.

3. Estimate the difference in various cylinders—check by pouring sand from one to the other.

4. Make a cone which has the same base and height as a cylinder (can) which you have. Pour sand from the cylinder to the cone. How many times does it fill the cone?

THE SPHERE

A solid figure analogous to a circle is a sphere. A sphere (Fig. 9.46) is a simple closed surface having a point O in its interior such that if A and B are *any* two points on the surface, $\overline{OA} = \overline{OB}$.

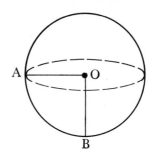

Figure 9.46

The earth is an example of a sphere. (It is flattened somewhat at the poles.) Many objects have the shape of a sphere: a ball, a balloon, ball bearings, and many other objects. The large spheres made of styrofoam are very helpful in teaching geography. Lines can be placed for latitude and longitude. Cuts can be made to show cross sections of the sphere. Technically, the sphere is the surface of the solid, not the solid itself.

Exercises.

1. Take a sphere made of styrofoam:
   a. Cut it through the center.
   b. Make other cuts parallel to the first.
   c. What is the shape of the cross section?
2. Cut out one-fourth of a sphere.
   a. Draw some radii.
   b. Measure to see if all radii are equal.

Motion Geometry

Making a tracing of a line, or an angle on a transparent sheet is an important activity in determining congruence of lines, angles, and polygons as well as other figures. The student should recognize after he has made a copy of figures on transparent sheets that they have all of the properties of the original figures. The tracing has the advantage of being able to be moved. This is important because it enables the student to compare the original figure with many other figures.

In motion geometry there are three basic operations. The *slide* is a motion for a certain distance in a certain direction. When a drawing is made on a transparency you can slide it to give it a new position or to measure another figure (see Fig. 9.47).

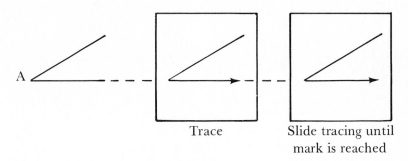

Trace   Slide tracing until mark is reached

Figure 9.47

The *flip* is a turning over of the transparency so that the figure is now a mirror image of the original figure position. The *turn* is the turning of a specified amount and direction about a fixed point. Turns can be clockwise or counterclockwise.

Tracing is the basis for determining congruency. Moving the copy from one position to another may be necessary in order to measure different figures. This may be done by sliding the copy from one figure to another, or it may be necessary to turn the copy so as to find corresponding parts. The very young child will probably not be able to make tracings. Children will gain skill in this task as they mature and they have better coordination.

The teacher can make use of the overhead projector in making tracings for young children. He could use a figure such as △ ABC (Fig. 9.48) drawn on one transparent sheet. Copies could be made on a second transparent sheet while the children watch.

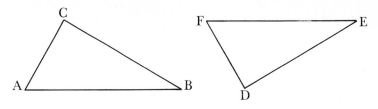

Figure 9.48

By turning the copy of ABC in Figure 9.48 to make A correspond with F, one can find that △ ABC ≅ △ DFE. The teacher should wait for the children to tell him how to turn the copy. Children can also learn that corresponding parts of congruent figures are also congruent. Ask questions to bring out which line segment in the copy corresponds to a given line in DEF.

After children are able to make copies and move them to find congruent figures, they should find examples of the use of congruent figures in such everyday situations as those suggested below:

1. The wheels of an automobile. (What would happen if the front wheels were not congruent?)
2. The Coke machine. (What happens if you put a dime in the nickel slot?)
3. Any other vending machine.
4. Parking meters.
5. Pair of shoe soles. (Would you find congruence by the tracing, slide or turn method?)
6. Find many other objects in the environment that children think are congruent.
   a. Find ways to check to see if they are congruent.
   b. Did you make a tracing?
   c. Could you match the objects to see if they were congruent without tracing?
   d. If you made a tracing did you have to slide, flip, or turn it to fit the model to be measured?
   e. Did you have to go through more than one of the above processes?

Motion geometry is also concerned with similarity and symmetry. These concepts are difficult for the elementary school age child, but many will be able to understand the basic concepts. Figure 9.49 illustrates similarity and can be used in the following exercise:

1. Make a copy of △ ABC on a transparent sheet.
2. Slide the copy over △ DEF so that ∡ C coincides with △ F.
   a. Would ∡ C be congruent to ∡ F?
   b. Is ∡ 1 congruent to ∡ 2?
   c. Is ∡ 3 congruent to ∡ 4?
   d. Is AB parallel to DE?
3. Name the parts in △ ABC that are congruent to △ DEF.
4. Name the parts in △ ABC that are not congruent to △ DEF.
5. If the two triangles are similar, make a definition of similar triangles. (Children would have to know something about parallel lines and corresponding angles in order to understand this concept.)

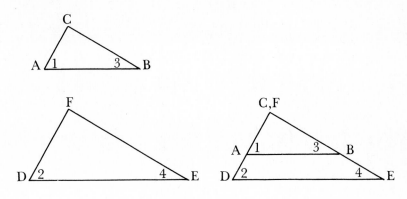

Figure 9.49

Symmetry is often studied through the technique of flipping or folding. Triangles that can be folded to get a mirror image are symmetric. The isosceles triangle ABC in Figure 9.50 has one line of symmetry. These questions could be asked when studying such a triangle:

    a. Are the two sides congruent?
    b. Is angle A congruent to angle B?

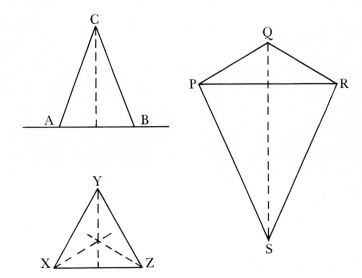

Figure 9.50

Equilateral triangles (△ X YZ) have three lines of symmetry. They can be folded in any of the three lines. (Scalene triangles have no lines of symmetry.) The traditional shape of a kite would be symmetric. The line of symmetry, QS, would be perpendicular to the crossbar PR. Questions like the following could be asked:

    a. Which triangles would be congruent?
    b. What corresponding sides would be congruent?
    c. Which angles would be congruent?
    d. Draw other figures that would be symmetrical.

The following activities illustrate symmetry further:

1. Fold a piece of paper, cut out a design, and note the symmetry.
    a. Butterfly (one fold).
    b. A Christmas tree (one fold).
    c. A snowflake (three folds).
    d. A bird (one fold).

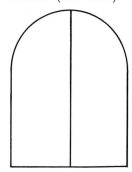

2. With compass and rule, draw a stained glass window making the line of symmetry a vertical line down the center. Make the two sides symmetrical. What is the easiest way to make the second side?

Motion geometry is a growing and expanding concept. Children should have material to work with and freedom to experiment. The experimentation can be carried on by teams of students, with the teacher serving as a resource person. Children appear to have more interest when they work as teams. Each person receives ideas from other students; they challenge each other's ideas and cause students to produce proof that their ideas are tenable.

After they have learned the basic concepts, students should be asked to find examples from the environment. They can depict these with scale drawings or, in some instances, can bring the real objects into the classroom. They can even take slides of examples of congruency, symmetry, and similarity. They will then be forced to devise a way of proving the relationship.

Children who have made observations of this nature, have drawn figures, and made tracings will have readiness for more difficult concepts in mathematics and science. They will also be more perceptive about shapes and sizes of objects in their environment.

Related References

Colciani, Mary P. et al. *Modern Geometry.* Boston: Houghton Mifflin Company, 1963.

Phillips, Jo McKeeby and Zwoyer, Russell E. *Motion Geometry.* New York: Harper & Row, Publishers, 1969.

School Mathematics Study Group, *Elementary School Mathematics.* 30, 16 mm films, 30 minutes each. National Council of Teachers of Mathematics, Washington, D.C.: The Council, 1963.

School Mathematics Study Group, *Studies in Mathematics.* vol. 9. Board of Trustees of the Leland Stanford Junior University, 1963.

Wheeler, Olive. *Geometry in the Elementary School.* Dallas: Hester and Associates (five filmstrips with cassette tapes; Lines and Points, Triangles, Quadrilaterals, Polygons, Solid Figures), 1971.

CHAPTER 10

DECIMAL FRACTIONS AND PERCENTS

In the chapter on rational numbers, the concept of a fraction was developed, followed by the development of methods of understanding and computing with fractions. The consistency of the operations with whole numbers and operations with rational numbers was repeatedly emphasized, and this same consistency will pertain to decimal fractions. The concept will not be new, but previously learned materials will be applied to new situations. It should also be kept in mind that in most programs, decimal fractions are introduced after students have gained a reasonable mastery of common fractions. Thus, this chapter will be concerned with a brief developmental history of decimal fractions; the meaning of decimal fractions; operations with decimal fractions; and the meaning and application of percent.

History of the Development of Decimal Fractions

As discussed in Chapter 5, the basic idea of decimal fractions was probably developed by the Babylonians. It should be remembered, however, that although they developed the basic idea, they did not develop decimal fractions as we use them, because they used a base 60 system of place value. The Babylonian concept of fractions was based upon expressing all of their fractions so that the denominator was always the base, or a positive power of the base.

It took some twenty centuries to develop this mathematical idea into the form that we now know and use. The writings of two sixteenth-century mathematicians, Christoff Rudolff and Simon Stevin, presented the idea of decimal fractions; from their ideas other mathematicians developed the notation of decimal fractions in use today. Thus, another piece of the numerical puzzle fell into place and modern man's system of numeration became more complete.

Not only does the concept of decimal fractions provide a system of expressing fractions in a manner consistent with our scheme of place-value notation, but it also enables us to go beyond the implied division of common fractions so that a small number can now be divided by a larger number. It should also be noted that the development of the concept of decimal fractions makes possible the extension of place-value notation to the right of the units' place as many places as we need or desire.

MEANINGS OF DECIMAL FRACTIONS

The term *decimal,* literally translated, means "ten." Since the system of numeration used by most people is base ten, we can say that we have a decimal system of numeration. This means that we have decimal whole numbers as well as decimal fractions, and decimal mixed numbers. (It would probably be better to refer to each type by their whole correct name, rather than just as decimals.) It should also be noted that fractions such as $\frac{3}{10}, \frac{19}{100}$, and so on, are decimal fractions, but they are expressed in the form of common fractions. The term *decimal fractions* as used in this book will refer to fractions expressed in the form of .7, .032, and so forth. An important aspect of decimal fractions that should be kept constantly before the students is the fact that decimal fractions are not new or different fractions, but are merely *fractions in a special form.*

The most distinguishing and unique feature about decimal fractions is the method of expression. Numerals are used to express the numerator, but the implied denominator, which is not written, is designated by the position (place value) of the numerals in the numerator; therefore, the denominator of decimal fractions will always be ten or a power of ten (such as 100, 1,000, 10,000, and so on), even though it is not written.

THE DECIMAL POINT

Another unique feature of decimal fractions is the decimal point (often erroneously referred to as the decimal). Decimal fractions are always preceded by the decimal point (for example: .6, .013, .01, and so on). The purpose of the decimal point is to serve as a punctuation mark or road sign to indicate that the whole number or numbers have ended, and the fractional part of the number is beginning. We could use almost any other type of mark or symbol to serve as a separator of whole numbers and fractions, but, for convenience and consistency it has been agreed that the period-like decimal point will be used.

It should be pointed out that the use and importance of the decimal point is often misrepresented and overemphasized. Children are often left with the impression that the decimal point is the reference point of our numeration system, or that the decimal point has some kind of place value of its own. Such is not the case and teachers should take precautions to prevent this misconception. In some instances, children may even come to think of the decimal point in the way they think of the numerals that represent numbers. Care must be taken by the teacher to ensure that students recognize the decimal point as a separator of whole numbers and fractional numbers and as a mechanical aid for aligning like numbers in the algorism. In computation, the operation that is being performed is performed on numbers and not the decimal point. The decimal point does not enter into the computation. It can be stressed that one of the great advantages of working with decimal fractions is that you do not have to get a common denominator in order to add or subtract these fractions. This is because of the place-value scheme inherent in decimal fractions which makes all fractions of this kind tenths, hundredths, thousandths, or other multiples of ten; and the role of the decimal point is that of assisting in aligning like numbers. Instead of emphasizing the decimal point, time should be spent on developing the importance of the units' (ones') place in our place-value system of notation, because all numbers (both fractions and whole numbers) derive their value from their relationship to the unit (one).

THE IMPORTANCE OF THE UNITS' (ONES') PLACE

Children and teachers have often missed or overlooked the importance of the units' place. This probably resulted from failure to fully understand the place-value system of notation. In developing the place-value system, each position to the left of the units' position derives its value from its relation to the unit. For example, 18 derives its value because it is 18 times greater than the unit (one). With decimal fractions, the place-value system is extended to the right of the units' position; in a similar fashion, fractional numbers also derive their value in relation to the units place. The decimal fraction .3 derives its value because it is three-tenths as great as the unit (one). Thus, the units place is the reference point of our numeration system, since any number derives its value by its relationship to the unit (one).

Students being introduced to, and working with, decimal fractions will often look for patterns and relationships to aid their understanding. If they have the impression that the decimal point is the point of reference, it will probably seem illogical for the *tenths'* position to be the first position to the right of the decimal point while the *tens'* position is the second position to the left of the decimal point. The same difficulty is encountered when comparing other positions to the right and left of the decimal point.

By using the correct point of reference, the units' place, a symmetrical relationship will be discovered by the student. In this symmetrical relationship, the *tens'* place will be the *first* position to the *left* of the units' place, while the *tenths'* place will be the *first* position to the *right* of the units' place; the *hundreds'* position will be the second position to the left and the *hundredths'* place will be the second position to the right of the units' place; and so on. Figure 10.1 illustrates this symmetrical relationship:

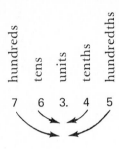

Figure 10.1

This symmetrical relationship can also be seen if we observe a place-value chart. In our study of numeration systems (Chap. 5), it was shown that by use of exponents and the base being used it was possible to determine the positional value of numbers. However, since the exponents used in determining positional value of whole numbers were always positive integers, some other method must be used with decimal fractions. It was probably quite natural and logical that mathematicians decided to use exponents of negative integers to denote decimal fractions. For example, if 10^2 means 10×10 or 100, then 10^{-2} means $\frac{1}{10} \times \frac{1}{10}$ or $\frac{1}{100}$. By studying the place-value chart in Figure 10.2, the symmetry of our place-value system of numeration, as well as the importance of the units, can be seen.

Thousands	Hundreds	Tens	Units (Ones)	Tenths	Hundredths	Thousandths
10^3	10^2	10^1	10^0	10^{-1}	10^{-2}	10^{-3}

Figure 10.2

KINDS OF DECIMALS

The discussion of fractional numbers in Chapter 7 explained that fractions in the form of $\frac{a}{b}$ were often referred to as common and improper fractions (although this terminology was not considered to be desirable). In a similar manner, decimal fractions are sometimes referred to as pure decimal fractions (when the value of the fraction is less than one) and mixed decimal numbers (when the value is greater than one and contains both whole numbers and decimal fractions). In order to try to avoid confusion, when we refer to decimal fractions with a value less than one, they will be called simply *decimal fractions* (for example, .7, .39, .016, and so forth). When the value is greater than one, and contains decimal fractions, these will be referred to as *mixed decimal numbers* (for example, 1.03, 15.2, 6.721, and so on).

READING DECIMAL FRACTIONS

The reading of decimal fractions is developed through understanding of the place-value scheme utilized by these fractions and then having numerous opportunities to practice reading decimal fractions. As you may suspect, learning to read decimal fractions is considerably like reading decimal whole numbers and this similarity can be extended to assist students in their reading of decimal fractions. It should also be noted that there are some differences in designating decimal fractions and decimal numbers so that decimal fractions can be distinguished from decimal numbers, particularly in oral communication. It is the recognition of these differences and careful pronunciation of them that enable precision and conciseness to be developed in communication.

Decimal fractions are read initially as if they were decimal whole numbers; then they are named by the positional name of the last digit on the right. For example, .312 would be read initially as "three hundred twelve"; then the fractional name of the last digit on the right (that is, the 2 occupying the thousandths' position in this instance) is added to the initial numerical reading. Putting both the initial step and the naming step together, .312 would be read as "three hundred twelve thousandths." It is the suffix *ths* that distinguishes the reading of this numeral from decimal whole numbers, therefore, careful enunciation of the *ths* is necessary. The reading of mixed decimal numbers is accomplished by first reading the decimal whole number in the normal manner; this is followed by the word "and" to separate the decimal whole number and fraction, and then the decimal fraction is read in the normal manner. The reading of 136.28 would be "one hundred thirty six *and* twenty eight hundredths."

CHANGING FROM FRACTIONAL FORM
TO DECIMAL FRACTIONS

Since the decimal fraction is a special kind of fraction that is written in a special way, the student should have little trouble in converting from one form to the other. Probably changing from decimal fractions to equivalent fractions should be taught first, because the concept of equivalent fractions has already been developed. (It should be remembered that equivalent fractions were developed from the concept that Numbers Have Many Names.) In changing decimal fractions to fractions, the pupils should be guided to discover that any decimal fraction can be written in the fractional form of $\frac{a}{b}$, (Fig. 10.3).

$$.7 = \frac{7}{10} \qquad \frac{3}{4} = .75$$

$$.41 = \frac{41}{100} \quad \text{or} \quad \frac{1}{2} = .50$$

$$.038 = \frac{38}{1000} \qquad \frac{5}{8} = .625$$

Figure 10.3

Nothing really new has had to be learned in changing decimal fractions to fractions. The child makes an application of what he has already learned.

Another important aspect of equivalent fractions that can also be developed at this time is the relationship (or equivalence) that results from annexing a zero, or zeros, after the last digit of a decimal fraction (for example, .3 = .30 = .300 = .3000 and so on). Zero usually describes the empty set and means "not any." This has been the case with decimal whole numbers and, in a general way, it is also true for decimal fractions. In decimal whole numbers, a zero annexed after the last digit changes the value of the number to a number ten times greater. In contrast, the annexing of a zero, or zeros, after the last digit in a decimal fraction does not change the value of the fraction, only the fraction's name. This is because decimal fractions are located to the right of the point of reference, the units' position. As children gain experience with this type of equivalent fractions, they can soon be guided into generalizing that annexing a zero, or zeros, after the last digit of a decimal fraction does not change the value of the fraction, but it does change the name of the fraction. The changing of fractions to decimal fractions requires an understanding of the division process when decimal fractions are involved. For this reason, changing fractions to decimal fractions will be postponed until after the study of the division process as it pertains to the decimal fraction.

Operations with Decimal Fractions

Before beginning any computation with decimal fractions, it must be remembered that readiness must precede computation. Readiness for computing with decimal fractions should include reasonable mastery and understanding of the basic operations with whole numbers, understanding of the concepts of fractions, reasonable mastery and understanding of the basic operations with fractions, and a reasonable mastery and understanding of numeration, particularly as it pertains to decimal fractions. Without all of the preceding understanding prior to computing with decimal fractions, the pupil's learning could easily become confused and muddled. The resultant learning, if any, could be of a shallow, mechanical nature. Time spent in developing these preoperational understandings will pay great dividends in future mastery for the pupils.

ADDITION

To the authors' knowledge there are no adequate concrete materials for use with decimal fractions except the number line. Since decimal fractions are not usually introduced until the upper elementary grades, the students will have acquired certain basic skills and understandings in operations with numbers. Therefore, most of the students will be operating at a more abstract level in their learning than when they were learning operations with whole numbers. Consequently, it will probably not be necessary to work at the concrete level as long as was necessary with whole numbers and fractions. It should also be remembered from the chapter on rational numbers that the emphasis should be on extending previously mastered skills and understanding rather than on learning something new. Learning to add decimal fractions will be very similar to learning to add whole numbers. Also, as the operation of addition is being learned, the students can be inductively guided to discover that many of the properties of addition also hold true for adding decimal fractions. The rule of likeness will be very important in learning to add and subtract decimal fractions. Although the decimal point is not a point of reference, it is a mechanical aid to help ensure that only like numerals are added. Thus, by keeping decimal points aligned, we are also aligning like numbers, so that when we add, we will be adding only like numbers.

The actual introduction of addition of decimal fractions should be done with the number line in which tenths are added to tenths and the sum is less than one, like this for the sum .3 + .4:

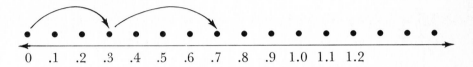

```
0   .1   .2   .3   .4   .5   .6   .7   .8   .9   1.0  1.1  1.2
```

After the students work the problem on the number line, the teacher should then symbolize what they have done by writing the algorism on either the chalkboard or overhead projector, like this:

$$
\begin{array}{c}
.3 \\
+ .4 \\
\hline
\end{array}
\equiv
\begin{array}{c}
3 \text{ tenths} \\
+ 4 \text{ tenths} \\
\hline
7 \text{ tenths}
\end{array}
\equiv
\begin{array}{c}
.3 \\
+ .4 \\
\hline
.7
\end{array}
$$

After observing the teacher symbolize what they had performed on the number line by writing the algorism, the students should be guided into their own symbolization of each of the problems that they worked on their number lines. As children are able, they should make the algorism without the number line. The next step after mastering tenths added to tenths without regrouping, would be the addition of hundredths added to hundredths without regrouping. The students initially work the problem using the number line, like this:

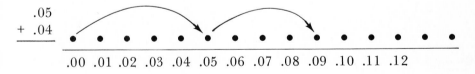

```
.05
+ .04
```

```
.00 .01 .02 .03 .04 .05 .06 .07 .08 .09 .10 .11 .12
```

Following this, the teachers symbolizes the algorism in this manner:

$$
\begin{array}{c}
.05 \\
+ .04 \\
\hline
\end{array}
\equiv
\begin{array}{c}
5 \text{ hundredths} \\
+ 4 \text{ hundredths} \\
\hline
9 \text{ hundredths}
\end{array}
\equiv
\begin{array}{c}
.05 \\
+ .04 \\
\hline
.09
\end{array}
$$

During the time students are developing mastery of the process, the teacher should regularly emphasize that the decimal point was a mechanical aid to assist in the alignment of like numbers. When the teacher was satisfied that his students had reasonable mastery working with these types of addition, the students could then be guided into adding decimal fractions that required regrouping. The students would once more work the problem initially on the line, like this:

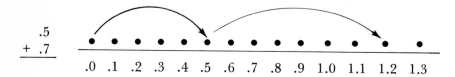

$$
\begin{array}{r}
.5 \\
+ \ .7 \\
\end{array}
$$

.0 .1 .2 .3 .4 .5 .6 .7 .8 .9 1.0 1.1 1.2 1.3

The teacher would then symbolize the algorism for the students in this manner:

$$
\begin{array}{r}
.5 \\
+ \ .7 \\
\end{array}
\equiv
\begin{array}{r}
5 \text{ tenths} \\
+ \ 7 \text{ tenths} \\
\hline
12 \text{ tenths} = 1.2
\end{array}
\equiv
\begin{array}{r}
.5 \\
+ \ .7 \\
\hline
1.2
\end{array}
$$

This would then be followed by addition of mixed decimal numbers in which it is not necessary to regroup, like this:

$$
\begin{array}{r}
1.2 \\
+ \ 1.5 \\
\end{array}
$$

.0 .1 .2 .3 .4 .5 .6 .7 .8 .9 1.0 1.1 1.2 1.3 1.4 1.5 1.6 1.7 1.8 1.9 2.0 2.1 2.2 2.3 2.4 2.5 2.6 2.7 2.8 2.9

Following mastery of addition on the number line of mixed decimal numbers without regrouping, a transition should then be made to a place-value chart, such as shown in Figure 10.4.

	10^1	10^2	10^3
	tenths	hundredths	thousandths
	.4	6	3
.463	.3	4	8
+ .348			
.811	.8	1	1

Figure 10.4

During this time of teaching the algorism of adding fractions, the teacher should help the students remember that even in adding decimal fractions we are still grouping by tens. This means that any time we get as many as ten, or more, in any one column, we must regroup so that the proper numbers will be in the appropriate columns.

After the students have reasonable understanding of adding decimal fractions using the place-value chart, the next step should be to extend their learning to adding mixed decimal numbers, first without regrouping, using the place-value chart shown in Figure 10.5.

	tens	ones	tenths	hundredths	thousandths
1.34		1	.3	4	
+ 2.45	+	2	.4	5	
3.79		3	.7	9	

Figure 10.5

This would then be followed by adding decimal fractions or mixed decimal numbers that involved regrouping (Fig. 10.6).

	tens	ones	tenths	hundredths	thousandths
3.64		3	.6	4	
+ 5.78	+	5	.7	8	
9.42		9	.4	2	

Figure 10.6

The transition from adding decimal fractions using the place-value chart to the more conventional algorism should not cause any great problems.

The use of annexing zeros after the last digit of a decimal fraction was earlier discussed as a means of developing equivalent fractions. This use of zero can assist students in adding or subtracting ragged decimal fractions. *Ragged decimal fractions* are decimal fractions that do not have the same number of places represented to the right of the decimal point. The following is an example of an addition problem involving ragged decimal fractions.

$$.02 + .145 + .7 + .0081$$

Placed in the traditional vertical form, it would be shown like the first set of numbers in Figure 10.7. The role of the decimal point in aligning like numbers is apparent, but since each of the decimal fractions are different, they each have a different number of digits to the right of the decimal point. This results in some of the decimal fractions having blank spaces following the last digit, thus giving a "ragged" appearance. This causes some students to be confused as what to do as they attempt to add the various columns. Since it is possible to annex zeros after the last digit in a decimal fraction without changing the value of the fraction, the student can annex zeros after the last digit as many times as necessary so that all decimal fractions have the same number of places. This is shown in the second set of numbers in Figure 10.7.

$$
\begin{array}{rcr}
.02 & & .0200 \\
.145 & & .1450 \\
.7 & & .7000 \\
+\ .0081 & \equiv & +\ .0081 \\
\hline
\end{array}
$$

Figure 10.7

Annexing zeros in this manner is an intermediate step, and most students will soon realize that they do not have to perform this step in order to solve this type of addition.

SUBTRACTING

There are certain aspects of readiness for subtracting decimal fractions, just as in adding decimal fractions. The students must have a reasonable mastery and understanding of the system of numeration, subtracting whole numbers, and subtracting fractions. If students are having difficulties in learning operations with decimal fractions, the problem may very well be that they did not sufficiently master the previous concepts and not decimal fractions themselves. Since we are stressing the similarities of operations with whole numbers, fractions, and decimal fractions, the teacher would probably be wise to spend some time periodically reviewing and reinforcing previous learnings. The introduction of subtracting decimal fractions, as in adding, would be done with the number line in which tenths would be subtracted from tenths without having to regroup, like this:

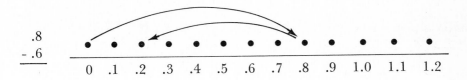

It will be remembered from operations with whole numbers that in using the number line to perform subtraction, you first moved down the number line to the value of the minuend (in this example, .8), then reversed directions and moved back toward the starting point, counting off the value of the subtrahend (in this example, .6). Again, the teacher would symbolize in the algorism what the students had performed on the number line, like this:

$$\begin{array}{ccccc} .8 & & 8 \text{ tenths} & & .8 \\ \underline{-\ .6} & \equiv & \underline{-\ 6 \text{ tenths}} & \equiv & \underline{-\ .6} \\ & & 2 \text{ tenths} & & .2 \end{array}$$

Gradually, the students would be guided into their own symbolization in the algorism of what they had performed on the number line, and finally to computing with just the algorism. Following this basic sequence of subtracting tenths from tenths, the students would be introduced to subtracting hundredths from hundredths, without regrouping, in essentially the same sequence that was used in the subtraction of tenths, for example:

$$\begin{array}{c} .09 \\ \underline{-\ .03} \end{array}$$

.00 .01 .02 .03 .04 .05 .06 .07 .08 .09 .10 .11

After the students work the problem on the number line, the teacher would symbolize the operation in the algorism, like this:

$$\begin{array}{ccccc} .09 & & 9 \text{ hundredths} & & .09 \\ \underline{-\ .03} & \equiv & \underline{-\ 3 \text{ hundredths}} & \equiv & \underline{-\ .03} \\ & & 6 \text{ hundredths} & & .06 \end{array}$$

The students would then be guided into working on their own in making the transition from working on the number line to working with the algorism. The teacher would also assist the students in maintaining an awareness of the role and function of the decimal point as mastery in computation was being developed. As students achieve reasonable mastery of the introductory phases of subtraction, they would then be guided by the teacher into a more difficult phase of subtraction that required regrouping, in a manner similar to the following example:

$$
\begin{array}{r}
.12 \\
- .08 \\
\hline
\end{array}
$$

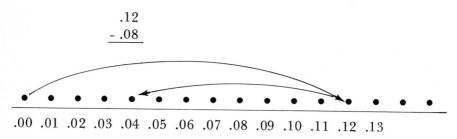

.00 .01 .02 .03 .04 .05 .06 .07 .08 .09 .10 .11 .12 .13

The teacher would symbolize the operation, like this:

$$
\begin{array}{r}
.12 \\
- .08 \\
\hline
\end{array}
\;\equiv\;
\begin{array}{r}
12 \text{ hundredths} \\
- \;\; 8 \text{ hundredths} \\
\hline
4 \text{ hundredths}
\end{array}
\;\equiv\;
\begin{array}{r}
.12 \\
- .08 \\
\hline
.04
\end{array}
$$

A transition to the algorism could then be made by the students, under teacher guidance. This would be followed by subtracting mixed decimal numbers that did not require regrouping, like this:

$$
\begin{array}{r}
2.8 \\
- 1.5 \\
\hline
\end{array}
$$

.0 .1 .2 .3 .4 .5 .6 .7 .8 .9 1.0 1.1 1.2 1.3 1.4 1.5 1.6 1.7 1.8 1.9 2.0 2.1 2.2 2.3 2.4 2.5 2.6 2.7 2.8 2.9

As the students master understanding of these operations, they will be ready for the transition from the number line to the place-value chart (Fig. 10.8).

	ones	tenths	hundredths	thousandths
.369 - .157 --- .212		.3	6	9
	-	.1	5	7
		.2	1	2

Figure 10.8

The importance of the rule of likeness and keeping the decimal point aligned so that only like numbers will be subtracted should also be kept constantly before the pupils. After reasonable mastery of subtracting decimals in the place-value chart without regrouping, the next step would be to extend their learning to subtracting mixed decimal numbers without regrouping. This is shown in Figure 10.9.

	tens	ones	tenths	hundredths
5.36 - 1.24 --- 4.12		5	.3	6
	-	1	.2	4
		4	.1	2

Figure 10.9

Since the pupils should already have mastered regrouping with whole numbers before beginning decimal fractions, there should not be much difficulty encountered. Therefore, subtraction not requiring regrouping would be followed by subtracting fractions or mixed decimal numbers that did require regrouping, as in Figure 10.10.

	10^1	10^0	10^{-1}	10^{-2}	10^{-3}
7.31 - 4.62 --- 2.69		7	.3	1	
	-	4	.6	2	
		2	.6	9	

Figure 10.10

MULTIPLICATION

Most students in the conventional math programs learned to multiply numbers involving decimal fractions in almost a mechanical process and did not understand why the process worked. Learning to multiply decimal fractions need not be mechanical learning, however. It will be remembered that decimal fractions are simply a special kind of fractions written in a special way, with the denominator not written, but determined by a place value scheme. The previously learned algorism of multiplication of fractions can also be utilized:

$$\frac{\text{numerator} \times \text{numerator}}{\text{denominator} \times \text{denominator}}$$

In multiplying decimal fractions or mixed decimal numbers, we will still be multiplying numerator times numerator and denominator times denominator (except that the denominator of the decimal fraction will not be written, but determined by a place-value scheme). For example:

$$\frac{2}{10} \times \frac{4}{10} = \frac{8}{100} \quad \text{or} \quad \begin{array}{r} .2 \\ \times\ .4 \\ \hline .08 \end{array}$$

(We multiplied tenths times tenths, so the answer must be hundredths.)

(tenths × tenths = hundredths)

It will be recalled from Chapter 5, that in multiplying numbers with exponents, you actually add the exponents (example: $10^2 \times 10^3 = 10^5$). This will also hold true when decimal fractions are multiplied:

$$\frac{1}{10^2} \times \frac{1}{10^1} = \frac{1}{10^3}.$$

When multiplying decimal fractions, the reason that you have the same number of places in the product that are in both factors added together is because of the rule of adding exponents when you multiply. This rule of adding exponents is implied in multiplying decimal fractions and is often overlooked and not understood. As children work with the multiplication of decimal fractions, they can gradually be guided to develop a rule for multiplying. Remember that it is the students who must develop the rule in their own terms, with teacher guidance, as they develop understanding of what they are doing.

The beginning phase of teaching the multiplication of decimal fractions will relate as much as possible to multiplication of whole numbers, and in many ways will be developed in a similar manner. The teacher should assist the students in recalling that multiplication is a special kind of addition in which equal-size sets are put together. Students should initially perform the operation on the number line, after which the teacher should symbolize the operation by writing in the algorism. To begin multiplication of decimal fractions, the multiplication of a decimal fraction and a whole number would be used, because it relates so closely to multiplication of whole numbers, like this for the product .4 × 3:

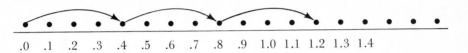

.0 .1 .2 .3 .4 .5 .6 .7 .8 .9 1.0 1.1 1.2 1.3 1.4

The teacher would write:

$$\begin{matrix} .4 \\ .4 \\ +\ .4 \end{matrix} \equiv (3\ \text{sets of .4}) \equiv \dfrac{\begin{matrix} 4\ \text{tenths} \\ \times\ 3 \end{matrix}}{12\ \text{tenths}\ =\ 1.2} \equiv \dfrac{\begin{matrix} .4 \\ \times\ \ \ 3 \end{matrix}}{1.2}$$

As the students make the transition to writing the algorism, and begin to develop mastery of this process, they should be guided by the teacher to develop a rudimentary rule for placing the decimal point in the product. Then the students should be guided to explore the multiplication of a whole number times a decimal fraction. In this multiplication, the students will need to utilize a rectangular array (Fig. 10.11), similar to the manner in which fractions were multiplied in Chapter 8.

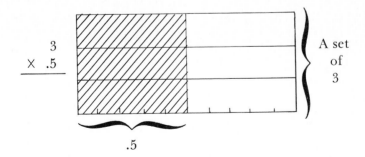

$$\begin{matrix} 3 \\ \times\ .5 \end{matrix}$$

A set of 3

.5

Figure 10.11

The teacher would symbolize what the students had performed by writing the algorism, like this:

$$
\begin{array}{ccc}
3 & 3 & 3 \\
\times\ .5 \equiv & \times\ \ 5\ \text{tenths} \equiv & \times\ \ .5 \\
\hline
& 15\ \text{tenths} & 1.5
\end{array}
$$

The student should then progress to the multiplication of a decimal fraction by a decimal fraction. At this point, it becomes slightly more difficult to illustrate the operation, especially when multiplying decimal fractions other than tenths. For this reason, this phase would begin with the multiplication of tenths multiplied by tenths, with the goal of having the students develop enough understanding in this phase that they will be able to work in the algorism by the time they are ready to multiply decimal fractions other than tenths. A typical problem in this phase is shown in Figure 10.12.

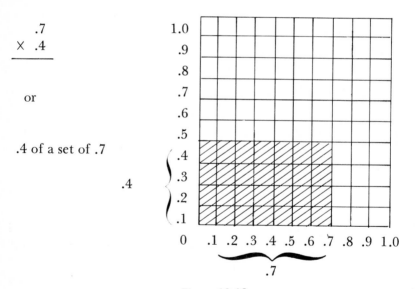

Figure 10.12

During this time, the teacher should be guiding the students toward the development of the generalization that there will be as many places in the product as the sum of the number of places in both factors. The students would be led to recall that in multiplying fractions, $\frac{7}{10} \times \frac{4}{10} = \frac{28}{100}$. In decimal fractions, .7 × .4 = .28, or when tenths are multiplied by tenths the product is hundredths. Expanding this idea leads to tenths times hundredths for a product of thousandths; hundredths times hundredths for a product of ten thousandths; and so on. The skillful teacher will guide the students to discover the relationship between the number of places in the product and the number of places in both factors.

The next phase in the multiplication process would be the multiplication of mixed decimal numbers. By this time, the students should have reasonable mastery of multiplying a whole number times a decimal fraction; a decimal fraction times a decimal fraction; and a whole number times a whole number. With these skills, it becomes simply a matter of combining all three into one operation by using the distributive property of multiplication, like this:

$$
\begin{aligned}
\begin{array}{r} 6.8 \\ \times\ 3.5 \\ \hline \end{array} \equiv\ 3.5 \times 6.8 &= (3 + .5) \times (6 + .8) \\
&= (3 \times 6) + (3 \times .8) + (.5 \times 6) + (.5 \times .8) \\
&= 18 + 2.4 + 3.0 + .40
\end{aligned}
$$

This process is shown in expanded form below:

$$
\begin{array}{r}
6 + .8 \\
\times\ (3 + .5) \\
\hline
.40 \longrightarrow (\text{the product of } .5 \times .8) \\
3.0 \longrightarrow (\text{the product of } .5 \times 6) \\
2.4 \longrightarrow (\text{the product of } 3 \times .8) \\
18 \longrightarrow (\text{the product of } 3 \times 6) \\
\hline
23.80
\end{array}
$$

After some work with this type of problem, the students will probably be able to combine some steps so that it looks more like the traditional algorism below:

$$
\begin{array}{r}
6.8 \\
\times\ 3.5 \\
\hline
3.40 \longrightarrow (\text{the product of } .5 \times 6.8) \\
20.4 \longrightarrow (\text{the product of } 3 \times 6.8) \\
\hline
23.80
\end{array}
$$

As the algorism is being developed, it may help students to put the decimal points in the partial product, which is in contrast to the traditional way. The following two methods of solutions for the same problem illustrate the difference. Observe carefully the differences in these two methods.

A.
$$
\begin{array}{r}
4.23 \\
\times \quad 3.2 \\
\hline
.846 \\
12.69 \\
\hline
13.536
\end{array}
$$

B.
$$
\begin{array}{r}
4.23 \\
\times \quad 3.2 \\
\hline
846 \\
1269 \\
\hline
13.536
\end{array}
$$

In solution A, the first partial product is .2 of 4.23, which is .846; the second partial product is 3 times 4.23, which is 12.69. In the more traditional method, solution B, the decimal points are ignored in the partial products and the multiplication is performed as if it were 423 × 32. The decimal point is then placed in the product. This is the method that probably most students will eventually use, but not until they have developed their own rule from their acquired understanding.

DIVISION

It has been emphasized in preceding chapters that division is the most difficult of the basic operations for children to master. So it is with division of decimal fractions. However, there are some approaches that a teacher may utilize that will help children understand this operation. The same approach that was used in learning division of whole numbers will be utilized in learning division of decimal fractions. The partial quotient, or subtractive method, of division presented in Chapter 6 can be utilized effectively in division of either decimal fractions or mixed decimal numbers. Also, students who mastered this operation to a reasonable degree should not experience much difficulty in making the transition from division of whole numbers to division of decimal fractions.

Since there is a distinct relationship between division involving whole numbers and division involving decimal fractions, the beginning phase of division involving decimal fractions should relate as much as possible to division of whole numbers. This initial phase can also be related to the initial phase of division of fractions quite well. Measurement type division will be used at first, because of the ease of relating to division of whole numbers. Measurement division measures a total quantity into groups of a specified size and then the total number of groups that were contained in the total can be determined. A typical problem of this type would involve a whole number measured by a decimal fraction, with the resulting answer being the number of equal groups. The following illustration presents a typical measurement division problem involving a decimal fraction.

2 ÷ 5 (2 measured by .5 will result in how many groups?)

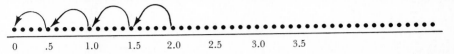

| 0 | .5 | 1.0 | 1.5 | 2.0 | 2.5 | 3.0 | 3.5 |

After the student performs the operation on the number line, the teacher should symbolize the algorism as shown in Figure 10.13.

```
.5 / 2.0
    - .5 | 1
    ─────
     1.5
    - .5 | 1
    ─────
     1.0
    - .5 | 1
    ─────
      .5
    - .5 | 1
    ─────
      0  | 4 (groups of .5)
```

Figure 10.13

(The zero is used to show 0 tenths because you must divide tenths by tenths in order to get units.) By encouraging and guiding students to interpret what the indicated division means, the obtained answer will be more realistic and understandable. In the preceding example (Fig. 10.13), it does not seem plausible that 2 ÷ .5 would yield an answer greater than either of these terms. However, when the problem is interpreted as 2 measured by .5 to yield 4 groups of .5, then it becomes plausible. It should be noted that in this initial phase care should be exercised to avoid division problems that result in incomplete division.

After some time has been spent developing reasonable mastery of this phase, the students should then be guided into problems involving partitioning division. Partitioning division parts a total group into a specified number of groups, with the resulting answer being the number in each equal group. This type of problem could be typified by a decimal fraction divided by a whole number, as in Figure 10.14, which could be symbolized in the algorism that follows:

```
4 / .8
  - .8 | .2 (the size of each equal group)
  ─────
    0  |
```

.8 ÷ 4   (.8 parted into 4 groups will result in what size groups?)

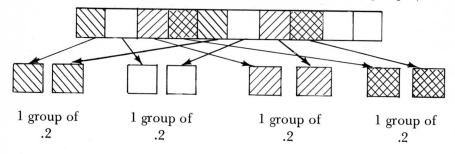

1 group of   1 group of   1 group of   1 group of
.2   .2   .2   .2

Figure 10.14

Following reasonable mastery of this phase, the students could then progress to the division of a mixed decimal number by a whole number, as in Figure 10.15.

$$29.24 \div 4$$

```
4 / 29.24
  - 28.00    7.00
    1.24
  -  1.20     .30
     .04
  -   .04     .01
            7.31
```

Figure 10.15

It will be noticed that in using the subtractive, or partial quotient, method of division, the problem of placing the decimal in the quotient, which is inherent in the traditional method, does not exist. Figure 10.16 may help clarify this.

$$3.864 \div 2.3$$

```
2.3 / 3.864
      2.300    1.00
      1.564
      1.380     .60
       .184
       .184     .08
              1.68
```

Figure 10.16

It will be recalled from Chapter 6 that most children can become as fast and proficient in dividing using the subtractive method as using the traditional method. Consequently, by using the subtractive method, pupils will not have to learn the confusing traditional method that involves "pointing off" so many decimal places before you begin dividing.

Students can be guided to discover a generalization that will assist them in checking their answers. In the multiplication of decimal fractions, it was learned that the number of places in the product was the sum of the number of places on both factors. Since division can be considered the inverse of multiplication, it then follows that the number of places in the quotient will be the *difference* between the number of places in the dividend and the number of places in the divisor. Using the previous example (Fig. 10.16), this relationship can be illustrated as follows:

$$3.864 \quad \div \quad 2.3 \ = \ 1.68$$

$$(3 \text{ places minus } 1 \text{ place} \ = \ 2 \text{ places})$$

Since decimal fraction denominators are all either ten or powers of ten, the idea of division of numbers with exponents that was presented in Chapter 5 can be applied to division of decimal fractions as well. That is, to divide numbers with exponents, you simply subtract the exponents. In decimal fractions, the number of places to the right of the decimal point is as indicative of the power of the number as an exponent. Consequently, this idea of subtracting the number of places in the divisor from the number of places in the dividend to find the number of places that will be in the quotient is valid.

Converting Common Fractions
to Decimal Fractions

Earlier in this chapter, a method was discussed for converting decimal fractions to common fractions. At this time, a method will be presented for converting common fractions to decimal fractions. It will be remembered that a common fraction is an indicated division. When we perform this indicated division, the resultant quotient will be a decimal fraction. The fractions $\frac{5}{8}$ and $\frac{3}{4}$ are converted into decimal fractions in Figure 10.17.

$$8 \, \big/ \, \overline{\begin{array}{l} 5.000 \\ \underline{4.8} \quad .6 \\ .20 \\ \underline{.16} \quad .02 \\ .040 \\ \underline{.040} \quad .005 \end{array}} $$

$$\frac{5}{8} = .625 \qquad .625$$

$$\frac{3}{4} = .75$$

$$4 \, \big/ \, \overline{\begin{array}{l} 3.0 \\ \underline{2.8} \quad .7 \\ .20 \\ \underline{.20} \quad .05 \\ .75 \end{array}} $$

Figure 10.17

It can be pointed out that there are certain equivalence relations between fractions and decimal fractions that are used a great deal more often than any of the equivalence relations. These relationships are so useful that they are considered by many to be basic relationships. These basic equivalence relations are listed in Figure 10.18.

$$\frac{1}{10} = .10 \qquad\qquad \frac{1}{2} = .50$$

$$\frac{1}{8} = .125 \qquad\qquad \frac{3}{5} = .60$$

$$\frac{1}{5} = .20 \qquad\qquad \frac{2}{3} = .66\frac{2}{3}$$

$$\frac{1}{4} = .25 \qquad\qquad \frac{7}{10} = .70$$

$$\frac{3}{10} = .30 \qquad\qquad \frac{3}{4} = .75$$

$$\frac{1}{3} = .33\frac{1}{3} \qquad\qquad \frac{4}{5} = .80$$

$$\frac{3}{8} = .375 \qquad\qquad \frac{7}{8} = .875$$

$$\frac{2}{5} = .40 \qquad\qquad \frac{9}{10} = .90$$

Figure 10.18

The astute teacher will make many opportunities for his students to encounter these basic relations so they will be well acquainted with them. The students should not be required to memorize them, but from experience with and use of them, they will gradually become a part of their instant recall ability. Only the students who see the equivalency readily should use them, since this concept is often confusing to immature students.

Percent

Percent is a topic closely related to decimal fractions and can be profitably studied by most students after reasonable mastery of decimal fractions. Decimal fractions have been presented in this chapter as a special form of fractions whose implied denominator is always ten or a power of ten. Percent can be thought of as a special form of the decimal fraction, since percent translated means hundredths. Since percent is just another name for hundredths, mathematicians have agreed to let the percent symbol (%) mean the same as hundredths. By using the percent symbol (%), we do not have to use a decimal point for the hundredths position of a number. For example, 75% is just another name for .75; conversely, .37 is another name for 37%, and so on.

As a teacher guides understanding of percent, he should be cognizant of the fact that the work done with percents in the elementary school is basically the foundation for later work to be done with percents in junior and senior high school. In fact there are some who believe that the study of percent should be postponed until junior high school. The authors believe that it is best not to teach those things that may inhibit later learning. Some authors recommend teaching the application of percent by using proportion, or by learning some complicated method of computing. Either of these methods may inhibit learning, especially when students encounter a fractional part of one percent (for example, 1/2%), because the students do not usually understand what is meant. It would seem, then, that the work done in the elementary school on percent could be spent most profitably by developing better understanding of percent during a major portion of the time, and then, if application of percent is to be studied, developing the relatedness of percent to decimal fractions. In this way the previous learning of decimal fractions can be utilized so that essentially little that is new will have to be learned to work with percent. The following examples will illustrate how problems with percent can be worked by decimal fractions.

Example 1: (Finding a certain percent of a number.) 60% of 25 is what number?

$$\begin{array}{r} 25 \\ \times\ .60 \\ \hline 15.00 \end{array}$$

Change 60% to .60 and then find .60 of 25. What is 60 hundredths of 25?

Example 2: (Finding what percent one number is of another number.) 15 is what percent of 25? 15 is how many hundredths of 25?

$$25\ \overline{\smash{\big)}\ \begin{array}{l}15.0 \\ 15\ 0\end{array}}\quad \begin{array}{l}.6 \\ \hline .6\end{array}$$

$$\frac{15}{25} = .6 = .60 = 60\%$$

(We would start by comparing 15 to 25 in fractional form; then performing the indicated division. The quotient, .6, would then be changed to its equivalent fraction in hundredths, .60, and then converted to percent, 60%.)

Example 3: (Finding the whole quantity when a certain percent of it is known.) 60% of what number is 15?

$$.60 \times \square = 15$$

or

$$\square = \frac{15}{.60}$$

$$.60\ \overline{\smash{\big)}\ \begin{array}{l}15.00 \\ 12\ 00 \\ \hline 3\ 00 \\ 3\ 00 \\ \hline\end{array}}\quad \begin{array}{l}20 \\ \\ 5 \\ \\ \hline 25\end{array}$$

$$\frac{15}{.60} = 25$$

(We would start by establishing that .60 of what number is 15 can be solved similarly to problems we encountered in operations with whole numbers (i.e., $5 \times \square = 30$). These problems were solved by actually using the inverse of the process indicated.)

By relating the application of percent to decimal fractions, and by spending enough time in developing the meaning of percents, we will probably be less likely to inhibit future learning about percent than if we tried to teach one of the more complicated methods at this time.

One of the difficulties encountered by many students, and some adults as well, is understanding and interpreting percent greater than 100% and percent less than 1%. It was previously pointed out that elementary school students have a great deal of difficulty in understanding and working with fractional parts of 1%. The authors recommend that teachers not attempt to teach or have students work with percent less than 1%. There are numerous other ideas in percent that are much more useful and valuable to elementary school children, the idea being that the time spent on percent should be spent on those things that will be of most use to the students.

Percent greater than 100%, on the other hand, can be developed and used by elementary school children, particularly in the upper intermediate grades. This idea of percent greater than 100% can be developed by first establishing that 100% is a whole and very similar to one whole object or group. The students might then be asked how they would interpret 200%, if 100% meant one whole? This discussion could include the comparison of 100% and 200%, both numerically and with actual objects. Not a great deal of time would be spent on developing concepts of percent greater than 100% and the concept would not be attempted at all until after the basic ideas of percent had been developed. Percent such as 125%, 150%, 175%, 200%, 250%, 300%, and possibly a few others would be worked with by the students. The important thing is that students have enough experience with percent greater than 100% to get the general idea of what a percent greater than 100% means.

Extending Your Thinking

1. Multiply the following by using the method of placing the decimal point in the partial product:
    a. 3.25 × 1.4
    b. .027 × .38
    c. 55 × .46
    d. .81 × .69

2. Perform the following divisions by using the Greenwood (or subtractive) method of division:
    a. 36.52 ÷ 7
    b. 5.89 ÷ 3.4
    c. .917 ÷ 6.1
    d. .454 ÷ .21

3. Using a rectangular array, illustrate the following multiplications:

    a. .3 X .9
    b. .6 X .8
    c. .4 X .7
    d. .7 X .8

4. Change the following fractions to their equivalent decimal fractions:

    a. $\dfrac{2}{5}$

    b. $\dfrac{3}{4}$

    c. $\dfrac{5}{16}$

    d. $\dfrac{7}{12}$

5. Change the following decimal fractions to their equivalent fractions:

    a. .38
    b. .75
    c. .19
    d. .54

6. Add the following on a number line, then do the same addition using a place-value chart:

    a. .8 + .9
    b. 1.5 + 1.8
    c. 2.7 + .6
    d. 1.9 + 2.4

7. Perform the following subtractions on a number line, then do the same subtractions using a place-value chart:

    a. .7 − .5
    b. 1.3 − .8
    c. 3.3 − 1.9
    d. 4.1 − 3.2

8. Plan and describe three activities that would assist students in understanding the role and importance of the units' place being the reference point of our system of numeration.

9. Identify four situations that could be used to guide children's understanding of the relationship between decimal fractions and percent.

10. Plan and describe three activities that would provide children with opportunities to practice converting the most frequently used fractions to percent, and vice versa.

ANSWERS TO SELECTED QUESTIONS

1d.
$$
\begin{array}{r}
69 \\
\times\ .81 \\
\hline
.69 \\
55.2 \\
\hline
55.89
\end{array}
$$

2b.

3a.   .3 × .9

(The shaded portion is .27; therefore, .3 × .9 = .27)

4b.

5d. $.54 = \dfrac{54}{100} = \dfrac{27}{50}$

6a.   .8 + .9

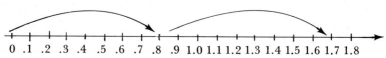

ones	tenths	hundredths
	8	
	9	
1	7	

Related References

Dwight, Leslie A. *Modern Mathematics for the Elementary Teacher.* New York: Holt, Rinehart & Winston, Inc. 1966. pp. 429-58.

The National Council of Teachers of Mathematics, *Topics in Mathematics for Elementary School Teachers.* 29th Yearbook, Washington, D.C.: The National Council of Teachers of Mathematics, 1964. pp. 303-32.

Riedesel, Alan C. *Guiding Discovery in Elementary School Mathematics.* New York: Appleton-Century-Crofts, 1967. pp. 244-62.

School Mathematics Study Group, *Studies in Mathematics.* Vol. 9, rev. ed. Palo Alto, Calif.: Stanford University, 1963. pp. 293-314.

Spencer, Peter and Brydegaard, Marguerite. *Building Mathematical Competence in the Elementary School.* rev. ed. New York: Holt, Rinehart & Winston, Inc. 1966. pp. 173-93.

Swenson, Esther J. *Teaching Arithmetic to Children.* New York: The Macmillan Company, 1964. pp. 417-36.

UNIT THREE
ENRICHMENT ACTIVITIES AND SUPPLEMENTARY INFORMATION

CHAPTER 11

PUZZLES AND GAMES

Considerable emphasis was given in earlier chapters to the need for change of pace activities in a mathematics program to maintain student interest. It should also be obvious that as skills and concepts are introduced and developed, there comes a time when the student must eventually practice these skills himself in order to master them. The purpose of this chapter is to suggest some ways that change of pace can be introduced into a mathematics program. Such reinforcement activities should not be selected at random. There should be a definite reason for their use and the teacher should understand the mathematical rationale involved.

Certain activities in this chapter might be classified as "gimmicks" by some people, but any danger in using this type of activity lies in the way it is used and not in the activity itself. Only if used incorrectly, might such activities inhibit learning or result in mechanical learning rather than the developing and expanding of concepts.

In many instances, students feel that mathematics is shrouded in mysticism and that teachers have some secret way of working and explaining problems. If these students are not guided in their learning so that insight and understanding is developed, their learning experiences will only serve to confirm a feeling of frustration. When students develop such a feeling toward mathematics, it is generally the result of the method used by the teacher rather than from the activity itself. Any activity, method, and/or model that results in conceptual development and understanding is pedagogically sound. The key, then, to correctly using any type of enrichment material is the predetermined purpose that the teacher has for using it and the method he uses in teaching it. Generally, the most effective learning experiences for students result from activities understood well enough by the teacher so that he has insight into their conceptual basis and then utilizes this insight to guide student discovery. The topics of this chapter can serve to enrich and enlarge the learning and understanding of students.

Cross-number Puzzles

The cross-number puzzle provides students with opportunities for interesting and challenging practice in basic operations. It is an activity that can be adapted to almost any level of sophistication and at the same time maintain a high level of interest. It should be remembered that people who have developed proficiency in computing have generally developed this skill over a period of years by using it regularly and having reasonable success with it. This section will present some ways of using the cross-number puzzle to encourage practice in the basic operations of addition, subtraction, multiplication, and division. The activities that will be described in this section are generally abstract in nature because most of them are designed to be used *after* the child has developed basic concepts of operations with appropriate concrete materials.

RATIONALE FOR CROSS-NUMBER PUZZLES

The ideas on which the activities presented in this section are based may seem on the surface to be disguised drill. In actuality they present an opportunity to develop more thinking and insight than does a conventional drill activity. As a student explores these activities, the concepts and generalizations that span arithmetic and mathematics reveal themselves in many circumstances and varied situations. There are also many built-in opportunities for the teacher to create *why*-type questions which are challenging and generate additional questions, rather than standard, conclusion-type answers. The process of searching will require the student to utilize his skill in computation and thereby reinforce the instant or automatic recall of basic facts that must become a part of his mental repertory for functional competency in mathematics. The cross-number puzzle idea also adapts quite conveniently to multilevel activities to better enable teachers to provide for the wide range of student ability found in most classrooms.

ADDITION

There are some general rules (Fig. 11.1) that the teacher should establish with the children before beginning to work with cross-number puzzles.

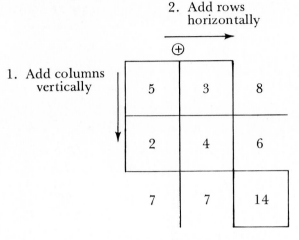

2. Add rows horizontally

1. Add columns vertically

3. Add column subtotals and put total in answer box

4. Add row subtotals and compare this total with number in answer box

Figure 11.1

The following rules can be used when working with an addition puzzle:

1. Add columns vertically and place subtotals in appropriate space.

2. Add rows horizontally and place subtotals in the appropriate space.

3. Add the column of subtotals (on the right side of the puzzle) vertically and place the total in the lower right-hand answer box.

4. Add the subtotals (at the bottom of the puzzle) horizontally and compare this total with the number in the answer box.

The rationale for the cross-number puzzle is based on the *associative property* of addition. It will be remembered that the associative property of addition enables us to add three or more numbers in any order that we desire. Also, since addition is a binary operation (that is, we add only two numbers at one time, regardless of how many numbers are to be added) the subtotals are then added to get the final total. The student should *not* be left with the feeling that the cross-number puzzle works because of magic or that the mathematics involved is something

mystical. The teacher should gradually guide the students to an understanding of why this puzzle works and eventually to a generalization, in
their terms. of the associative property of addition.

The young child might be introduced to the cross-number puzzle
sometime after he has a beginning mastery of the easier addition facts.
The teacher will probably want to start the introduction by using concrete materials (Fig. 11.2), such as geometric shapes or counting blocks.
The teacher would have the students determine how many counting
blocks were in each set, something like this: "How can we find out
how many blocks are in each box?" (By counting.)

(Pointing to the box that is upper left): "How many blocks are in
this set?" (Three.)

"Do you agree with Billy (that there are three blocks)?" (Yes.)

"Tell me how you know this." (By counting.)

(Pointing to the box that is upper right): "How many blocks are in
this set?" (Four.)

The questioning continues in like manner until the number of objects
in each set has been determined. As the students determine the number of objects in each set, the teacher writes the translation in number
symbols on the overhead projector or chalkboard, as shown in Figure
11.2.

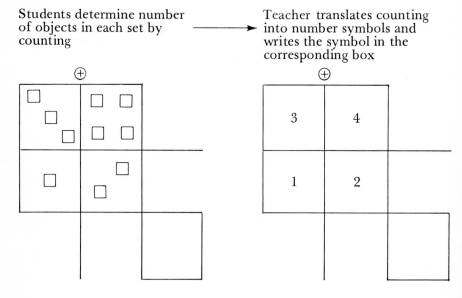

Students determine number of objects in each set by counting ⟶ Teacher translates counting into number symbols and writes the symbol in the corresponding box

Figure 11.2

The teacher then has the students put together the two sets on the left (this is the union of sets), determine how many blocks are now together, and the teacher then writes that number as the subtotal under the 3 and 1. The two sets on the right side would be put together and counted in similar fashion and the teacher would similarly write in the subtotal under 4 and 2. The objects in the two subtotal columns would then be put together (another union of sets) and the teacher writes in the total in the answer box. After that, the number of objects would be determined by combining horizontally the upper left and the upper right boxes, with the teacher writing in the subtotal; and the lower left and lower right boxes combined, with the teacher writing in the subtotal. These two subtotals would then be put together into one group and that total compared with the total in the answer box. The completed cross-number puzzle is shown in Figure 11.3.

$\oplus$

3	4	7
1	2	3
4	6	10

From this one cross-number puzzle, practice is provided in the following addition facts:

$$3 + 1 = 4$$
$$4 + 2 = 6$$
$$3 + 4 = 7$$
$$1 + 2 = 3$$
$$4 + 6 = 10$$
$$7 + 3 = 10$$

Figure 11.3

For a time, the teacher would continue having the children determine the number of objects in each set and telling where the number symbol should be placed in other cross-number puzzles. Then, when the teacher was reasonably sure that the students were understanding not only how, but also why the number symbols were placed as they were, the students could be gradually guided into working the puzzles independently.

After the students have gained reasonable mastery of the basic cross-number puzzle and the missing addend-type problem has been introduced, the modification shown in Figure 11.4 can be used:

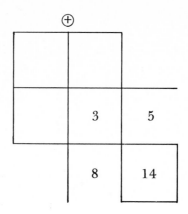

Figure 11.4

The students would be questioned about possible ways to solve this puzzle with the given information. The students will probably need some time to reflect on this and explore various ideas. Gradually, with teacher guidance, the relevant pieces of information can be put together and a solution reached. For example, we know (from the preceding cross-number puzzles) that the two subtotals at the bottom of the puzzle must total 14. This solution is simply the missing addend problem, that is, what number plus 8 is equal to 14. In a like manner, the other blanks of the puzzle can be filled in, using the missing addend. From this one cross-number puzzle, practice is provided in the following missing addend problems:

$$\square + 8 = 14 \qquad \square + 3 = 8$$

$$\square + 3 = 5 \qquad \square + 5 = 9$$

$$\square + 5 = 14 \qquad \square + 2 = 6$$

As students progress in their ability to add, cross-number puzzles can be designed (Fig. 11.5) to give practice in these newly acquired skills. The teacher can vary addition puzzles by supplying the addend on some puzzles and encouraging the student to find the subtotals and totals. In other puzzles, the teacher may give some of the addends and some of the subtotals, and the student finds the missing parts of the puzzle. After some practice with these puzzles, the student should be able to complete a puzzle when numerals are placed in *any four spaces of the puzzle.*

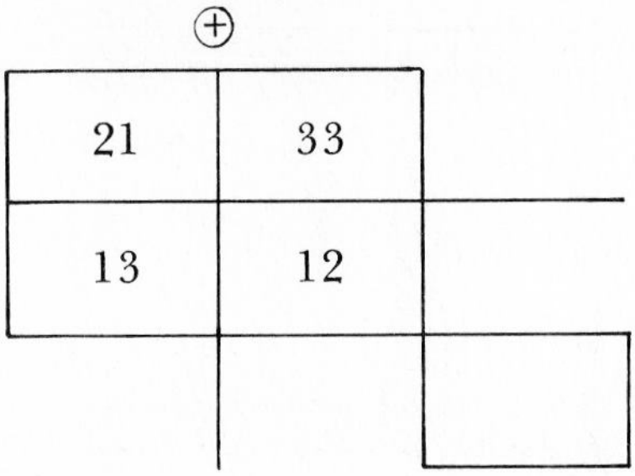

$\oplus$		
21	33	
13	12	

adding two-digit
numbers (with or
without bridging)

$\oplus$		
114	312	
121	433	

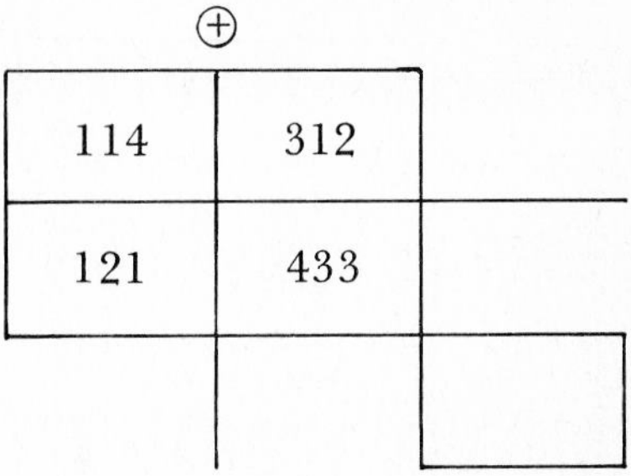

adding three-digit
numbers (with or
without bridging)

$\oplus$		
$\frac{1}{12}$	$\frac{3}{12}$	
$\frac{2}{12}$	$\frac{5}{12}$	

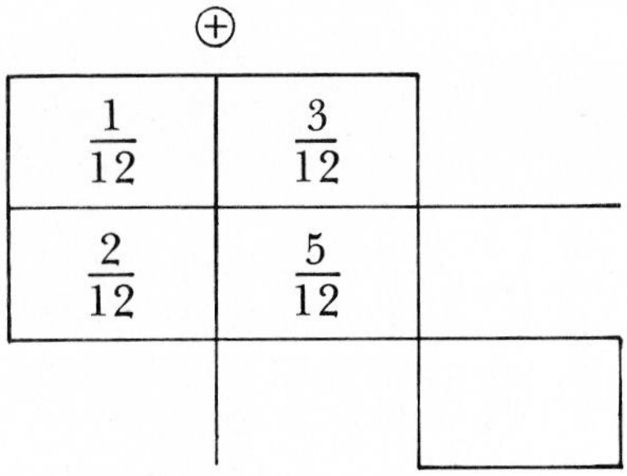

adding fractions with
like denominators

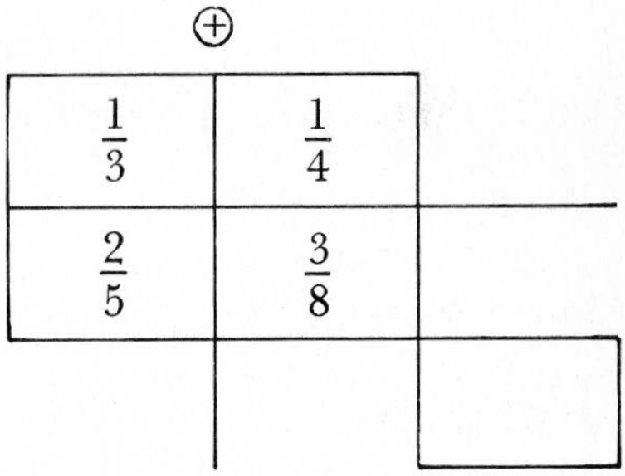

$\oplus$		
$\frac{1}{3}$	$\frac{1}{4}$	
$\frac{2}{5}$	$\frac{3}{8}$	

adding fractions with
different denominators

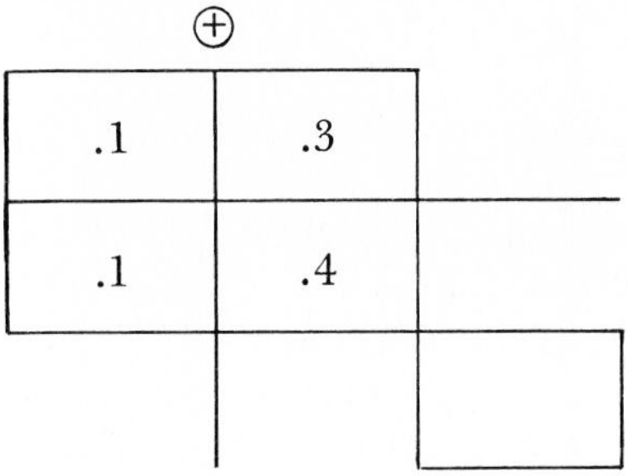

$\oplus$		
.1	.3	
.1	.4	

adding decimal
fractions

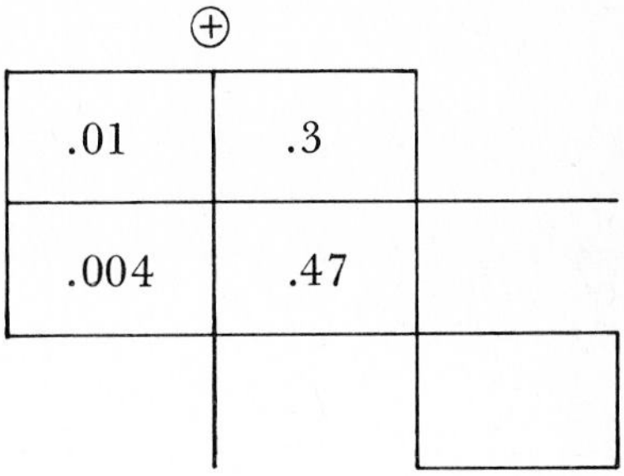

$\oplus$		
.01	.3	
.004	.47	

adding decimal
fractions

Figure 11.5

Another dimension can be added to the cross-number puzzle when the teacher feels the students are ready. The teacher asks, "What do you suppose would happen if we put a pair of 'ears' on each of the upper corners of the puzzle and after adding vertically and horizontally, we also add diagonally and put the diagonal subtotals in the 'ears'?"

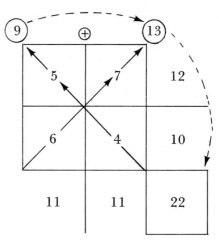

Figure 11.6

It often surprises the students that the two subtotals in the "ears" also give the same total as the two subtotals of the rows or columns (Fig. 11.6). Once again it is the *associative* property of addition, not magic, that makes it possible to do this.

SUBTRACTION

It was indicated in the chapter on basic operations with whole numbers that subtraction did not have the same properites as addition, nor could the same things be done in subtraction as in addition. For example, addition was commutative and associative, but subtraction was neither. It follows, then, that subtraction cross-number puzzles will have more limitations than addition puzzles. Be careful, then, in selecting subtraction problems to put in cross-number puzzles, because some problems may present the student with a situation that he must accept as unsolvable, at least for the time being. Figure 11.7 illustrates a subtraction cross-number puzzle that works.

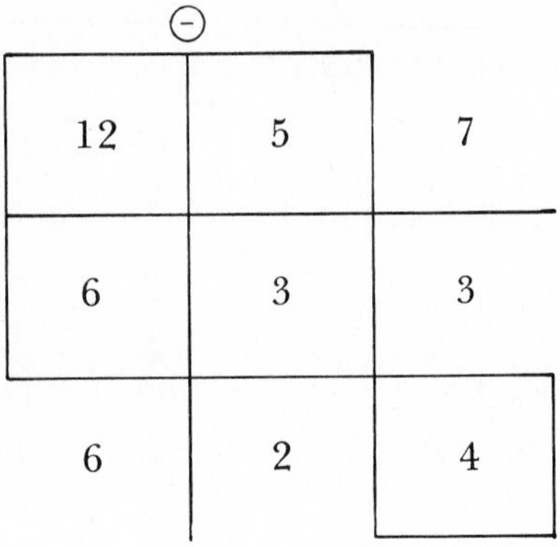

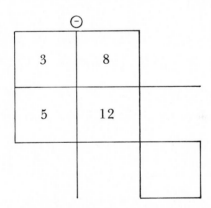

Figure 11.7

However, not just any arrangement of numbers will work (Fig. 11.8), because we might end up having to subtract a large number from a small number.

Figure 11.8

One way to avoid this complication would be to agree in advance that, when necessary, the smaller number will be subtracted from the larger number until the children are introduced to directed numbers. It can also be said that not just any four numbers in a cross-number puzzle will work in subtraction. The teacher should check to see that the puzzle is solvable before giving it to the children.

When the teacher feels that the students have gained reasonable mastery of the basic subtraction facts, a variation can be introduced. This variation will require the student to find the missing parts of the puzzle, as illustrated in Figure 11.9. There are, of course, many other variations of the subtraction puzzle, including subtraction of fractions and subtraction of decimal fractions (Fig. 11.9).

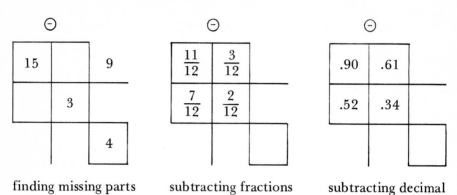

finding missing parts   subtracting fractions   subtracting decimal fractions

Figure 11.9

After the students have gained some mastery working cross-number puzzles using subtraction, the teacher may want to suggest that the students put "ears" on the subtraction puzzle and see what happens (Fig. 11.10.)

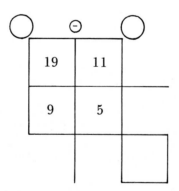

Figure 11.10

The children will usually find, after some groping around, that the subtraction cross-number puzzle with "ears" do not behave like the addition puzzle with "ears." This could be an interesting problem for the children: to discover why not. If we analyze our work with the subtraction puzzle, and also remember some of the properties of subtraction from Chapter 6 on basic operation with whole numbers, it becomes apparent that subtraction is *not* commutative or associative. This is why the subtraction puzzle with "ears" does not work.

MULTIPLICATION

Since multiplication is so closely related to addition, the multiplication cross-number puzzle will behave very similarly to that for addition. If children have previously worked with cross-number puzzles in addition and have some mastery of the basic multiplication facts, it is not too difficult for them to make a transition to the multiplication puzzle. Figure 11.11 illustrates the general type of puzzle that can be used by students in the early phase of multiplication.

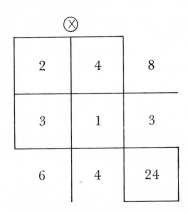

Figure 11.11

In analyzing why this puzzle works, it should be apparent that we are multiplying four numbers together for a product. When we multiply horizontally, we pair the factors one way and when we multiply vertically, we pair the factors another way. Yet regardless of which way we pair the factors, we still get the same final product. This, of course, is just another way of stating the *associative property of multiplication*.

Once more it can be seen that these puzzles work not because of happenstance, but because of the laws that govern mathematics.

As students gain competency in multiplication, variations of the multiplication puzzle can be introduced, as shown in Figure 11.12.

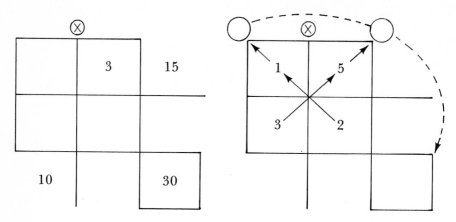

working with the missing multiplicand (or multiplier)

placing "ears" on the puzzle and multiplying diagonally as well as horizontally and vertically

Figure 11.12

Cross-number puzzles that utilize multiplication of fractions or multiplication of decimal fractions can also be developed for student practice.

Another variation of the cross-number puzzle can be made so that both addition and multiplication are used. It will be recalled that the distributive property of multiplication combines both multiplication and addition. Since this variation is different from the regular multiplication puzzle, note the distinguishing physical characteristics of this puzzle (Fig. 11.13), which are: the double lines at the top and right hand side; the answer box located in the lower left corner rather than the lower right corner; and the "ears" diagonally opposite each other. There will also be some differences in the rules governing the working of the puzzle. The solution to the puzzle in Figure 11.13 is shown in Figure 11.14.

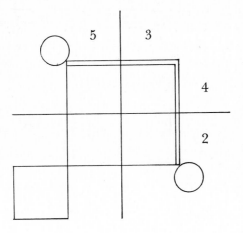

Figure 11.13

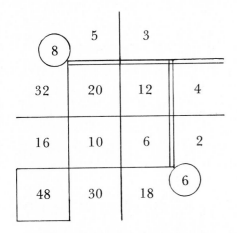

Figure 11.14

The cross-number puzzle provides practice in the following facts:

4 X 3 = 12	12 + 6 = 18
4 X 5 = 20	20 + 10 = 18
2 X 3 = 6	20 + 12 = 32
2 X 5 = 10	10 + 6 = 16
6 X 8 = 48	32 + 16 = 48
	30 + 18 = 48

The rules to be used in this multiplication cross-number puzzle are:

1. When you cross a double line, multiply.
2. When you cross a single line, add.

It will also probably be noticed that the "ears" on this puzzle do not serve the same function as those used in addition.

This multiplication cross-number puzzle works because of the *distributive property of multiplication* and the *associative property of addition*. In Figure 11.14, the factor 8 was distributed into 5 and 3, while the factor 6 was distributed into 4 and 2. The partial products could be added in any order because of the associative property of addition.

DIVISION

Since division is a special kind of subtraction, the same kind of limitations will be encountered in the division puzzles as in the sub-traction puzzles. We should also expect to observe the same type of rules in division puzzles as were observed in the subtraction puzzles (that is, the larger number should be divided by the smaller number). Caution should be taken in selecting the numbers to be used in the puzzle because students may encounter problems containing fractions in the answer before they are ready for this phase of division. Figure 11.15 illustrates how division cross-number puzzles can first be used to reinforce basic division facts.

$\div$

18	9	2
6	3	2
3	3	1

Figure 11.15

As students gain competency in division, variations can be introduced in a manner similar to the way in which variations were introduced for the other basic operations. One variation is suggested in Figure 11.16.

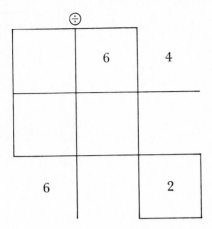

Figure 11.16

Another variation (Fig. 11.17) would be to place a pair of "ears" on the division puzzle in a manner similar to that used with other puzzles. The students could then be given an opportunity to discuss and predict what they think will happen when they work the puzzle with "ears."

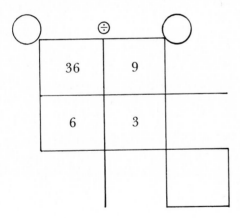

Figure 11.17

After trying several of these division puzzles with "ears," the students can be guided to an understanding of why the "ears" do not work in the case of division.

Other variations of the division puzzle would include using fractions and decimal fractions, but these are not nearly as effective learning situations as the division puzzle using whole numbers. Although fractions or decimal fractions work quite nicely in puzzles using addition, subtraction, or multiplication, such is not the case in division puzzles. In division using fractions or decimal fractions, the student would need more complete mastery of the operation *before* he would profit from working with them in cross-number puzzles. Since these activities are intended to provide interesting practice, it would be of questionable value to use fractions or decimal fractions in division puzzles.

The cross-number puzzle is an interesting and challenging method of helping students gain practice in the skill of computation. It is possible to work puzzles such as these because they are governed by the laws of mathematics. From working these puzzles, students can be guided to an appreciation and understanding of the structure of mathematics. These puzzles were not designed to teach a skill; they were designed to help reinforce the skill *after* a certain mastery had been achieved. After the student has gained some experience in working basic puzzles, it is possible to develop many variations from the basic puzzle. The addition and/or multiplication puzzles are the most productive and effective in reinforcement, although there is also value in the other two types.

Number Machines

The number machine idea is usually an intriguing and fascinating way to challenge children to use, apply, and even extend what they have learned. A number machine is a fictitious machine that will perform various operations on numbers. In a sense it is a figment of our imagination, but real enough that we can draw a picture of it (Fig. 11.18), and describe how it operates. The way the number machine works is as follows: one or more numbers are dropped or fed into the input slot of the machine and the machine performs some type of operation on the number(s); as a result of the machine's operation on the number(s), another number is cranked out of the output slot.

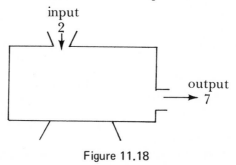

Figure 11.18

In the example shown in Figure 11.18, the number 2 is dropped in the input slot and the machine cranks out a 7 at the output slot.

The students try to discover what operation the machine performed. They do this by collecting sufficient information or data to find the pattern or rule used by the machine. The variety of different machines that can be created is limited only by the teacher's imagination.

RATIONALE FOR NUMBER MACHINES

The number machine is in reality a function machine. It may seem at first thought that functions are too difficult for elementary school children to cope with, since functions are generally associated with algebra and other kinds of higher mathematics. There are many instances, however, when elementary school teachers and students encounter functions, although they are probably not aware of it. For example, when the operation of addition or multiplication is applied to a pair of numbers, this can be viewed as a function. When a property of mathematics, such as the commutative property of addition, is stated, or when students work with formulas, such as finding the area of a triangle, these also can be thought of as working with functions. A *function*, then, can be described as a mathematical law or rule that governs the interdependence of two or more variables and expresses the exact nature of their relationship. This description is not a complete definition of function, but it will serve as a place to start thinking about functions.

The number machine, or function machine, is based on the concept that relationships may be determined between numbers or variables and generalizations can be developed therefrom. By using these ideas in an elementary school mathematics program, the teacher is laying some of the foundation for learning at the secondary level and beyond. These types of activities also permit children to apply what they know in an interesting and challenging situation. These activities are not designed to be included in the initial phase of teaching the basic operations, but they can be used quite effectively, after students have developed reasonable mastery of an operation, and they serve the purpose of providing enjoyable practice and reinforcement in computation as well as opportunities to look for relationships and to formulate rules. The first part of the discussion of number machines will present some ways this idea can be utilized at some of the lower elementary grades. The second part of the discussion will describe progressively more complex and difficult mathematical ideas that can be developed and/or reinforced.

USING NUMBER MACHINES

The number machine can be introduced to the students in several ways. One way that it might be introduced is for the teacher to describe a situation involving a machine that is capable of performing an operation on numbers. When certain numbers are fed into the machine, an operation on the numbers is performed, resulting in another number being emitted from the machine. In the beginning phases, the teacher would need to establish with the students that unless specified otherwise, it will work with whole numbers only.

The teacher begins by drawing a number machine (Fig. 11.19) on the chalkboard or overhead projector and demonstrating how it works. It is explained that when 2 and 3 are placed in the input slot, the machine does something to these numbers and cranks out a 5. The teacher could then have the children briefly discuss what they think happened inside the machine to cause it to perform like this. The children should not be allowed to jump to hasty conclusions; rather, they should be guided to see the need for more information. Even if some child, or children, suggest that the machine added the numbers, the teacher should suggest that they put in two more numbers (as shown in the second number machine, Fig. 11.19), and see what happens.

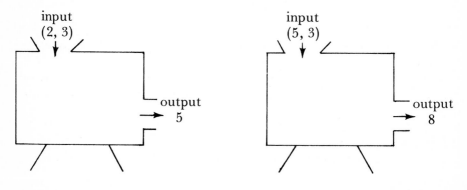

Figure 11.19

Some of the children will probably have a very good idea of what the machine is doing, but the teacher should continue guiding the search rather than telling. It must be remembered that just because one or two students make the desired response, this does not necessarily mean that all of the students understand. Next time the teacher might put two numbers in the number machine and have the students tell what number they think will come out and why (Fig. 11.20).

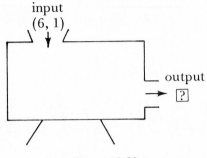

Figure 11.20

It may be that some students will still not know what is happening. If this is the case, the teacher should suggest looking at some more examples and recording this information in table form, like this:

Input	Output
2,3	5
5,3	8
6,1	7
4,5	9
3,5	8
2,1	3

After it is fairly certain that most, if not all, students know what operation the machine is performing, the students should then have several opportunities to work similar problems with the number machine. If the students wanted to name this machine, it might be called an *adder machine*.

At another time, a different type of number machine could be introduced to the children. This time when we put in one number we get a different number from the output tube, as shown in Figure 11.21.

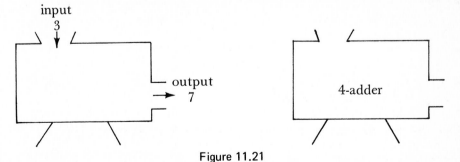

Figure 11.21

A record of what the machine does probably will help reveal its function:

Input	Output
3	7
8	12
1	5
4	8
5	10

After the children discover this machine's rule, they will probably want to label it a 4-adder, as also shown in Figure 11.21. This particular type of number machine makes use of the missing addend-type problem, such as $3 + \Box = 7$. The children will initially be guided to think, "How much more must I add to get this sum?" when solving this type of problem. There are many similar types of adder machines possible, such as the 3-adder, 5-adder, 6-adder, 7-adder, and so on. It should also be noted that it is not necessary for students to state their discoveries exactly as described here. It is important, however, that students state the rule they discover in such a manner that their idea is communicated. Children will usually state their rule in their own terminology and sometimes in a most surprising manner. The teacher should be concerned with guiding children to discover the rule, getting them to verbalize the rule, and if the rule does not communicate as well as desired, guiding the children to more precision in their statements.

Another type of machine that can be introduced to the students is shown in Figure 11.22.

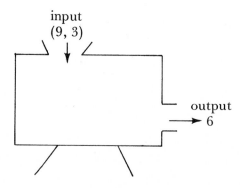

Figure 11.22

A record of this machine's activity is as follows:

Input	Output
9,3	6
5,4	1
10,7	3
8,4	4
7,5	
2,2	

(Can you complete the record?)

As you have probably surmised, this machine subtracts. The children will probably want to label the machine a subtracter. The subracter machine idea can be extended to the related machine in Figure 11.23.

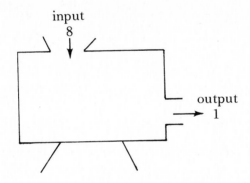

Figure 11.23

A record of this machine's activity would be:

Input	Output
8	1
12	5
14	7
10	3
9	2
11	4

The students will probably recognize what this machine's rule is and label it as shown in Figure 11.24.

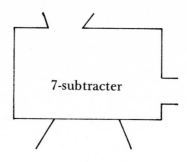

Figure 11.24

There are, of course, many other types of subtracter machines besides the 7-subtracter. There could be a 3-subtracter machine, a 5-subtracter machine, a 6-subtracter machine, a 2-subtracter machine, and so on. For a change of pace and an added dimension, the teacher can occasionally give the students an incomplete record, like this:

Input	8	12		10	7	
Output	2	6	3			5

The student's task would be to fill out the record and tell what kind of machine it is.

Another type of machine is shown in Figure 11.25.

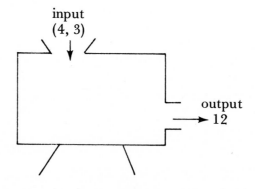

Figure 11.25

This machine's record would be:

Input	4,3	5,2	2,4	3,3	1,2	3,5
Output	12	10	8	9	2	15

This is a machine that multiplies, and probably it would be labeled the *multiplier machine*. From the multiplier machine, it is fairly logical to go to the machine in Figure 11.26.

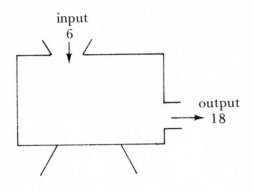

input
6

output
18

Figure 11.26

This machine's record:

Input	6	3	5	4	1	2
Output	18	9	15	12	3	6

This machine could be labeled the 3-multiplier, or the tripler machine. Once again for a change of pace, the students could be given an incomplete record of what a machine does, like this:

Input	10	3	8	1		9	6	
Output	50	15	40		25			35

The student's task in this situation is to fill in the empty blanks and identify the kind of machine that would make a record like this.

The division machine (Fig. 11.27) would be introduced in a manner similar to the other machines, but in a way that would be appropriate for division.

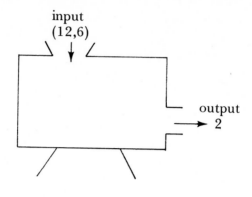

Figure 11.27

The record that this kind of machine would make is:

Input	(12,6)	(5,1)	(8,2)	(9,3)	(14,2)	(7,7)
Output	2	5	4	3	7	1

The children would probably want to label this machine a *divider machine*. Divider machines can also be explored from another angle. In this instance (Fig. 11.28), we will put a single number in the machine and get a number from the output; the student's task is to discover what kind of divider machine it is.

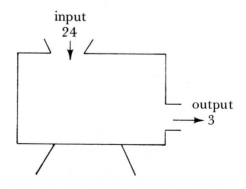

Figure 11.28

A record of this machine would be:

Input	Output
24	3
40	5
16	2
56	7
32	4
64	8

From the available information, it is fairly apparent that this is an 8-divider machine and this is probably what the students will want to call it. There are many other types of divider machines such as the 2-divider, 7-divider, 3-divider, 6-divider, and so on. Another possibility would be to give an incomplete record of a machine and have the students complete the record and identify the kind of machine used, something like this:

Input	6	21	18	9		3	
Output	2	7	6		5	1	8

With a little study, most students will recognize that this is the record of a 3-divider machine.

COMPLEX NUMBER MACHINES

The preceding description of activities with number machines has been concerned with the basic number machines. After students have worked these basic activities long enough for reasonable mastery, the number machine idea can be extended even further (see Fig. 11.29). The teacher can raise the question, "I wonder what would happen if we hooked two of these machines together." With the children's assistance, a record of the output of this combination could be developed.

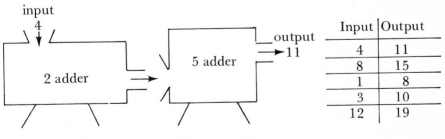

Input	Output
4	11
8	15
1	8
3	10
12	19

Figure 11.29

The teacher could raise other interesting possibilities with such questions as:

"Do you think it would change the record if we reversed the way the machines are hooked up?" (Try putting the same input numbers in the 5-adder first, and then the 2-adder.) "Would this be an illustration of the associative property of addition?"

"Is there one machine that we could find to do exactly the same work as these two machines?" (Try a 7-adder.)

Figure 11.30 shows another possibility for hooking up machines. In this case, an adder and a multiplier are used, and the record of performance of this hookup is shown.

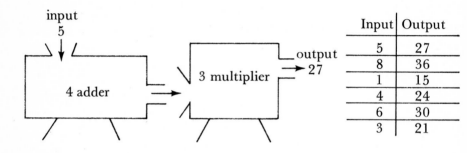

Input	Output
5	27
8	36
1	15
4	24
6	30
3	21

Figure 11.30

The teacher inquires:

"If we reversed this hookup (that is, put the 3-multiplier first followed by the 4-adder), and still used the same numbers, would we get different results?"

"What is the smallest number that we can get from the first hookup?"

As these machines are worked with, the astute teacher will likely recognize other instances in which the use of similar questions would stimulate productive thought.

By hooking up a multiplier and a divider (Fig. 11.31), another interesting possibility exists. The teacher asks:

"How would the results of the initial operation (of putting 6 into these number machines) compare with the results of $6 \times \frac{2}{3}$? How

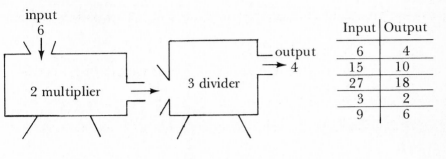

Input	Output
6	4
15	10
27	18
3	2
9	6

Figure 11.31

do the output numbers compare with the results you would get from multiplying each input number by $\frac{2}{3}$? If we reversed the order of the machines, would this affect the results in the record?"

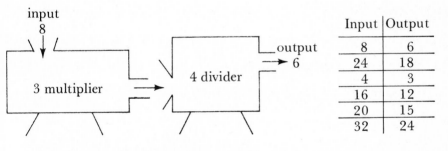

Input	Output
8	6
24	18
4	3
16	12
20	15
32	24

Figure 11.32

Perhaps another example of a multiplier and a divider hookup will be helpful (Fig. 11.32). In discussing the results obtained by hooking up a 3-multiplier and a 4-divider, the following questions could be asked:

"How do the output numbers compare with the results you would get from multiplying each of the input numbers by $\frac{3}{4}$? If we used only whole numbers, and exclude zero, in the input, what would be the smallest number that we could get from the output?"

By this time, the reader has recognized the almost unlimited variations and learning experiences possible with number machines. The ideas presented in this section are intended to serve as a starting point for the creation and development of other ideas. The remaining number machine ideas to be presented in this section will be presented in condensed form because the basic format is the same, as is the method by which the teacher guides the students is the same. Only the type of problem and the degree of difficulty are different.

If . . . Then . . . Situations. In an "If . . ., then . . ." situation, two machines are shown with an input number and an output number (Fig. 11.33). The students are to determine what kind of machine is necessary so that the indicated results are possible. It should be noted that there is often more than one correct answer.

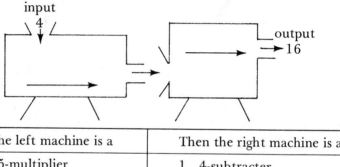

If the left machine is a	Then the right machine is a
1. 5-multiplier	1. 4-subtracter
2. 4-adder	2. 2-multiplier
3. 2-divider	3.
4.	4. 1-multiplier
5. 28-adder	5.
6.	6. 15-adder
7. 3-subtracter	7.

Figure 11.33

Factoring. Suppose we wanted to use only a multiplier machine and change 4 to 24. We would normally use our 6-multiplier machine (Fig. 11.34).

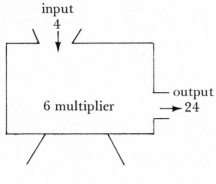

Figure 11.34

This operation could be shown by a drawing or diagram, like this:

When we get to the 6 machine, we find that it is broken. Can you think of a way to get 4 to 24 by using only multiplier machines? (Could we use a hookup of two or more machines to do the same job as a 6 multiplier?) The hookup shown in Figure 11.35 would be a possibility.

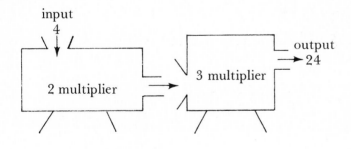

Figure 11.35

In planning which machines to use in the hookup, we could make a schematic diagram to check our plans before actually hooking up the machines. The example in Figure 11.35 could be shown in the following diagram:

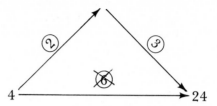

By using a hookup of a 2-multiplier and a 3-multiplier, we can do the same job as a 6-multiplier.

Another example requiring factoring would be when we started to change a 5 to 40 and find the 8-multiplier broken. If we are not sure what to do at this point, we can either start hooking up machines and observe what happens, or we can plan what needs to be done before we hook up the machines by sketching a diagram, like this:

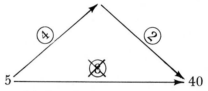

A hookup of the 4-multiplier and the 2-multiplier will do the same job as an 8-multiplier. Now, suppose we wanted to change a 5 to 40 and both the 8- and 4-multipliers were broken. We could diagram this hookup as follows:

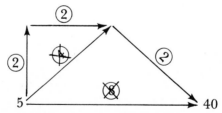

Prime Numbers. One day an accident happens and all of the even-numbered multiplier machines are broken. After surveying the damage, we find enough parts to fix only one of the even-numbered machines. (The parts of the odd-numbered machines will not interchange with even-numbered machines.) It will take several weeks to get the parts ordered from the factory to fix the other machines. Since we can fix only one machine, which even-numbered multiplier machine should we fix in order to be able to do the most things; With teacher guidance, the students can discover that all even numbers are multiples of 2 and, consequently, if we fix the 2-multiplier we can still accomplish all of the changing of numbers that we could previously. For example, to do the same job as a 4-multiplier, we would use the hookup shown in the following diagram:

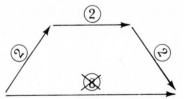

The diagram indicates that we run the number through the 2-multiplier twice. To do the same job as the 8-multiplier, we would diagram that hookup as follows:

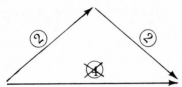

This time we ran the number through the 2-multiplier 3 times.

If we wanted to diagram the hookup that would do the same as a 10-multiplier, the following diagram would be used:

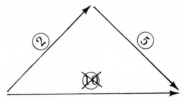

In this instance, we ran the number through the 2-multiplier and 5-multiplier. (Remember, all of the odd machines are in working order.)

We found that the 2-multiplier could do the same task, either by using it successively or hooked up with appropriate odd-numbered multipliers, as all of our even-numbered multipliers. Do you suppose there are other multiplier machines that we would not need because a certain other machine could also do their jobs? (At this point, we are seeking to uncover the prime numbers. With careful teacher guidance, the students should develop an understanding that the prime numbers are the building blocks of the number system, because all composite numbers can be expressed as the product of certain prime numbers.)

Powers and Exponents. The work done with prime numbers in the preceding activity can serve as a basis to launch a preliminary exploration of powers and exponents. We found, for example, that running a number through the 2-multiplier three times did the same thing as going through the 8-multiplier once. Although we could eventually do the same job with a 2-multiplier that could be done with an 8-multiplier, we had to use the 2-multiplier three times, whereas we only had to use the 8-multiplier once. It would seem, at this point, that there is a need to find some way to make our basic machines, such as the 2-multiplier, more efficient. Fortunately for us, mathematicians figured out a solution to our problem some time ago. They thought up the idea of a repeater machine; they called it the power that a number was raised to and symbolized the power with an exponent. The power to which a number is raised indicates the number of repeated multiplications by that number. We will use the idea of repeated multiplications and invent a little attachment that can be put on our multiplier machines to make the machines repeat as many times as we want (see Fig. 11.36). To accomplish this repeated multiplication, we merely set the dial on the attachment to the number of repeated multiplications. (The 2-multiplier with the repeater dial set on 3 would utilize 2 as a factor 3 times, or 2 $\times$ 2 $\times$ 2.)

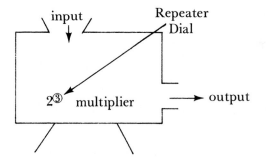

Figure 11.36

To do the job of a	Set the repeater dial of the 2 multiplier on:
4-multiplier	$2^2 = (2 \times 2)$
8-multiplier	$2^3 = (2 \times 2 \times 2)$
16-multiplier	$2^4 = (2 \times 2 \times 2 \times 2)$
32-multiplier	
64-multiplier	

(Can you complete the table?)

A similar type situation could be developed for the 3-multiplier and other numbers as well.

In summary, the number machine, or function machine, is based on the mathematical concept of function. Elementary school children, particularly in the intermediate grades, should be guided into learning experiences that will enable them to discover relationships between numbers. In describing these relationships, they can be led to discover and/or develop the appropriate generalizations. Those persons wishing to explore the use of number machines in greater depth are referred to a project developed by the University of Illinois Committee on School Mathematics (UICSM) entitled *Stretchers and Shrinkers* (Harper & Row), 1969.

What's My Rule?

This section is a continuation of the same type of activities that were introduced in the previous section on number machines. The basic idea to be developed once again is the search for patterns and regularity, and the communication of these discoveries. However, in this section the number machines will not be used, only the recorded data. The student's task will be to search the data in an effort to find some regularity or pattern in it that will allow him to develop a rule, and to understand what he has discovered well enough to communicate his idea. The educational implications for assisting and guiding students in developing this skill are almost too obvious to mention, yet in far too many instances students are given little or no opportunity for such mental development.

RATIONAL FOR "WHAT'S MY RULE?"

In adult life the ability to search out or detect patterns in objects, events, and data is used in many ways. In one instance we might search for a pattern in order to make a predicition; in another instance we might search for a pattern to determine the cause of a certain situation; in still another instance we may be searching for a pattern that will enable us to organize something more effectively; or we could be using this skill for numerous other reasons. Nearly any of the preceding reasons for detecting patterns would be justification enough to include this as part of the elementary curriculum. However valid and important as these reasons are, they are no more important than the power of rational thought and logic that can be developed from these kinds of experiences. The study of mathematics provides abundant patterns and relationships, and the ease with which numbers can be arranged and organized for systematic study makes the patterns more apparent.

The appeal of these types of activities to students may result from the stimulating mental activity they require, but this appeal may also result from a desire for orderliness in organizing the information we store in our brain. There seems to be inborn in man a necessity to organize information by some scheme or pattern. Those things that do not fit the anticipated plan confuse us for a time because we are uncertain where to assign them. It was noted in an earlier chapter that faster students are often intrigued by the ambiguous, if the ambiguity is not too extreme, whereas slower students tend to become frustrated by it. These different reactions by students probably result because the faster student knows how to organize information effectively to search for a pattern which will resolve or reduce the ambiguity, while the slower student usually does not know what to do. When students are left on their own to develop this skill, some will discover its usefulness and the power that it gives their intellect, others will discover some of the facets of organization by patterns but will not understand the significance of their discovery, and still others may never be aware of its existence. It is only through a planned, conscious effort by the teacher to provide experiences that promote searching for and using patterns that some students will ever cross this threshold of their mental capability.

ACTIVITIES FOR "WHAT'S MY RULE?"

At the primary level, the teacher can introduce this activity by telling the children that he has a secret he is not going to tell them—though he will help them discover his secret. When a student calls out a number, the teacher will respond with a number, like this:

Student A: "Five"
Teacher : "Six"
Student B: "Three"
Teacher : "Four"
Student C: "Nine"
Teacher : "Ten"
Student D: "Six"
Teacher : "Seven"

During the time that this activity is taking place, the teacher should start developing an awareness in students of the importance of keeping a record (Fig. 11.37) for an orderly, systematic study of the information.

Student's Number	Teacher's Reply
5	6
3	4
9	10
6	7

Figure 11.37

The teacher should caution the students that when they think they know his secret, or rule, they should not tell anyone else. When it is apparent that one or more students have discovered the rule, the teacher can ask each of these students to state a number and then give the number they think the teacher would use to reply. For example, the student might say, "If I said seven, I think you would answer with eight." In this way the secret is not given to the other children, but the teacher knows if the student has actually discovered his secret. The number line can also be used to help children discover the secret.

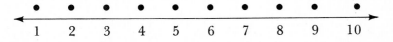

The teacher might direct the students like this; "When Jack called out 5 (points to 5 on the number line), I answered 6 (points to 6). When Sally called out 3 (points to 3 and also has students point to 3 on their number lines), I answered with 4 (everyone points to 4)," and so on. When all students have discovered the rule, or at least all students who are likely to in a reasonable time, the teacher asks the students to tell him what he was doing to get his answers. The students will probably say, "Adding one to the number." The teacher responds, "Yes, I was adding one more to get my answer." If the need exists, the teacher could then go back to the record and show how the rule would be applied to each number given by a student in order to determine the teacher's response.

Another activity could begin with a new secret rule. The teacher would guide the search in much the same manner as in the previous game, as shown in Figure 11.38. At the appropriate time, the teacher

Student's Number	Teacher's Reply
7	4
3	0
12	9
8	5

Figure 11.38

would ask the students to state the rule for this activity. The students will probably say that the teacher was taking a number three less than the one selected, or that the teacher was subtracting three from the other number.

In this and similar activities, the teacher may have to ask the children to select another number in the event that he is not ready to introduce negative numbers. For instance, if a child selects one, according to the rule the teacher's reply would be a negative two. The teacher can simply say, however, "I am sorry, but I will have to ask you to select another number." After a few times in which the teacher keeps the record on the chalkboard or overhead projector, students should do one or two activities without keeping a record. The teacher should then discuss with the children which way was the most helpful and what made that way more helpful than the other. In this manner, children can be guided to an awareness of the usefulness and importance of recording information. Also, at a later time when students are familiar with the general scheme of "What's My Rule?" activities, the teacher can occasionally choose a student to select the rule and respond to the other students' numbers.

Figure 11.39 shows some examples of "What's My Rule?" Many more possibilities can be initiated by the teacher.

A.		B.		C.	
Student	Teacher	Student	Teacher	Student	Teacher
10	2	6	3	5	20
4	8	14	7	3	12
9	3	4	2	8	32
5	7	18	9	10	40
6	6	10	5	7	28

Student	Teacher	Student	Teacher	Student	Teacher
8	16	9	9	12	5
6	12	2	2	6	11
1	2	0	0	8	9
10	20	6	6	10	7
3	6	3	3	3	14

Figure 11.39

The level of difficulty can be increased by having the students write the rule with symbols after they have discovered and verbalized it. If we were to use Figure 11.39a, for instance, the rule would be that the two numbers must total 12. With some assistance, the students would probably verbalize that the student's number plus the teacher's number should equal 12. The teacher would then write the symbols' S for student's number and T for teacher's number as follows: $S + T = 12$. After students observe the teacher write several such symbolizations, he can suggest that they try writing the rule. After they have all written a rule with symbols, the teacher leads a discussion of what they have done. If ideas for improvements do not come from the children, the teacher should make suggestions and then provide further opportunities to practice and develop this skill.

At a higher grade level, the complexity and difficulty should be increased slightly. A record that would require completing the data, discovering the rule, and symbolizing it can be introduced. This type of record might look like this:

	14	10	9	19					20		31
First Number	8	7	5	12	10	9	15	13	14		
Second Number	6	3	4	7	2	4	10	5		6	14
	2	4	1	5						11	

In working with this record, the student tries to determine the relationship between the first number and the second number in each column. This pair of numbers has been worked with in some way to produce the numbers above and below them. In the first example, 8 and 6 are worked with to produce 2, and then this same pair is involved in some operation that produces 14. Most students will probably realize fairly quickly that when 6 is subtracted from 8, the result is 2, and when 8 and 6 are added, the result is 14. The rule for the bottom row seems to be to subtract the second number from the first and the rule for the top row seems to be to add the two numbers. After checking the other columns, we find that our preliminary rules hold true. Now to write the rule:

Top Row = First number + Second number or F + S.

Bottom Row = First number – Second number of F – S.

Writing the rule in the record would look like this:

F + S	14	10	9	19
First Number	8	7	5	12
Second Number	6	3	4	7
F - S	2	4	1	5

This idea can be enlarged upon by placing additional rows on either side of the pair of numbers and using different rules for each row, like this:

1.		3	6	4	3	4			
2.		28	16	45	18	5			12
3. *First Number*		7	8	9	6	5	10	9	6
4. *Second Number*		4	2	5	3	1	4	1	
5.		22	20	28	18	12			
6.		6	12	8	6	8			

From observing the information in this record, the rules that could be developed will probably be similar to the following:

$$\text{Row } 1 = F - S$$
$$\text{Row } 2 = F \times S$$
$$\text{Row } 5 = 2 \times (F + S)$$
$$\text{Row } 6 = 2 \times (F - S)$$

As the records become progressively more difficult, the teacher will need to provide for differences in the ability of the students. One way the teacher can do this is by making several different records with differing degrees of difficulty so that all students will not be working at the same level, nor even the same number of problems. The teacher encourages all of the students to try additional and more difficult exercises, but their participation in the activity should be strictly voluntary.

A different type of activity can be used to assist in discovering and making generalizations. This activity can be developed from a very simple series of numbers that are related in some way, as in the following example:

$$1, 3, 6, 10, 15, 21, \ldots$$

In this series of numbers, the key to finding the pattern lies in uncovering the difference relationship of the adjacent numbers, namely that this difference progressively increases by one. Another series of numbers can be used to illustrate a different rule:

$$1, 2, 4, 8, 16, 32, \ldots$$

In this series of numbers, the key to the pattern is found by comparing adjacent numbers. Each succeeding number is twice as large as the preceding number.

Another series of numbers with still a different rule is:

$$1, 3, 4, 7, 11, 18, 29, \ldots$$

The key to finding this pattern lies in discovering that the sum of the first two numbers determines the third number; the sum of the second and third numbers determines the fourth; and so on. To restate this: we can determine any number beyond the first two in this series by obtaining the sum of the two preceding numbers. If we want to extend this idea of series numbers, we can use an additional row, or rows, of numbers that would also be related to the series,

2	5	12	23	36	__	__	__	136	__	__	__
	3	7	11	15	19	__	__	31	__	__	__
		4	4	4	4	__	__	4	__	__	__

or like this:

0	1	4	9	16	25	__	__	__	81	__	__
	1	3	5	7	__	__	__	15	__	__	__
		2	2	2	2	__	__	__	2	__	__

The key to finding the pattern in both of these illustrations lies in discovering the relationship between the offset number below and the two adjacent numbers above. In this instance, the offset number below is the difference of the two adjacent numbers above. Using this clue, it becomes reasonably easy to complete the record.

A slightly more difficult version of the same idea will involve finding a pattern both horizontally and vertically. A record of this type might look something like this:

1	1	2	3	5	8	__	__	__	55	__	__	__
3	1	4	5	9	__	__	__	60	__	__	__	__
4	2	6	8	__	__	__	__	__	__	246	__	__
__	__	10	13	23	36	__	__	__	__	__	652	__

In this activity, the key to the pattern is adding two adjoining numbers, whether horizontally or vertically, to get the next number in the horizontal or vertical series. The numbers placed farther to the right in the sequence are there to serve as checkpoints. As the student progressively fills in the blank spaces in the sequence, these checkpoints serve to confirm or deny that he is on the right path. If the checkpoint number fits in the sequence as the next number, it confirms that he is on the right track. In the event that the checkpoint number does not fit as the next number in his sequence, this would indicate to the student that something was wrong and he should go back to recheck his computation and/or the pattern he is using.

This section has presented additional ways to assist students in developing skill in discovering patterns and communicating generalizations about them. This skill is useful in a variety of ways, but many students never develop it to the point of being useful to them. Mathematics can serve as an effective model in searching for patterns because of the abundant patterns that permeate mathematics and because of the ease with which numbers can be arranged and organized so that patterns become more apparent. The ability to search for and discover patterns is not only useful in many everyday situations, but it also seems to be almost a necessity for the organization of information that is stored in the more useful areas of our intellect.

CHAPTER 12

TABLES, GRAPHS, AND STATISTICS

Some of the newer curriculum programs, specifically social studies and science, are placing more emphasis on the utilization of such mathematical skills as recording information or data and then organizing the data into visual form as a graph. Most courses of study in elementary school mathematics do not offer much provision for developing these skills, but it would seem that teachers, particularly in the intermediate grades, could profitably spend some of their time guiding students in acquiring these skills. This chapter will be primarily concerned with the uses of tables and graphs; a brief section on statistics is also included, however, because of its relevance to tables and graphs.

Rationale for Tables, Graphs, and Statistics

The importance of the ability to communicate has been emphasized repeatedly in this book, because communicating ideas, findings, and information is one of the most fundamental of all skills. Learning also depends to some extent on receiving and understanding communications and communicating with others. Communication, then, implies that there is both a sender and a receiver, although both do not necessarily have to be at the same place nor even of the same time period. For example, the great writers of other eras still communicate with us today through their works. This type of communication, however, often leaves some questions unanswered or some ideas not fully understood, because there is no chance for interaction between sender and receiver. The most advantageous and desirable type of communication probably occurs when both the sender and the receiver are in close enough proximity for them to interact with each other, usually at the oral level. While oral communications are usually more desirable, there are situations in which it is not possible to communicate orally. In these cases the communication must take some other form, such as writing, graphs, diagrams, charts, tables, and the like.

Communication, like learning, is possible at different levels of sophistication and complexity, and very likely the communique is an indication of the level of thought developed by the student. It may also be an indication of his mental maturity. With teacher guidance, students can often go beyond the simpler levels of learning (as presented in Bloom's Taxonomy from knowledge to comprehension) to the more complex levels of application, analysis, and even synthesis. Learning to work with and use tables and graphs is one way a teacher can aid students in extending their learning. The students will not only have the opportunity to gather facts, but they can also organize these facts so that application of what they have done and analysis of their findings is more likely to occur. In this way, students can be guided to varied situations that require application of what they know and gradually this can evolve into a meaningful analysis of the situation.

The three types of communication—oral, written, and pictorial—are used to complement each other, but the development of these skills should probably not be attempted simultaneously. A sequential approach to their development is probably the most effective. Communication is a multifaceted act requiring many skills and many opportunities to practice using them, and teachers at all levels must plan experiences that will lead to the development of the necessary skills. After children have learned to listen and speak, they begin to interpret pictures as a readiness for reading. When they interpret pictures that depict quantitative data, they are learning to interpret simple graphs. This development of written and pictorial communication could be started in third grade and would begin with the making of simple graphs and tables. Interpretation of simple data should be developed first. The making of inferences, predictions, and hypotheses would probably not be formally developed before the upper intermediate grades.

Tables

In previous chapters the importance of an orderly, systematic approach to problem-solving has been emphasized. Such an approach becomes even more important when information or data is being recorded. As more and more information is compiled, it becomes increasingly important to use an orderly, systematic approach. Without some type of organization of data, important relationships may be overlooked.

Suppose some students were making a number of trials and they recorded the following:

Trial 1-2	Trial 10-5
Trial 2-8	Trial 11-6
Trial 3-6	Trial 12-6
Trial 4-7	Trial 13-7
Trial 5-6	Trial 14-4
Trial 6-4	Trial 15-6
Trial 7-9	Trial 16-3
Trial 8-5	Trial 17-5
Trial 9-8	Trial 18-7

For this set of data, one of the most obvious approaches would be to arrange the trials from the smallest to the largest, as shown in Figure 12.1.

2	6
3	6
4	6
4	7
5	7
5	7
5	8
6	8
6	9

Figure 12.1

While this ordered arrangement is more useful than random arrangement, there is a better method for organizing the data. If we put a tally mark by the appropriate number for each time it occurred (Fig. 12.2), this would compress the data into a much smaller space and enable the viewer to appraise it much more quickly.

2 — /
3 — /
4 — //
5 — ///
6 — /////
7 — ///
8 — //
9 — /

Figure 12.2

This arrangement is known as a *frequency distribution.* As the name implies, the frequency with which each number occurs is tallied, thereby making a concise distribution which shows not only the range of scores but also how many times each score occurred. The frequency distribution is an orderly way to arrange data, and it is also useful because it can serve as a beginning step of statistical analysis of the data. With quantities that can be compared, frequency distribution makes it possible to become more aware of existing relationships.

It should be pointed out, however, that frequency distribution will not serve in all cases, since it is a statistical table. Another type of table is needed for mathematical variables which are dependent on each other for their values. For example, problems dealing with the variables of rate, time, and distance usually involve a relationship where one of the variables is dependent on the other variables. Distance in Figure 12.3 depends on the variables of rate and time, because the greater the time and the greater the rate, the greater the distance will be.

	Rate (MPH)	Time (hours)	Distance (miles)
1.	10	1	10
2.	10	2	20
3.	10	3	30
4.	20	1	20
5.	20	2	40
6.	20	3	60

Figure 12.3

It can be seen from the first entry that 10 mph for one hour would result in a distance of 10 miles. In the second entry, rate remains the same, but the time is doubled and so is the distance. In the fourth entry, the rate is doubled, but the time is the same (as no. 1) and the distance is doubled when compared to the first entry's distance. Now, consider the case of an ordered pair of numbers with some condition placed upon them, such as that their sum must be a certain number. Mathematically, we could express such a problem like this: $\square + \triangle = 6$.

Then we could depict this mathematical sentence in table form, as shown in Figure 12.4. It can be observed from Figure 12.4's table (or from the mathematical sentence) that when one of the variables, □ , is assigned a value, the other variable, △ , is dependent on it for its value.

□ + △ = 6	
□	△
6	0
5	1
4	2
3	3
2	4
1	5
0	6

Figure 12.4

When fairly large amounts of data are collected, they can probably be utilized and interpreted better if they are organized into some type of systematic arrangement. It should be mentioned again that even if there is a pattern of relationships present in the data, it is often not obvious from inspecting the data in table form alone. The organization of the data is generally the initial phase in a plan and not the final goal; from this arrangement of the data, it is possible to do something with the information that will probably lead to a better understanding. The next logical step in using this organized information would be to put it in the form of a graph so that comparisons and relationships can be observed visually.

Graphs

Graphs are a most useful tool in communicating and understanding relationships between objects and events. They permit a person to make visual comparisons in interpreting what is presented. In this section we will be concerned with the types of graphs and their uses.

Most elementary school children have had some limited experience with graphs because working with number lines is, in a sense, working with graphs; however, when working on the number line, the student is working only along the number line in either a forward or backward movement. In working with graphs, the student is, in a sense, working on two number lines simultaneously—one number line is drawn horizontally and one vertically.

Basically there are the same types of graphs as there are tables, statistical and mathematical. There are several kinds of statistical graphs: pictorial graphs, bar graphs, line graphs, and circle graphs. Each has particular advantages and disadvantages. Very briefly we will discuss the advantages and disadvantages of each kind:

1. A *pictograph* (Fig. 12.5) is the simplest type of graph to read, but it usually presents only approximate information, which is not as precise as other types.

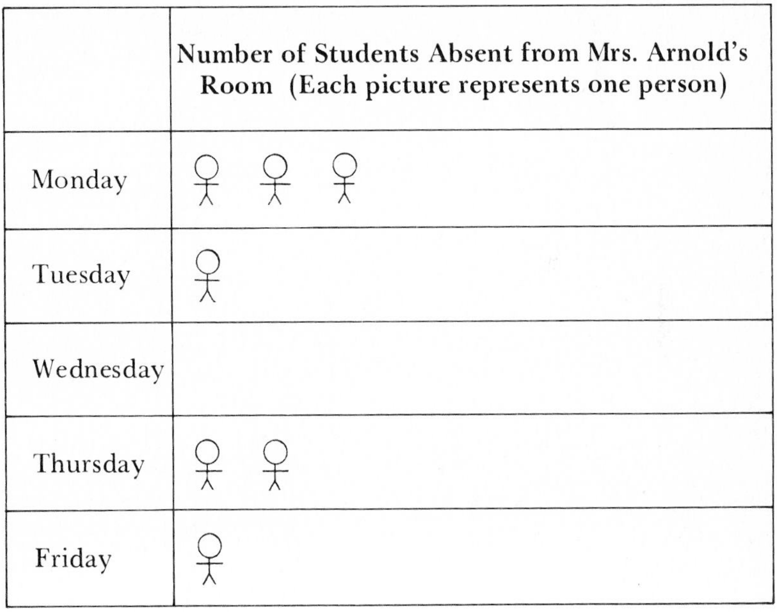

	Number of Students Absent from Mrs. Arnold's Room (Each picture represents one person)
Monday	♀ ♀ ♀
Tuesday	♀
Wednesday	
Thursday	♀ ♀
Friday	♀

Figure 12.5

Although it is possible to organize and construct graphs in several ways, it has been arbitrarily agreed that by observing certain basic rules, the resulting uniformity and convenience increases the probability of communication and understanding. There are many instances in everyday life which involve similar types of general agreement for convenience. For example, we normally read from left to right and we drive on the right-hand side of the street. There are other possible ways, but one method was arbitrarily decided upon and the general acceptance of this method produces regularity and convenience. Children can be guided to understand that while there are several ways to organize and construct graphs, the adherence to agreed-upon rules will increase the ease with which another person reads and interprets the graph. The basic rules for pictographs are:

a. The symbols used should be self-explanatory.
b. Only comparisons should be charted and not isolated statements.
c. When dealing with large numbers, the charts compare only approximate quantities, not exact amounts.
d. In the comparison, larger quantities are shown by using the appropriate number of symbols, not by using larger symbols. For example, a comparison of something twice as much as another thing would be represented by twice as many symbols, not symbols twice as large.

2. A *circle graph*, (Fig. 12.6) as the name indicates, utilizes a circle divided into appropriate parts to show relationships. For the circle graph to be used correctly and effectively, the relationship of the parts to the whole should be shown.

Figure 12.6

While the relationship of the parts to the whole are more apparent in a circle graph, the accurate construction necessary for this type of graph probably precludes its use to any great extent except in the higher intermediate grades. The basic rules for circle graphs are:

a. Find the sum of all the numbers involved.
b. Determine the percentage, or fraction, each part is of the total or whole.
c. Multiply 360° by each percent or fraction to get the size of each central angle. (A central angle is an angle with its vertex at the center of the circle. Its sides are radii of the circle.)
d. Construct a circle of any convenient radius.
e. Draw each specified angle at the center and extend the sides of each angle until they intersect the circle.
f. Label each part used in the representation.

3. The *bar graph* and histogram are usually more accurate in their construction but are a little more difficult to read than the pictograph. This particular kind of graph is probably more widely used than any of the others. The bar graph and the histogram are essentially the same

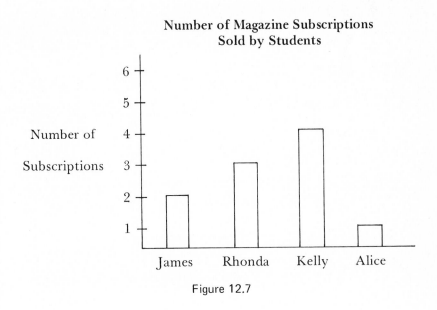

Number of Magazine Subscriptions Sold by Students

Figure 12.7

kind of graph, but their appearance is different. The bar graph (Fig. 12.7) uses rectangular bars of different length to denote quantity, while the histogram (Fig. 12.8) uses some form of individual tallies to denote quantity. Generally any information that can be put in a bar graph or histogram can also be put in a point or line graph, and vice versa, because these two types of graphs are closely related. When working with individually distinct elements, such as the sale of magazine

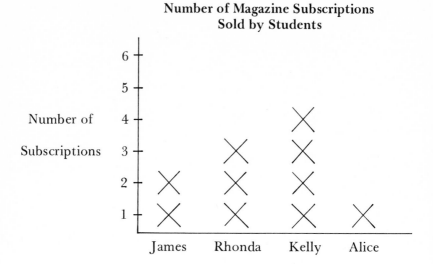

Figure 12.8

subscriptions, it is probably better to use the bar graph or histogram. When working with data or elements that are continuous or interdependent, the point or line graph will probably serve better. The basic rules for the bar graph or histogram are:

a. The bars, or individual tallies, should be placed vertically for ease of comparison.
b. The category that is named is placed along the horizontal axis.
c. The category that is measured or counted is placed along the vertical axis.
d. Each axis is labeled with descriptive terms, and the title for the entire graph should be descriptive.
e. The lines of the graph are labeled rather than the spaces. This is consistent with the manner in which the number line is labeled.

4. The *line graph* (Fig. 12.9) is used when there is a continuous set of data, such as changes over specified periods of time (and it is also used to represent a mathematical sentence). This graph can be misleading if the starting point is not zero and/or the scale is not the same on both axes of the graph. It should be noted, however, that when this type of graph is correctly constructed and used, it can be one of the most useful of all graphs. Each point on the graph represents a pair of measurements. After the points have been plotted, they are connected with

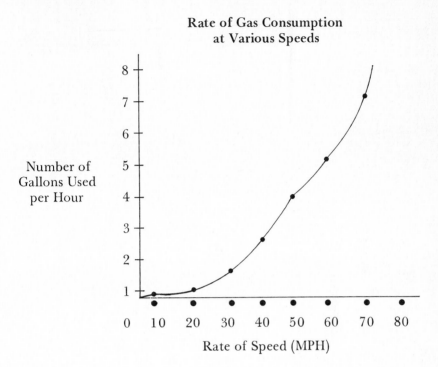

Figure 12.9

line segments, or—if a pattern appears—the points are connected with a smooth curve. The basic rules for a line graph are:

a. The categories (or variables) that are chosen, named, or manipulated are placed along the horizontal axis.
b. The categories (or variables) that are counted, measured, or over which we have no control except as they respond to the other variable are placed along the vertical axis.
c. The largest value needed on both axes is determined and placed at a convenient distance from the origin (or zero). The distance on each axis between zero and the largest value needed is subdivided into workable and convenient segments.
d. Each axis of the graph is labeled with descriptive terms, and the title for the graph should be descriptive.
e. The lines of the graph rather than the spaces are labeled.

From the line graph, it is possible to observe how one factor influences the behavior of the other and also to make certain kinds of predictions. It is often possible to discover a pattern, if one is present, even from measurements taken at irregular intervals. The real value of the line graph comes from its use in making reasonably accurate predictions about where other pieces of data would fit when only limited measurements are available. The ability to make predictions is one of the highest levels of comprehension in Bloom's Taxonomy because it requires the learner to project certain meanings based on judgments and basic understandings. Also required in the skill of predicting is the recognition and confidence of the regularity of certain things and events in the universe. With the discovery of this regularity or pattern, it is possible to extend what we know, with reasonable assurance, by means of mental activity rather than from physical activity or experience alone. From the development of this type of mental activity, it becomes possible to generate additional insights that enable the learner progressively to function at more complex levels of thought.

While predictions are useful as skill tools, however, they have certain limitations in their reliability. The diligent teacher will guide his students to recognize that certain predictions are more reliable than others. For example, predictions made within our range of data are generally fairly reliable. This kind of prediction is known as *interpolation*. Predictions made outside our range of data are generally not as reliable. This kind of prediction is known as *extrapolation*.

As students develop proficiency in making predictions and understanding the uses of predictions, they are also becoming more proficient in using and interpreting data. While it is probably not possible to teach all of the things our students are likely to need to know about predictions and interpreting data, it is possible to help them develop concepts and generalizations that they can apply in a useful way to meet most situations. Children in kindergarten through grade two are probably not mature enough to handle the concepts necessary to understand and work with graphs, but there are some prerequisite skills that can be developed during this time, since young children in these grade levels typically spend considerable time learning to distinguish likenesses and differences in objects and other things. The development of this skill is useful in many areas besides reading, since this forms the foundation for classification. Besides being a method of organization, classification is a powerful communications tool since it provides at least one means to communicate organization and relationships of objects or other things. The comprehension and reasonable mastery of these skills seem to enhance the development of other more complex skills used in describing relationships between objects and events. Of equal, or greater importance, is the development of oral communication skills in which children have many opportunities to practice and use these skills.

Young children can begin to work with graphs initially by reading picture graphs in much the same way that they read picture stories in the beginning phase of reading. After reading a picture graph, they should discuss with the teacher the meaning they derived from the graph. With careful teacher guidance, fundamental ideas about graphs will be developed. At a later time, when they have developed some skill in reading picture graphs, they can be guided into reading other simple graphs and discussing their meaning.

Starting about the third grade, children can be introduced to graphs by guiding them into a situation in which they will see a need to organize their information or data. Very likely before students will recognize the value and uses of tables and graphs, they will need to be involved in some type of problem situation where there exists a need for these skills. The teacher can then guide them in developing an organized, systematic method of handling and presenting the data. In the beginning phases, the teacher might arrange a situation where several groups of students are working with different sets of data. After each group has prepared its data, a student from another group can be asked to interpret the prepared data. In most cases the student interpreter will not be able to give much information from the data prepared by the group. The teacher and students should then discuss what is needed to improve the communicability of the prepared data. In the event one or more groups organized its data so that it could be interpreted reasonably well, the teacher and students would then discuss what features of the organization was helpful in understanding it. The students could then be guided to develop rules for presenting data so that people other than the person(s) collecting it could also get the correct information from it.

The initial organization of information would probably be in the form of a table or chart. From this arrangement of the data, the teacher would then guide the students to an understanding of the need and advantages of an orderly, systematic method of recording data and then organizing it into its most useful form. Following numerous opportunities to gather, record, and organize data, the students would be guided into utilizing this information, thus extending their learning.

The students probably will recognize that only limited or certain types of information can be obtained from a table. With this awareness on the part of the students, the teacher can then suggest that there are some other ways to obtain even more information from this data. The histogram can then be introduced and the various types of information that can be obtained from it can be discussed. After a period of time in which the students have developed reasonable competency in the interpretation of the histogram, the bar graph can be introduced and its uses discussed. Then, at still a later time, in a manner similar to that used with bar graphs, the point or line graph should be introduced and its uses discussed.

Most of the time spent in the third and fourth grades on graphs would be used in developing skill and understanding in gathering, recording, and organizing data, but some time would be spent on learning to interpret the data contained in the tables and graphs. As students progress to the upper intermediate grades, the emphasis should shift to the kinds of information that can be obtained from the interpretation. When the students are able to interpret information and generate additional thought patterns from the interpretation, they are using the higher mental processes described in Bloom's Taxonomy as comprehension and application. The development of these higher cognitive processes is receiving more and more emphasis in many of the newer curriculum programs, because the way in which a student uses what he knows indicates not only the effectiveness of his learning, but also often determines whether the student can go on to higher and more useful levels of thought.

MATHEMATICAL GRAPHS

Mathematical graphs usually take the form of some type of line graph, since most mathematical sentences involve dependent variables; consequently, mathematical sentences, or equations, that result in a line graph are known as linear equations, or sentences. With proper guidance from the teacher, the graphing of these less complex mathematical sentences is usually not too difficult for students in the intermediate grades.

Most students in the intermediate grades have encountered ordered pairs of numbers; therefore, this can serve as another way of applying previous learning. Most of these students will have worked with number lines and the introduction of a *number plane* can be described as working with two number lines (one horizontal and one vertical) at the same time. Consider the earlier example of a mathematical sentence so that the sum of two numbers would be 6. Figures 12.10 shows the table we made for the problem: $\square + \triangle = 6$, and how these numbers would be represented as points.

$$\square + \triangle = 6$$

$\square$	$\triangle$	
6	0	would be represented by the point $(6, 0)$
5	1	would be represented by the point $(5, 1)$
4	2	would be represented by the point $(4, 2)$
3	3	would be represented by the point $(3, 3)$
2	4	would be represented by the point $(2, 4)$
1	5	would be represented by the point $(1, 5)$
0	6	would be represented by the point $(0, 6)$

Figure 12.10

Any of these ordered pairs of numbers meets the requirement of totaling 6. We can now locate each of these ordered pairs of numbers on a number plane (Fig. 12.11). After the ordered pairs of numbers have been located, or—more correctly—after the points represented by the ordered pairs of numbers have been plotted on the number plane,

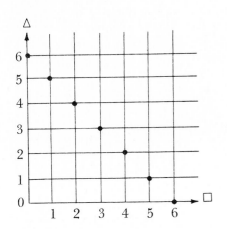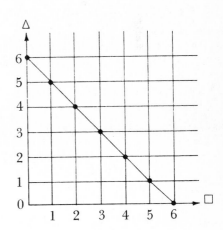

Figure 12.11

the students should be guided to observe that the points seem to make a straight line. The students could then connect each of these points with a line segment (also shown in Fig. 11.11) and decide if it appears to be a straight line.

There are many interesting discoveries awaiting students in working with mathematical graphs. For example: would $\square + \triangle = 6$ look the same on a number place as $\square - \triangle = 6$? Or how would the graph of $\square \times \triangle = 6$ compare with either $\square + \triangle = 6$ or $\square - \triangle = 6$? After graphing mathematical sentences, it may be that the teacher as well as the students will want to explore this idea further.

EDUCATIONAL IMPLICATIONS

Learning has been described as more than knowing something. It is the ability to use what you know. This would include not only applying the correct generalization at the right time and place, but also extending one's learning through the development and utilization of his rational powers of thought. Since it is not possible to have students experience all those things that they may possibly need, we must selectively choose those situations from which they are most likely to develop broad concepts and/or generalizations which can be applied to new situations. When students have developed the ability to make generalizations and can correctly apply them, they can blend this higher level of cognitive thinking with new experience.

Experience is vital to learning, especially in the initial stages, but if learning is to progress beyond the fundamental level, experience alone is not sufficient. The additional prerequisite of intellectual thought must be combined with experience for learning to be expanded and extend into the upper and more useful levels of the cognititve domain. Man has refined the ability to profit from and extend his learning from experience to a greater extent than probably any other living thing. It should be noted, however, that only the mental capacity to develop this ability is inherited. The ability itself must be developed.

The understanding and use of graphs by students is one way a teacher can guide students into experience opportunities that develop high level mental capabilities as well as a highly useful skill in communication. Thought processes necessary for this level of mental activitiy require the student to recognize the uniformity and regularity of our universe. Without this awareness, the patterns and relationships that permeate our existence and surroundings are reduced to the level of mere factual content. On the other hand, the assumption of regularity opens the possibility of patterns and relationships being extended to concepts and/or generalizations, as well as the possibility of the

xtension of rational thought in greater depth. This assumption makes
possible for us to predict that a certain thing will happen under
ertain conditions because of past experiences, learnings, and the like.
Vithout these attributes, we can only guess, with any guess being as
ood as any other. Predictions allow us to feel reasonably sure of our
rojected expectations, while guesses leave us with uncertainty.

Another mental operation is also possible from the assumption of
egularity. As patterns and relationships are interpreted it is possible to
xtend or project our thinking to a level beyond predicting by attempt-
ng to construct an explanation of occurrences. The mental operation
f constructing explanations based on facts or information is known as
nferring. With enough of the proper information, it is possible to con-
truct fairly reliable explanations or inferences of why certain things
ccur. Without enough of the proper information, we must sometimes
nodify or change our explanation (inference) as well as our expectation
prediction). Even with some uncertainty, predictions and/or inferences
re infinitely more valuable than guesses because from the development
f the ability to predict and infer comes the power of reasoning.

Statistics

The opening portion of this chapter dealt with topics closely related
o statistics. In fact many people consider tables and graphs an integral
art of statistics. Although statistics can be complicated and may require considerable depth of thought to be understood, there are parts
f statistics that are fairly familiar to most people. It is this part of
tatistics with which we will be concerned in this section.

Statistics involve organizing and analyzing data (usually in numerical
orm) so that the data can be understood and become useful. In other
vords, statistics provide one method of utilizing information in solving
problems by enabling us to see existing relationships and patterns, to
nake inferences and conclusions, and to formulate hypotheses so that
ve can operate in an organized, systematic manner above the level of
rial and error.

MEASURES OF CENTRAL TENDENCY

Probably the statistical concept that is most widely used and that has
the broadest application is the measure of central tendency. The measure of central tendency gives a single characteristic or measure that is
the most representative of a group or set of data. While it would be
difficult to remember the characteristics of each measure in a large
group, it is fairly easy and useful to remember a single representative

measure. There are, of course, limitations in the extent to which a single measure can represent the characteristics of a group, but each individual measure within the group will be more like the representative measure than like any other single measure. There are five basic statistical measures of central tendency, but in this section we shall be concerned with only the three most common: average, median, and mode.

Average. The average (also known as the mean) is probably the most used and best known of the three measures. "Average" has more than one meaning. For example, when we talk of the average student, we are talking of a typical student, but when we talk of a statistical average, we are talking about a different concept. When we refer to average in this section we will mean statistical average.

Most students in the intermediate grades will probably have come into contact with the concept of average in several different ways. They may have had an explanation of how their grades are averaged; they may have read about the average rainfall or some other condition in some of the other subject matter areas; or they may have come in contact with averages as they are used in sports in numerous other ways.

Suppose some students have obtained the following data:

16	14	14
18	15	15
13	13	17
15	16	12
14	15	16
17		

They can put this data in table form and into a graph and it will be more useful than in the above form. However, it will soon become evident that there are limitations on what can be done with this information in table and graph form. By determining the average, they will have one more piece of information about their data. To determine the average, all of the data would be added together and then this sum would be divided by the total number of measures that were added together. The resulting quotient will be the average. For example, the average of the previously mentioned students' data would be the sum of all the scores, 240, divided by the total number of scores, 16; that is, $240 \div 16 = 15$. If the students had placed the data in a frequency distribution, some of them might realize that the average can be computed from the frequency distribution in the manner shown in Figure 12.12.

Score	Frequency	(Score × Frequency
18	1	18
17	2	34
16	3	48
15	4	60
14	3	42
13	2	26
12	1	12
Totals	16	240

The average $= 240 \div 16 = 15$

Figure 12.12

Median. Another measure of central tendency is the median. As the term suggests, median is the exact middle score or measure in a distribution. Stated another way, the median score is that score which has as many scores above it as there are below. Since it is necessary to locate the exact midpoint in a set of data, the median is usually easier to compute from a frequency distribution in which the scores are ordered from largest to smallest, or vice versa. From the set of data previously used to compute the average, the median would be 15.

Mode. The mode is the score or measure that occurs most frequently in a distribution. Just as it was easier to compute the median from a frequency distribution, so it is also more convenient to compute the mode from a frequency distribution. The measure that occurred most frequently in the previous data is 15. Thus, in this particular set of data, the average, median, and mode were all the same: 15. These three measures may or may not always be the same; it will depend upon the distribution and frequency of the data involved.

The average is generally the most widely used and provides the most representative measure of these three measures of central tendency. There are, however, some disadvantages in using the average, particularly if one or more of the measures in a distribution is extremely large or extremely small. The obtained average then will usually not be as representative as the median or mode. One extremely important advantage of the average is that a group of averages can be averaged and be meaningful and accurate. The median is not affected as much by extremely large or small scores as the average, but it is not generally as useful a measure as the average because about all that can be said for a median is that there are as many scores above it as there are below it. The mode is even more unstable as a measure than the average or median, because it is possible to have more than one mode in the distribution; this is called a multimodal distribution.

MEASURES OF VARIABILITY

The measures of central tendency describe only a limited amount of information about a set of data. It is sometimes important to know how widely dispersed these measures are or how closely they tend to group together. The amount that the individual measures deviate from the average, or other measure of central tendency, is known as *variability*.

The simplest measure of variability would be the *range* of scores. This is determined by finding the difference between the largest and smallest score. This measure of variability, at best, is only a very rough measure and does not usually provide much additional information about the data. In fact if the data is arranged into a frequency distribution, the range can be determined from this.

A better and more useful measure of variability is the *standard deviation*. Elementary school children should *not* be taught how to compute the standard deviation, however, because it involves mathematical skills that most are not ready to master or use in a meaningful way. The standard deviation is mentioned here as background information for the teacher so that he can be aware of topics to be developed at the junior and senior high school level. The standard deviation is probably the most useful and widely used measure of variability; most of the more complicated statistical analyses utilize the standard deviation as a basic component of the analysis.

Two sets of data may have the same average, yet the distribution of scores in one of the sets may be far more dispersed than in the other. The standard deviation provides an indication of how closely or how widely the scores are dispersed around the average. A small standard deviation indicates that most of the scores are clustered fairly close to the average, while a large standard deviation indicates that most of the scores are dispersed over a fairly wide range. A teacher desiring more information about standard deviation, or other measures of variability, can find this in any good book on tests and measurements, or any beginning book on statistics.

Extending Your Thinking

1. Construct a frequency distribution and find the mean, median, and mode of the following group of scores:

87	96	85	89	76	87
68	81	69	74	83	62
91	93	87	79	87	95
78	80	90	96	92	78
77	70	97	87	73	86

2. Construct a bar graph to show the preference of ice cream flavors of students in Mrs. Thornhill's room. The following data was collected in a class survey:

Vanilla—8

Chocolate—13

Strawberry—6

Banana nut—4

3. A group of children were changing the water in their aquarium. They decided to keep a record of how fast the siphon they were using removed the old water. From the data presented below, construct a line graph.

Time elapsed (in minutes)	Total gallons of water removed
2	3
4	5
6	6
8	6.5

4. Using the graph constructed for no. 3, what is your prediction of the total number of gallons of water removed at the end of three minutes? At the end of ten minutes?

5. In which of the predictions that you made in no. 4 do you have the most confidence? Why?

6. What would you have to do to test your predictions?

7. How would you explain why the water was removed much faster during the first four minutes than during the last four minutes? How would you test your explanation?

8. How are the two tests that you constructed in nos. 6 and 7 alike? How are they different?

ANSWERS TO SELECTED QUESTIONS

2.

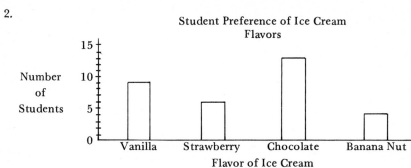

3.

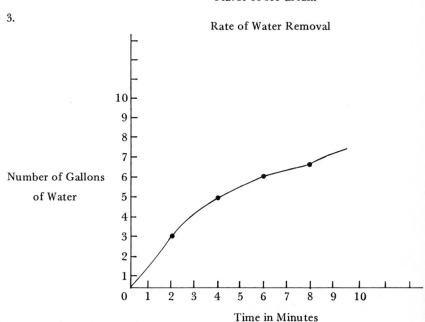

4. At the end of three minutes, there would be approximately four gallons. At the end of ten minutes, there would be approximately 6.75 gallons.
5. We should feel most confident about the prediction at the end of three minutes, because it came between two known measurements, while the prediction at ten minutes was beyond our last measurement.
6. We would need more data or observations. Consequently, to test our prediction we would need to repeat or duplicate our experiment and obtain measurements at the end of three minutes and ten minutes.
7. One explanation could be that there was more water pressure during the first four minutes because there was more water in the tank. To test this explanation, we would need to set up an experiment to determine the relationship between the amount of water and the pressure. By doing this, we would obtain a new set of data or observations.
8. The two tests were similar in that they both required us to obtain more data and observations. The two tests differ in that in the test of the prediction we repeated or duplicated the previous experience, while in the test of the explanation we created a different experiment to collect new data.

Related References

Commission on Science Education, *Commentary for Teachers.* 3rd expanded ed. Washington, D.C.: The American Association for the Advancement of Science, 1968. pp. 112-21, 134-44, 187-204.

Duncan, Ernest and Quast, W.G. *Modern School Mathematics.* New York: Houghton Mifflin Company, 1968. Chap. 5.

Heddens, James W. *Today's Mathematics.* Chicago: Science Research Associates, 1964. pp. 457-63, 473-80.

CHAPTER 13

DIRECTED NUMBERS

In our study of mathematics up to this point we have been concerned only with the size or magnitude of a number. Consequently, we have encountered limitations as to what could be done in certain situations. For example, it was not possible to subtract a larger number from a smaller number. With the development of directed numbers, this becomes possible, because now we can consider not only magnitude but also direction of numbers. This chapter will be concerned with the development of directed numbers, the concepts involved, and methods to use in operations with directed numbers.

Rationale for Directed Numbers

Many people associate directed numbers with algebra because it was in this study area that they first became acquainted with the idea of these types of numbers, particularly negative numbers. The fact that many students fail to develop sufficient understanding of this number concept undoubtedly accounts for much of the difficulty and frustration they experience with algebra. Operations with directed numbers and natural numbers are both considered to be complete arithmetic systems and both systems have been applied to the field of algebra. It is well-known that algebra is highly abstract in nature and, consequently, when students encounter the idea of directed numbers for the first time in algebra they are being forced to learn this new system at the abstract level.

To further compound the problem, there seems to be little agreement at the secondary level on the best way to teach directed numbers. One solution may be to introduce directed numbers in the elementary school program at a time when the basic operations with whole numbers have been mastered. In this way, the operations in this new system can be developed as an extension of previously learned ideas. At one time, the concept of directed numbers was considered to be too difficult for elementary school children. Recent research indicates however, that the more mature elementary school student seems to be capable of working with and understanding basic ideas and operations in this system. Some of the newer curriculum programs are even introducing negative numbers at the primary level. In the final analysis, the teacher must decide whether or not his class is ready to cope with the concept.

HISTORY OF DIRECTED NUMBERS

The discussion in Chapter 8 described how the basic idea of fractions was known for several hundred years before people understood how to use them effectively. In almost direct contrast to fractions, negative numbers were searched for over a period of several hundred years and during most of this time mathematicians were not exactly sure what they were seeking. They did know, however, that their number system was not complete as it existed. There is evidence that sometime about 800 A.D., the Hindus and the Arabs attempted to develop the concept of negative numbers but apparently they were not successful, or else a record of their efforts was not preserved by mathematical writers. In about 1300, the Italian mathematician Fibonacci attempted to describe and interpret negative numbers, but he too apparently was not successful in this effort, although he made several outstanding mathematical contributions. Even as recently as the early 1800s most mathematicians were not ready to accept negative numbers. One English mathematician even implied that negative numbers were the work of the devil himself and should be ignored (and there have probably been several hundred thousand algebra students since who would agree with him). Despite the resistance of some mathematicians, however, negative numbers have achieved acceptance in the last 100 years.

DESCRIPTION OF DIRECTED NUMBERS
AND CONCEPTS INVOLVED

It will be remembered from Chapter 5 that an integer was described as any number that could be expressed as the difference of any two natural numbers. With the development of negative numbers to go with positive numbers and zero, mathematicians were finally able to describe the whole set of integers. By being able to describe the set of integers, mathematicians were able to complete another piece of the puzzle and give us a better picture of the structure of our number system.

Directed numbers are often referred to as *signed numbers*, but since elementary school children seem to understand what is meant by "directed" more easily than by "signed" numbers, we will use only the term directed numbers, in this book. As the term implies, these are numbers in which not only the magnitude of the number is considered, but also the direction.

In developing the concept of directed numbers, we must first guide the students to realize that for every point on the number line that we have used, there is a corresponding negative point. This negative point is the same distance to the left of zero as the other number is to the right of zero. For example, the point $^+5$ would be five units to the right of zero, and its corresponding negative point, $^-5$, would be five units to the left of zero. The pupils should eventually generalize that the negative portion of the number line is simply a mirror reflection of the positive portion. (The positive portion of the number line is the portion with which the students are already familiar.)

Previously, zero has had the function of a place holder and cardinal number of the empty set. With directed numbers, zero now also assumes the role of separating the positive numbers from the negative numbers. Since zero is neither positive nor negative, or—as some mathematicians believe—it is both positive and negative, it serves as a separator and an origin (or starting point) for numbers extending infinitely in both directions.

The next concept that should probably be developed has to do with ordering numbers from smallest to largest. Prior to studying directed numbers, this was not much of a problem, because two sets could be compared and it could be determined if one set was equal to, greater than, or less than the other set. Comparisons of this type with negative numbers are more difficult to show. By using the number line, particularly the positive section in the beginning phase, the pupils can be guided to generalize that in comparing two numbers on the number line, the number farthest to the right is the greater number. This means that $7 > 5$, $10 > 8$, and so on. However, since the negative side of the number line is a mirror reflection of the positive side, this same generalization must hold for the negative side as well, like this: $(^-1) > (^-3)$, $(^-5) > (^-7)$, and so on. This is to say that although 1 is the smallest positive whole number, $(^-1)$ is the largest negative whole number because it is the negative number farthest to the right.

In earlier contacts with operations such as addition, the pupil probably has developed some incomplete concepts; for example, when adding any two nonzero numbers you get an answer larger than either addend. With directed numbers, this does not necessarily hold true. For example: $(^-4) + (^+3) = (^-1)$. We did not get a sum larger than the second term, but we did get an answer larger than the original term, $(^-4)$, because we *added* to $(^-4)$.

Another concept that probably should be developed before beginning formal operations with directed numbers is the concept of *absolute value*. This term has considerable use in higher mathematics and it particularly relates to directed numbers. *Absolute value* means that the value of a number is determined by its value without regard to whether it is designated as positive or negative. The symbol | | is used to designate absolute value. (For example, |6| would designate the absolute value of 6 on a number line.)

Introducing Directed Numbers

Since there are no good concrete materials at this time that can serve as models, most of the work with directed numbers will need to be done at the semiconcrete and abstract levels. This means that students who do not operate efficiently at the abstract level should probably not be introduced to directed numbers. Since most children are not working efficiently at the abstract level until about the fourth grade, these activities would probably be of most benefit to students in the intermediate grades. The students will also need to have a reasonable mastery of the basic operations with counting numbers. (If the reader uses a number line to work through each example in the remainder of this discussion, the operations presented will be more meaningful.)

Many children at the primary level can understand the meaning of directed numbers, but this does not necessarily mean that this is the best time to introduce this idea to them. The astute teacher will introduce these concepts when his students are ready, providing also that these concepts will be useful in future problem-solving. Some of the children may have vague ideas of directed numbers—for example, a temperature report of ⁻12 degrees. These vague ideas generally are not a sufficient base on which to build other concepts. A good starting place is a number line because most children will have worked with it in other learning situations. The teacher can place a number line on the chalkboard, like this:

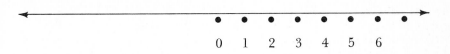

Through discussion, pupils establish the fact that each point is named because of the number of units it is from zero: point 1 is one unit from zero, point 2 is two units from zero, and so on. The teacher can then question what the point would be called if he stood at zero and moved one unit to the left. After some discussion, most children will agree that the point one unit to the left of zero should also be called one, like this:

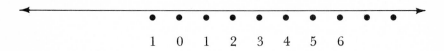

$$1 \quad 0 \quad 1 \quad 2 \quad 3 \quad 4 \quad 5 \quad 6$$

In similar fashion, additional points can be established left of zero at 2, 3, 4, 5, and 6, so that the number line now looks like this:

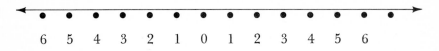

$$6 \quad 5 \quad 4 \quad 3 \quad 2 \quad 1 \quad 0 \quad 1 \quad 2 \quad 3 \quad 4 \quad 5 \quad 6$$

Now a need arises for some means of distinguishing between numbers to the left of zero and numbers to the right. The teacher can ask a student to come to the board and point to 5 on the number line. If the child asks "Which one?" the teacher points out that probably some method is needed to distinguish between the numbers. If the child goes to the board and points to one of the numerals, the teacher can ask why he thinks that is the one meant (thus also establishing a need to distinguish between the numbers).

After the need has been established, the teacher explains that mathematicians have devised a method of distinguishing between these numbers by putting a certain sign or symbol by each of the numbers to the left of zero and a different sign by each of the numbers to the right of zero. It was arbitrarily decided to label all the numbers on one side of zero as negative numbers (written like this, $^-1, ^-2, ^-3, \ldots$) and all the other numbers on the other side of zero as positive numbers (written like this, $^+1, ^+2, ^+3, \ldots$). It should be noted that when directed numbers are written, the sign is written to the *upper left* of the numeral (like this, $^-7$ or $^+3$), so that the positive and negative signs are not confused with the plus sign of addition or the minus sign of subtraction. Although the signs look identical, the *positive and negative signs indicate a direction from zero, while plus and minus signs indicate an operation on numbers.*

After the children have gained some understanding that directed numbers indicate not only magnitude but also direction, the teacher guides them to the realization that the portion of the number line designated as positive and negative is an arbitrary designation. It does not matter which side we designate as positive, because the other side must be negative. In most instances we have become accustomed to having the right side designated as positive and the left side as negative— but it does not *have* to be just this way. The teacher can assist the students in understanding this in several ways. One of the most effective ways would be to place the following number line on the chalkboard:

$$0 \qquad \qquad ^-3$$

The teacher then explains that he had designated the point (three units from zero) as negative three. Then he has students locate and label other points, such as $^+4, ^-5, ^+1$, and so on, until all points are labeled. This type of activity can be repeated several times, with the teacher (or a student) designating one side of the number line as positive or negative, and the other side automatically becoming the other direction. A vertical number line can also be used in a similar manner to further assist children in developing and refining this idea.

Operations with Directed Numbers

In teaching operations with directed numbers, we will need to emphasize that the laws, or properties, that have previously been learned are still valid; operations with directed numbers will be consistent with this previous knowledge. Many students who fail to attain a reasonable mastery of algebra are often confused in the preliminary stages when they first encounter directed, or signed, numbers because they seem to conflict with previous learning. Continued emphasis on the consistency of what they are learning with what they have learned, aids students in their understanding and helps prevent possible frustration at a later date.

Before beginning to teach addition of directed numbers, a teacher should make a number line on the floor. Using masking tape is an easy and inexpensive way of making one or more number lines on the floor, and since most classroom floors are covered with some type of rubber or vinyl tile, these make convenient units for the number line. The importance of direction becomes much more apparent to a student when he steps off the indicated operation on the number line, but since it is not likely that all of the children will be able to work on the floor number lines at the same time, it will be necessary that the students remaining at their desks also have number lines to work with in performing the various operations.

It would be advantageous to develop a set of rules to use when working on the floor number line. It will be remembered that the rules we develop must be consistent with what we have done in the past. The first rules that we should develop would be the general rules that will hold true for all operations. After developing the general rules, we would then develop specific rules for each operation.

General Rules:

1. Standing at the starting point, zero, we can face in one of two directions, either positive (+) or negative (−):

negative direction (−)   positive direction (+)

2. After we have faced in one of the two directions, we can walk in one of two directions: either forward or backward. Since walking forward is most natural, it will be considered positive (+), and moving backward (opposite the direction we are facing) will be considered negative (−).

ADDITION OF DIRECTED NUMBERS

In the beginning phase of addition, it is probably best to work with problems where both addends have like signs. After a reasonable time, students can then be led to make a generalization concerning adding directed numbers with like signs. To add ($^+$4) + ($^+$3), the student starts at zero on the number line, facing the positive direction, and moves as indicated:

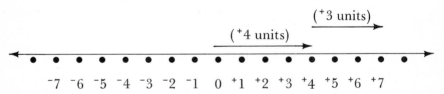

As the students work this problem, they will move four units in a positive direction and then move three more positive units to arrive at $^+$7, which is the sum. After working several such problems, the children will probably realize that this is just the way they worked addition problems. Next, the students should be introduced to adding two negative numbers, such as ($^-$4) + ($^-$3):

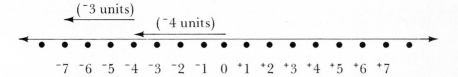

Starting at zero, the students would first move four units in a negative direction, then three more negative units and arrive at ⁻7, which is the sum. Again, after working several similar problems, the children will probably observe that the addition of two negative numbers is not very different from adding positive numbers. Gradually, after students have worked a considerable number of addition problems where both addends have the same sign, they can then be guided to make a generalization or rule about what they have found. To assist the students in formulating the rule, the teacher may need to list a number of examples on the chalkboard, like this:

$$(^+4) + (^+3) = {}^+7 \qquad (^-2) + (^-4) = {}^-6$$
$$(^+5) + (^+4) = {}^+9 \qquad (^-6) + (^-5) = {}^-11$$
$$(^+3) + (^+1) = {}^+4 \qquad (^-2) + (^-2) = {}^-4$$
$$(^+7) + (^+5) = {}^+12 \qquad (^-4) + (^-3) = {}^-7$$

Then, with teacher guidance, the students can probably make their generalization. In their terms, it will likely be something similar to this: When adding directed numbers that have like signs, add the numbers and keep the same sign.

In adding directed numbers where the signs are different, the students will probably observe that this appears to be the same as the previously learned operation of subtraction of counting numbers. However, while the answers are the same, the operations are different. This shows the addition, (⁺4) + (⁻3):

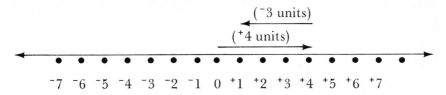

The students move four positive units on their number line, then three negative units, and arrive at ⁺1, which is the sum. They may need some guidance to remember that this is still addition, or a putting-together process. After the students have worked several similar problems, the teacher introduces this type of problem, ($^-$4) + ($^+$3):

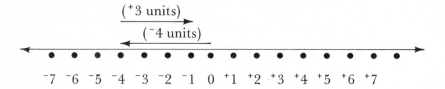

In solving this problem, the student moves four units in a negative direction, then three positive units, and arrives at $^-$1, which is the answer.

When the students have worked enough addition problems in which the addends have different signs to be ready to make a generalization, they can be guided inductively to generalize in their own terms: To add two numbers whose signs are different, you subtract the number with the smallest absolute value from the larger number, and keep the sign of the larger number in the answer.

When the students have gained reasonable mastery of adding numbers when their signs are alike and when they are different, the teacher can introduce problems in which there are three or more addends. First, would be three or more addends with all of their signs alike. Later, the three or more addends would have the signs mixed, like this: ($^-$4) + ($^+$5) + ($^-$3).

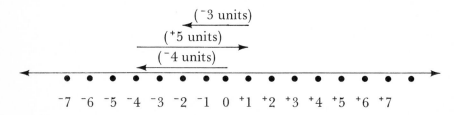

The solution is: ($^-$4) + ($^+$5) + ($^-$3) = $^-$2.

SUBTRACTING DIRECTED NUMBERS

Subtraction has been described as the inverse of addition, or the process that undoes addition. While inverse does not exactly mean opposite, in working with directed numbers it is quite natural to think of an inverse as being opposite, especially when working on a number line. This is true because we can move in only two directions on the number line, and if we are undoing some movement, then we are surely going in the opposite direction. It is important that the teacher encourage the students to decide what operation they need to perform on the problem before working it. For example, the problem ($^+$7) − ($^+$3) would be interpreted something like this: move seven positive units from zero; then, because subtraction is an inverse of addition, move three units in the direction opposite that moved when adding. To subtract ($^+$7) − ($^+$3), we would proceed like this:

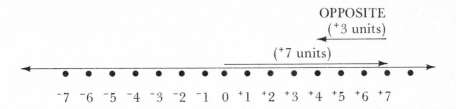

The student would move seven positive units, then think of subtraction as opposite, and move three units opposite the positive direction to arrive at $^+$4, which is the answer.

To subtract ($^-$7) − ($^-$3), we could proceed like this:

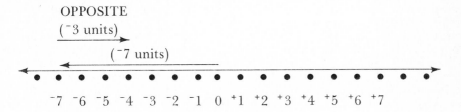

In this problem, the student would move seven negative units, then think of subtraction as opposite and move three units opposite the negative direction to arrive at $^-$4, which is the answer.

The teacher must be aware that subtraction of directed numbers with different signs usually produces an answer that is larger than either original number. The children will probably need some assistance in understanding this, since it is in direct contrast to what they had previously experienced about subtraction. It might be helpful to remind students that directed numbers and counting numbers are different kinds of numbers; therefore, we will not always get exactly the same kind of answers from working with directed numbers as we did from working with counting numbers. The subtraction of directed numbers with different signs would be done like this for ($^+$4) − ($^-$3):

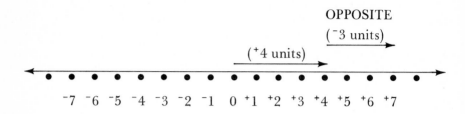

The student would move four positive units, then think of subtraction as opposite and move three units opposite the negative direction to arrive at $^+$7, which is the answer. To work the other type of problem, ($^-$4) − ($^+$3), the student would proceed as follows:

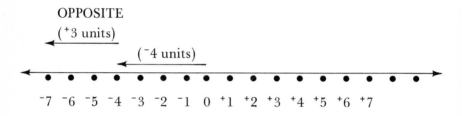

The student would move four negative units, then think of subtraction as opposite and move three units opposite the positive direction to arrive at $^-$7, which is the answer.

As students work with subtraction of directed numbers, the teacher must remember that they must discover the properties of subtraction and make the generalizations in their own terms. The initial generalization that students usually make about subtracting directed numbers is that you do the opposite of what the subtrahend indicates. At a later time, with teacher guidance, this generalization can be refined to: In subtracting directed numbers, change the sign of the subtrahend and then proceed as in addition of directed numbers. The teacher must realize that subtraction of directed numbers is more difficult to understand than addition and more time and guidance will be required in developing these generalizations.

Another way that subtraction of directed numbers can be taught is to utilize the missing addend type of problem to solve subtraction. It should be pointed out, however, that this method generally does not develop understanding as well as the previously described method. The missing addend method is presented only as background information for the teacher, since some textbook authors present this method in their texts. To work a problem such as (⁻4) – (⁺3) with this method, the student would restate the problem as (⁺3) + □ = (⁻4). Now the student must determine *how many* units he must count and *what direction* he must move to get there. In this particular problem, he would have to move from (⁺3) in a negative direction to reach (⁻4), like this:

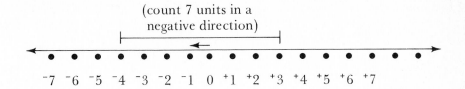

(count 7 units in a negative direction)

Therefore, (⁺3) – ⁻7 = (⁻4) or (⁻4) – (⁺3) = ⁻7. An additional example would be: (⁺7) – (⁺3). To solve this problem, the student must restate the problem as addition, (⁺3) + □ = (⁺7). Next, he must then determine *how many* units and in *what direction* to count to go from (⁺3) to (⁺7), like this:

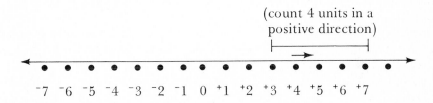

(count 4 units in a positive direction)

Using this method, (⁺3) + ⁺4 = (⁺7) or (⁺7) – (⁺3) = ⁺4.

MULTIPLICATION OF DIRECTED NUMBERS

It will be remembered that in a preceding part of this chapter it was emphasized that new operations must be consistent with previously learned operations. It was shown that adding two positive (⁺) numbers was consistent with the previously learned operation of addition, and that subtracting one positive number from another was shown to be consistent with the previously learned operation of subtraction. Multiplication will also be shown to be consistent with previously learned operations of multiplication. Multiplication was shown as the putting together of equal-size sets. To multiply directed numbers, we will also stress putting together equal-size sets, but we must also consider direction. To state this another way, 3 X 2 will still mean 3 sets of 2 and the product will still be 6, but the sign of the product will be determined by what occurs as a result of the signs of the multiplier and the multiplicand. In order to develop understanding, it is vital that the teacher encourage and assist students in interpreting what process is indicated in each multiplication problem before attempting to get a solution. After the students have discovered the rules governing multiplication of directed numbers, it probably will not be necessary to continue formal interpretation of each problem. By this time the students will be able to work the multiplication algorism with an understanding of why it works. Multiplication of directed numbers would proceed something like this: The problem: ($^+$3) X ($^+$2). The interpretation: 3 sets of positive 2. It looks like this on the number line:

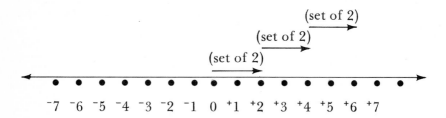

Therefore, ($^+$3) X ($^+$2) = $^+$6.

The next type of problem to be introduced would be ($^+$3) X ($^-$2). The interpretation: 3 sets of negative 2. It would look like this on the number line:

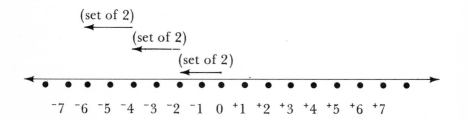

The solution to this problem would be: ($^+$3) X ($^-$2) = $^-$6.

The two preceding types of problems are presented initially because they can be related more directly to conventional multiplication problems than can the remaining two types of directed number multiplication problems. When the students first encounter a negative multiplier, such as ($^-$3) X ($^+$2), they will probably need some assistance in interpreting what this means. A comparison between the first example used and this one could be helpful, like this:

Problem	Interpretation
1. ($^+$3) × ($^+$2)	1. 3 sets of positive 2
2. ($^-$3) × ($^+$2)	2. (when comparing these two problems, it can be seen that the multiplicands, ($^+$2), are the same, but the multipliers are different. Therefore, the ($^-$3) will be interpreted as "the opposite direction.") ($^-$3) × ($^+$2) will be interpreted as opposite the direction of 3 sets of $^+$2.

The number line looks like this:

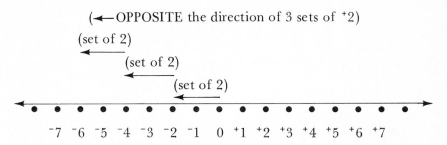

The solution to this problem would be ($^-$3) × ($^+$2) = $^-$6.

After working more of these problems, some students may have enough understanding to shorten their interpretation to something like this: "Opposite the direction indicated by the multiplicand." This beginning generalization is fine, but the teacher must not lose sight of the fact that we are seeking to guide students to discover the rules that govern multiplication of directed numbers, not just short cuts.

The remaining type of problem can be illustrated with ($^-$3) × ($^-$2). Here again, a comparison between this problem and a previous example may be helpful.

Problem	Interpretation
1. ($^+$3) × ($^-$2)	1. 3 sets of $^-$2
2. ($^-$3) × ($^-$2)	2. ($^-$3) is interpreted as opposite the direction of 3 sets of $^-$2.

The number line looks like this:

(OPPOSITE the direction of 3 sets of ⁻2 ⟶)

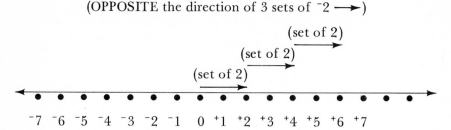

The solution to this problem would be (⁻3) × (⁻2) = ⁺6.

The work children do on the number line and the multiplication algorism is aimed at having them discover the rules that govern the multiplication of directed numbers for themselves. After the children have had considerable experience working these problems, the teacher helps them organize their information so that the rule becomes more apparent. There are several ways of organizing this information, but one effective way is to use a chart or table, something like this:

Problems with (⁺) products	Problems with (⁻) products
(⁺3) × (⁺2)	(⁻3) × (⁺2)
(⁻3) × (⁻2)	(⁺3) × (⁻2)
(⁺4) × (⁺4)	(⁻4) × (⁺4)
(⁻4) × (⁻4)	(⁺4) × (⁻4)
(⁺5) × (⁺2)	(⁻5) × (⁺2)
(⁻5) × (⁻2)	(⁺5) × (⁻2)

With some guidance, most of the children will realize that all of the problems on the left have numbers with like signs and produce positive products, while all of the problems on the right have different signs and produce negative products. From this realization, it is only a short step to making a generalization about multiplying directed numbers. The rule, in the students' own terms, would be something like this: Multiply the two numbers as we have always done; then, if the signs of the two numbers are alike, the product will be positive, but if the signs of the two numbers are different, the product will be negative.

DIVISION OF DIRECTED NUMBERS

Division is by far the most difficult operation to learn and understand, not only with counting numbers, but with directed numbers as well. Consequently, this operation with directed numbers will be more difficult to explain than the other three operations. For this reason, the teacher will want to consider carefully which students are ready for this operation and to what extent it should be studied.

Division was described as a special form of subtraction in which equal-size sets were taken away from a total quantity, and it was also described as the inverse of multiplication. Division of directed numbers will be presented as successive subtraction of equal-size sets, because this can be presented more clearly on the number line than can division shown as the inverse of multiplication.

Once again, interpretation of what the problem asks before attempting a solution is vital for the development of understanding. The students will find many similarities between division of counting numbers and division of directed numbers, but without interpretation of the problem, the answer will probably have no meaning. For example, the problem $8 \div 4$ will have 2 as its solution in both counting numbers and directed numbers, but in the case of directed numbers, whether it is positive or negative is as important as the number answer. It can also be pointed out that the solution to some problems (such as $(^-8) \div (^-4) = {}^+2$) seemingly presents a paradox unless a careful analysis or interpretation has been made prior to the solution.

In the following illustrations of division of directed numbers, the same basic problem, $8 \div 4 = \square$, will be used, but with a different combination of signs for the dividend and the divisor in each illustration. It will be recalled that division is a process that involves breaking a total quantity, or whole, into equal-size parts. For this reason, division on the number line is started at the point indicated by the dividend (in this case, 8 is the dividend) and working back toward zero. This is in contrast to what we did in addition and the other two operations when we started at zero and worked outward or away from zero. The divisor indicates either the size of each equal set (measurement division) or it indicates the number of equal sets (partitioning division) to be taken from the whole quantity.

Up to this point, the interpretation of division of counting numbers and division of directed numbers is the same. With directed numbers, however, direction must be taken into consideration and this involves two major aspects vital to understanding. They are: (1) division is an inverse, therefore, we will think of it as opposite; and (2) whether we reach zero by a forward movement or backward movement will determine if the quotient is positive or negative. Consequently, if we separate the total quantity into equal sets by a *forward* movement the quotient will be *positive*; if we separate the equal sets by a *backward* movement the quotient will be *negative*.

To illustrate division of directed numbers, the problem ($^+8$) ÷ ($^+4$) = □ will be used first because it relates so closely to the division learned with counting numbers.

The problem: ($^+8$) ÷ ($^+4$) = □. The interpretation: ($^+8$) will be measured into sets of 4. The positive (+) sign of the 4 indicates that we initially face in a positive direction; however, since division is an inverse, we turn to face *opposite* the indicated positive direction. We now start at ($^+8$) and measure off sets of 4 until we reach zero. We will be measuring in a *forward* direction, so the quotient will be *positive*. The number line looks like this:

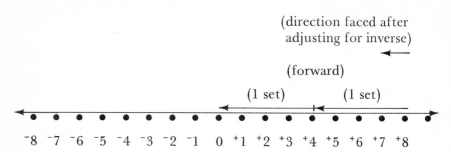

The solution: ($^+8$) ÷ ($^+4$) = $\boxed{^+2}$.

The next division problem will be ($^-8$) ÷ ($^+4$). The problem: ($^-8$) − ($^+4$) = □. The interpretation: ($^-8$) will be measured into sets of 4. The (+) sign of the 4 indicates facing in a (+) direction, but division is an inverse, so we face *opposite* the (+) direction, or in a negative direction. Starting at ($^-8$), we measure off sets of 4 toward zero. We will be measuring in a *backward* direction, so the quotient will be *negative*. The number line looks like this:

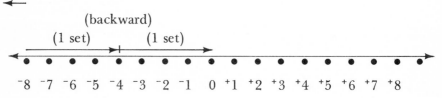

The solution: ($^-8$) ÷ ($^+4$) = $\boxed{2}$.

The third type of problem illustrated will be ($^+8$) ÷ ($^-4$). The problem: ($^+8$) ÷ ($^-4$) = □. The interpretation: ($^+8$) will be measured into sets of 4. The (⁻) sign of the 4 indicates that we face in a (⁻) direction, but division is an inverse so we face *opposite* the (⁻) direction. Starting at (⁺8), we measure off sets of 4. We will be measuring in a backward *direction* toward zero, so the quotient will be *negative*. The number line looks like this:

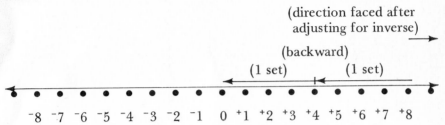

The solution: (⁺8) ÷ (⁻4) = ⁻2 . The final illustration of division of directed numbers will be (⁻8) ÷ (⁻4). The problem: (⁻8) ÷ (⁻4) = □. The interpretation: (⁻8) will be measured into sets of 4. The (⁻) sign of the 4 indicates facing in a (⁻) direction, but division is an inverse so we face *opposite* the (⁻) direction, or in a positive direction. Starting at (8), we measure off sets of 4. We will be measuring in a *forward* direction toward zero, so the quotient will be *positive*. The number line looks like this:

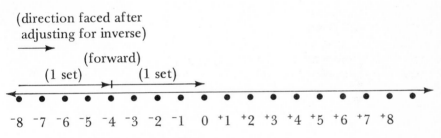

The solution: (⁻8) ÷ (⁻4) = ⁺2 .

After the students have worked several examples of each type of problem, the teacher begins guiding toward a generalization or rule for dividing directed numbers. A method of organizing the information, similar to the methods used with the other processes, will probably be helpful, like this:

Problems with (⁺) quotients	Problems with (⁻) quotients
(⁺8) ÷ (⁺4) (⁻8) ÷ (⁻4)	(⁻8) ÷ (⁺4) (⁺8) ÷ (⁻4)

This chart has only a limited number of examples to illustrate the idea. When used with children, many more examples would be needed in both sides of the chart before the realization of the pattern or rule becomes apparent. When it does become apparent, the students will be ready to verbalize the generalization. This generalization should be in the student's own terms and would be something like this: To divide directed numbers, divide like we always have and if the signs are alike the quotient will be positive (+); if the signs are different, the quotient will be negative.

The teacher must guide the pupils to realize that in division of directed numbers, not only is the number of equal sets taken from the dividend important, but also the manner in which they are taken.

CHAPTER 14

MEASUREMENT

The study and development of measurement was probably among man's first attempts to apply abstract mathematics to a practical situation. It seems likely that man's need for a more precise system of numeration arose partially from his need for more precise ways of measuring and comparing. Conversely, as man developed a more complete numeration system he could measure more exactly. The need of having some method to compare things has existed from the time of early man to the present. Our everyday lives are governed to some extent by various aspects of measurement. The importance of the topic cannot be denied, but there is some disagreement on the extent to which measurement should be taught in the elementary school. Some authorities contend that measurement cannot rightfully be considered as a part of mathematics because it does not have the structure and completeness of mathematics. Other authorities believe that measurement is probably the most important aspect of mathematics because it provides opportunities to make practical applications of mathematical learnings and skills. The authors of this text take the median position that measurement is a part of mathematics and is important, but that it does not have the same magnitude of importance as understanding the basic operations, or understanding our system of numeration. Many aspects of measurement are included quite naturally in the study of geometry (as presented in Chapter 9), while other aspects of measurement are essential parts of other subject matter areas. It would seem that unless some provision is made to teach essential concepts and understandings of measurement as a part of mathematics, they will not be adequately learned in other subject matter areas, or by incidental learning. This chapter will present the nature of measurement, the need of a standard unit of measure and the arbitrary nature of units of measure, and the need for understanding the most common units of measure.

Rationale for Measurement

Much of mathematics as we know it was developed as a result of man's need to measure something. There seems to be little doubt that primitive man's need for a more comprehensive number system resulted from his need for more accuracy and precision in his measurement. In other words, there came a time when it was necessary to know not only that one thing was more than another, but also how much more. Historical records reveal that every civilization of any consequence developed some type of measurement system that was fairly effective. Not only is a well-developed number system a prerequisite for a highly developed civilization, but also a reasonably effective system of measurement must be developed to go with the number system.

Some mathematicians contend that arithmetic can be resolved into the search for the solution to only two basic questions: "How many?" and "How much?" When the student seeks to answer the "How many?" type question, he must use some form of counting to reach a solution. When he seeks to answer a "How much?" type question, he must use some form of measuring to reach a solution. There seems to be very little awareness on the part of most people of the extent to which we depend on forms of measurement in our everyday living. Measurement can be logically thought of, then, as one of the most important and fundamental areas in arithmetic.

THE NATURE OF MEASUREMENT

Measurement can be described as the process of comparing. If we are comparing two objects in which there are extreme differences, we can use our senses to determine that one object is more or less than the other. As the differences become less and less pronounced, it becomes more and more difficult for us to distinguish the differences with just our senses. If we must make a decision in this situation, then we usually employ some instrument or device to assist our senses. The device or instrument that we use can be a standard instrument with standard units for measuring, or it can be something not usually considered as a measuring instrument, such as a broom handle, paper clip, or even a tin can. Whether the unit of measurement is standard or nonstandard, it is still an arbitrary unit, because somewhere, sometime, a decision had to be arbitrarily made to use it as a unit of measure. If we choose to use a standard unit of measure, such as a foot or a pound, it will be less difficult to communicate about it; also it will come nearer to meaning the same thing to different people than a nonstandard unit.

Measurement became very important in communicating and as a means of communication. Since all men were not the same size, a comparison that a small man would make might not be accurate for a large man. It may also have been necessary to know how much larger or smaller something was, rather than just that it was larger or smaller. As man developed a need for more precision in measurement, he probably resorted to comparing things to various parts of his body because they were always available for making comparisons, and they were reasonably easy to use in communicating so that another person could understand the comparison.

Measurement can be either direct or indirect in nature. If the length of two objects is to be compared and the objects are placed side by side, then a direct comparison can be made. This is known as *direct measurement*. There are situations, however, in which it may be inconvenient or impossible to make direct comparisons. In this case, the things to be compared can be measured by some other object and then the measurements can be compared rather than the objects themselves. When objects are measured by some common unit and their measurements compared, this is known as *indirect measurement*.

In the elementary school mathematics program, students should develop the following basic ideas:

1. Measurement is the process of comparing. A measurement requires naming the unit of measure to be used and determining how many of the units were used.

2. The three characteristics that can be measured mathematically are: distance (meaning length, area, volume, and so forth), time, and mass (or weight).

3. Measuring with known, standard units facilitates communication and understanding.

4. Objects may be compared indirectly by comparing each object to the same measuring instrument or unit of measure.

THE NEED FOR STANDARD
UNITS OF MEASURE

As people and their units of measure became more specific, governments began defining standard units of measure by law. Because measurement was such a vital part of trade and commerce, there also developed a need for units of measure of varying size (and value). With the establishment of standard units of measurements it became possible to take known units of measurement, compare them, and communicate the results to others.

Elementary school children should not be expected to accept the teacher's word that it is important to establish standard units of measure. The teacher can inductively guide students to discover the importance of having standard units of measure. For example, a teacher might take some large sheets of construction paper (12 x 18") and ask the students to remove everything from the top of their desks and then see if they can determine the size (or dimensions) of the paper without using rulers, yardsticks, or other similar standard measuring instruments. In time, some students will decide that they could use the width of their hand, the length of a finger, or some other similar measure. After discussing the effectiveness of these methods, most students would agree that there probably is a better way. The teacher could then ask the students what they might do to have a better method of measuring. This discussion could be guided so that the need of a measuring instrument is established.

The teacher could then provide each student, or each small group of students, with an unmarked strip of poster board (or a similar strip of other rather rigid material) that he had previously prepared to use as a measuring instrument. In preparing these strips, the teacher cuts them so that there are four or five different lengths and so that none of them measures exactly the length or width of the construction paper. As students or groups report their measurements, the teacher records them on the chalkboard. It soon becomes apparent that there were several different measurements and that these measurements were not very precise. The teacher then asks the children if they think that the reason they got different measurements was because the pieces of construction paper were of different sizes. The children would probably compare all of the pieces of paper and conclude that they were the same size. Someone might suggest that the measuring instruments were not the same size, or the students could be guided to compare measuring strips.

After the students decide that the different lengths of measuring strips caused the different measurements, the teacher asks them what they should do next. Probably the suggestion will be made that all measuring strips be the same length. The teacher might have a separate group of measuring strips the same length already prepared. With these, after the students again measure their pieces of paper and compare the measurements, they will find that this time the measurements are more alike.

With some guidance from the teacher, students will realize that even though their measurements are more alike, the precision leaves something to be desired. For example, some students may have reported the length as nearly 5 units, other students may have reported the length as more than 4 units, but less than 5 units, and so on. The teacher can now ask what they can do to make their measurements more exact. After some discussion (and teacher guidance), the students will probably decide that if they create some smaller subunits on their measuring strips, they will be able to be more exact. The students might later decide it is also necessary to create and use fractional parts of the subunit for more exactness.

The teacher then needs to guide students in generalizing about what they have discovered concerning the importance of standard units of measure and the need for units of varying size. In their terminology, the generalizations that students develop may be something like this: If we are going to tell others about our measurements or compare them, the measurements must be made in some standard unit of measure, and to be exact in our measurements, it is sometimes necessary for the standard unit to be subdivided into standard subunits (or enlarged into standard larger units).

Students could also be guided to generalize that measurement expresses a combination of two things: the measure (or how many were measured), and a standard unit of measure. For example, if we measured the length of a room at 25 feet, 25 would be the measure and a foot the standard unit of measure. Using a yardstick, the room would be $8\frac{1}{3}$ yards; $8\frac{1}{3}$ would be the measure and a yard the standard unit.

The standard units of measure that a society or culture uses are arbitrarily chosen and then objects are measured in terms of these units. We could create in our classroom an entirely different set of units to measure with, and as long as we created certain standard units that everyone in the room agreed to use, we could measure, compare, and communicate within our room as effectively using our own method as when using the method that is in general use. When we tried to talk with someone outside of our room, however, we would probably have trouble making him understand. For a system of measurement to be effective, then, it must not only have standard units of measure but it must also have general acceptance and use.

Systems and Types of Measurement

There are basically two different systems of measurement in use today: the *English system*, using such measures as inches, feet, pounds, gallons, and the like, and the *metric system* using such measures as centimeters, meters, liters, kilograms, and the like. Regardless of which system is used, certain types of measurements can be made by either system. The measurements made most often are linear measurement (or length), surface measurement (or area), and space measurement (or volume). Although other types of measurement can be made (with some measurements being possible in either system and some measurements possible in only one system), we shall be primarily concerned with linear, surface, and space measurement.

Linear Measurement. Linear literally means "line," so linear measurement essentially means measuring lines to determine their length. Students will need to experiment with several different ways of measuring a line segment in order to decide which kind of standard unit would be best for measuring line segments. They might try using a curved segment, a straight segment, a zigzag segment, a broken segment, and other types as well. After trying to measure with several different types, they will probably conclude that the straight segment serves best as a standard unit. By the time most students study linear measurement, they will probably have had some experience using the number line. To an extent, the operations performed on the number line are worked using linear measurement. Most elementary school children will have rulers marked off in inches on one side and centimeters on the other side. They can be given opportunities to construct line segments of various lengths, with emphasis on accuracy of their construction. At a later time, they can construct several line segments of different lengths and exchange papers with a partner. After the exchange, they can measure each line segment with both the English and the metric system to see with which system they can be the most exact.

During the time students are making measurements of line segments, they should be guided to discover that line segments do not always measure exactly a standard unit, or exact multiples of a standard unit. After students experiment with ways to become exact, they can be guided inductively to generalize, in their own terms, that when more exactness is needed, it is necessary to use the next smaller standard unit, and sometimes even the next smaller unit. Figure 14.1 illustrates how one measuring instrument does not give an exact measure of a line segment, but—by using a smaller standard unit—a more exact measure is obtained. Line $\overline{AB}$ is almost 3 units long; it is exactly $2\frac{7}{8}$ units long.

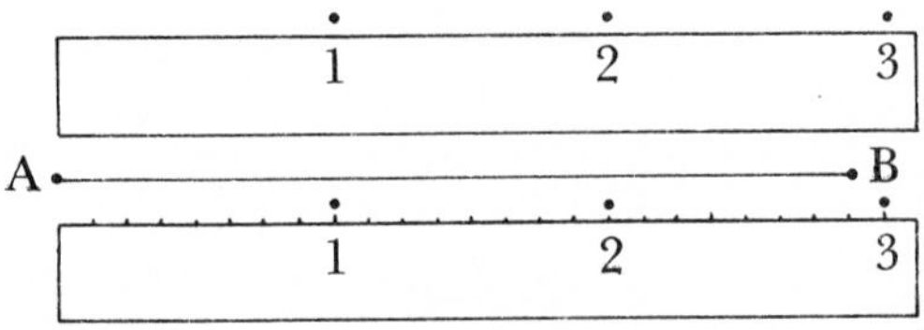

Figure 14.1

The students might next see if they can measure a curved line segment with their ruler. If they cannot, the teacher might ask for suggestions on how the length of a curved line segment could be determined. In these, as well as in many other ways, students can develop the fundamental concepts of linear measurement by being actively involved—and with teacher guidance.

Surface Measurement. This measurement is concerned basically with determining the area, or the amount of covered surface. Students first need to decide upon the standard unit to be used. They can be given opportunities to determine the size of a given area using several geometric shapes, such as those shown in Figure 14.2. If the students are

Figure 14.2

given enough time and opportunities to measure surface area with the different shapes, they will probably conclude that the square is the most practical. The circle, in most cases, will leave gaps that are not covered, since it will not fit exactly on all parts of the surface being measured. The same can be said for the triangle, hexagon, and trapezoid. The rectangle does almost as well as the square in measuring the surface, but determining and describing the ideal dimensions of the most appropriate rectangle would be difficult. The square has been selected as the standard unit of measure for surface measurement because it can be made to more nearly fit any surface than any of the other shapes. Figure 14.3 shows how small squares are used to measure the surface area inside an irregular curve. Just as students discovered

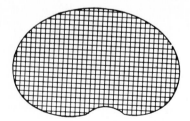

Figure 14.3

that more preciseness could be obtained in linear measurement, so they can be guided to discover that by making the size of the standard unit smaller, a more exact measurement can be made.

The geo plane (described in Chap. 9) is an excellent model for elementary school students to work with in studying surface measurement. They can begin by establishing the standard unit to be used on the geo plane. Although the teacher knows (and the students may also) the dimensions of the geo plane and the distance between two nails, the teacher would want to refer to the distance between two nails as a standard unit, rather than so many inches, and encourage students to do this also. Surface measure units would be referred to as square units, not so many square inches. The teacher could then guide the students using the geo plane in some of the following activities:

1. Develop the concept that perimeter is the distance around the figure. Find the perimeter of various squares and rectangles. It will probably be better at this time not to work on finding the perimeter of triangles or irregular polygons, but just establish the basic concept of perimeter. The teacher can then inductively guide students to make a rule for finding the perimeter.

2. What is the surface area of the smallest square on the geo plane? (One square unit. This is establishing the standard unit of measure.)

3. Determine the surface area of a square—
   a. in which each side is twice as long as the standard unit (four square units).
   b. in which each side is three times as long as the standard unit (nine square units). Have students hypothesize what the area would be if length of each side is four times greater than standard unit (16 square units)—then hypothesize when each side is five times greater than standard unit (25 square units). Have students make a chart or table of what they have done in previous steps to see if they can find any relationships between the length of the side of a square and its area—or rule for finding area of a square.

4. Determine the surface area of rectangle:
   a. 2 units long and 1 unit wide (2 square units).
   b. 3 units long and 1 unit wide (3 square units).
   c. 3 units long and 2 units wide (6 square units).

After finding the area of a number of rectangles, guide students to generalize a rule for finding area of rectangle. (Refer to Chap. 9 if more information is needed.)

5. Surround the four nails of a standard square unit with a rubber band. Remove the rubber band from *one* of the four nails so that it is now around only three of the nails (see Fig. 14.4).

    a. What kind of figure have we made? (A triangle.)

    b. What is the surface area of this triangle? ($\frac{1}{2}$ square unit). The teacher can guide the students to discover that this triangle divides the square unit into two equal parts. Since we know the area of the square unit, the area of the triangle would be $\frac{1}{2}$ of the square unit.

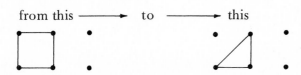

from this ⟶ to ⟶ this

Figure 14.4

    c. Have students hypothesize what they think would happen to the area of the triangle if we moved the apex of the altitude over one unit to the right (or left) so that the resulting triangle is the same as in Figure 14.5. What is the area of the new triangle? ($\frac{1}{2}$ square unit.) If students have difficulty finding the

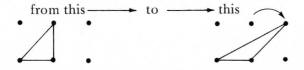

from this ⟶ to ⟶ this

Figure 14.5

area of the new triangle, the teacher might guide them to realize they need to utilize their standard square unit. For example, they can find the area of a rectangle that would enclose the new triangle. They know the area of the rectangle, but the triangle does not cover all of the rectangle. See if they can determine the area of the rectangle not included in the triangle. By sub-tracting the area not included in the triangle from the total area of the rectangle, the remaining area would be the triangle's area.

d. Hypothesize what would happen to the area of the triangle if we moved the apex one more unit to the right (Fig. 14.6). What is the area of this new triangle? ($\frac{1}{2}$ square unit.) Find this area in a way similar to that with which you found the area in preceding exercise c.

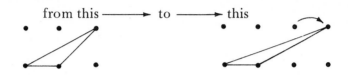

from this ⟶ to ⟶ this

Figure 14.6

e. Hypothesize what would happen to the area of the triangle if we moved the apex one more unit to the right. (It would still be $\frac{1}{2}$ square unit.) Guide students to make a list of things about the triangle that changed when the apex was moved and then a list of things about the triangle that remained the same, even though the apex was moved. Using the list of things that remained unchanged, guide students to develop a rule for finding the area of a triangle.

6. Using similar methods, develop rules for finding surface area of other plane figures such as parallelogram, trapezoid, and the like.

These have been just some of the exercises that can be done on the geo plane. It is recommended that the teacher or college student work out for themselves on a geo plane both these activities and those described in Chapter 9. There are many interesting discoveries awaiting the person who does some experimenting with the geo plane.

Space Measurement. The measurement of volume is concerned with determining how much space an object occupies. The teacher will want to begin by having students determine what would be the most appropriate standard unit to use in space measurement. The procedure would be similar to that used in determining linear measurement and surface measurement, except that now the students will experiment with solid figures. After experimenting with the solid figures, the students will probably conclude that the cube is the most appropriate standard unit because it will more nearly fill the empty space of a solid than any of the other kinds of solid figures. With the establishment of a standard unit for space measurement, students can be guided to discover a rule for determining the volume of a cube, using smaller cubes to determine the space to be measured. In similar ways, rules can be developed for other solid figures.

THE METRIC SYSTEM

Most elementary school mathematics programs have done little to develop understanding of the metric system. In the past, educators apparently felt that elementary students had little need for experience with metric measurement. There is a growing trend, however, to include more metric measurement in the elementary school curriculum, not only in mathematics but other subjects as well. The basic aim of this trend is to help students develop understanding of the basis of the metric system and the more common units of metric measurement, such as the meter, centimeter, gram, and liter.

The metric system's most appealing characteristic is its close relationship to our decimal system of numeration. Each of its units of measure is ten times larger than the preceding unit and one-tenth as large as the next larger unit. This means that a unit of metric measure can be converted to a larger or smaller unit by shifting the decimal point to the appropriate place. After having some opportunity to work with and study a metric chart of measurements, students will probably discover the relationships and advantages of the metric system. Figure 14.7 gives a partial metric chart of the more common metric measurements.

The English system of measurement has been used in most English-speaking nations, but now seems to be on the decline. It is not generally as easy to convert from one unit to another unit in the English system as it is in the metric system. The English system does, however, offer advantages that are not found in the metric system. For example, it is usually easier to think of $\frac{1}{2}$ of an inch, or $\frac{1}{2}$ of $\frac{1}{2}\left(\frac{1}{4}\right)$, of an inch, than $\frac{1}{10}$ of a centimeter, or $\frac{1}{10}$ of $\frac{1}{10}\left(\frac{1}{100}\right)$, of a centimeter. The important point to remember is not the advantages or disadvantages of these systems, but the fact that we need to guide our students so that they have a reasonable understanding of both systems and mastery of working with both. Some teachers lose sight of this fact and place great emphasis on memorizing measurement tables. Most of these tables

Linear Measurement—(basic unit of measure is the meter)

10 millimeters	=	1 centimeter
10 centimeters	=	1 decimeter
10 decimeters	=	1 meter
1,000 meters	=	1 kilometer

Surface Measurement—(basic unit of measure is square centimeter)

100 square millimeters	=	1 square centimeter
100 square centimeters	=	1 square decimeter
10,000 square centimeters	=	1 square meter

Space Measurement—(basic unit of measure is the liter)

10 milliliters	=	1 centiliter	=	.01 liter
10 centiliters	=	1 deciliter	=	.1 liter
10 deciliters	=	1 liter		
1,000 liters	=	1 kiloliter		

Weight—(basic unit of measure is the gram)

10 milligrams	=	1 centigram	=	.01 gram
10 centigrams	=	1 decigram	=	.1 gram
10 decigrams	=	1 gram		
1,000 grams	=	1 kilogram		

Figure 14.7

contain measures that are either archaic or seldom used. The time spent memorizing obsolete measures is wasted. Instead of demanding that time be spent memorizing tables, the teacher could create numerous situations where students would need to utilize the measures. Measures that are frequently used by the student, soon become a part of his working skills and mean more to him than if they had been memorized. Most textbooks contain tables of measures with which students should become familiar under teacher guidance. The students should be allowed to use these tables any time they need them. Students will usually learn some of these units through use and realize that it is easier to learn the more common units of measure than to have to continue looking them up in a book.

CHAPTER 15

DIFFERENT METHODS OF COMPUTATION

Students are often taught only one way to compute and, in some cases, this is adequate. There are instances, however, when students could profit from and enjoy learning other methods of computation. The methods presented in this selection are intended to be used for enrichment and enjoyment, not as a replacement for the conventional methods generally taught in the elementary school. Therefore, these ideas should be introduced only to those students who have a clear understanding of the conventional algorisms and have achieved reasonable mastery of them. Algorisms will be presented in this chapter for different ways to compute in subtraction, multiplication, and division, and check-of-nines methods for checking computation will be discussed.

In most instances the conventional methods of computing have gained acceptance because they were practical and reasonably easy to learn and use. History reveals that these schemes of computing were developed over several centuries. They have now been refined to the extent that we probably would have to resort to machines (such as adding machine, calculator, or computer) in order to improve on them. It can also be said that man has been able to use these computational schemes to develop countless noteworthy achievements, so their practicality can hardly be questioned. Other methods of computation are presented here as a means of opening other areas for children to explore. From their inquiry, it is possible that the children will gain a better insight into why our conventional algorisms evolved and how they can serve man as a most effective tool. It is also known that many elementary school students enjoy working with these other methods. If the student's inquiry is enjoyable, then this greatly enhances the likelihood that the learning that occurs will be more meaningful.

The teacher is cautioned that unless extreme care is exercised in presenting and working activities of the type presented in this chapter, the students may experience only a mechanical type of learning. On the other hand, any activity or device that promotes understanding of what is learned must be considered pedagogically sound. This suggests then, that *how* the teacher uses the activity determines the quality of learning that occurs.

It should be noted that just reading about these methods of computation probably will not develop sufficient understanding of them to enable the teacher to teach these ideas to students in a meaningful way. Since only a limited number of examples will be used to illustrate each method, it is recommended that the reader work through each example problem and in some cases make up additional problems of his own, in order to develop understanding of the algorism.

Equal-additions Method of Subtraction

At first glance, it may seem rather odd that we can help solve subtraction by using addition. Consider this situation: two children are climbing a ladder and they are told to stop where they are. Child A is on the sixth rung and Child B is on the second rung of the ladder (Fig. 15.1). We would say that there was a difference of 4 rungs in their position on the ladder. Now if each child climbed 5 more steps (Child A is now at 11 and Child B is now at 7), there still would remain a difference of 4 rungs in their positions because they both climbed the same amount.

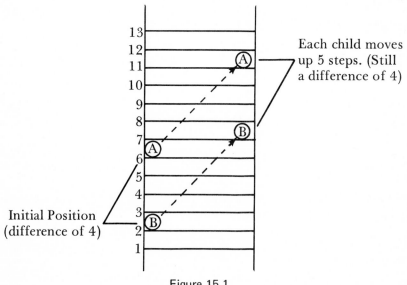

Figure 15.1

This problem illustrates a property of subtraction that can be helpful in certain situations. This property of subtraction allows us to add the same amount to both the minuend and the subtrahend without changing the difference. Now when this idea is applied to a problem situation, such as 51-28 (one of the more difficult two-digit problems) it is possible to change the problem from a difficult problem to an easier one, like this:

$$
\begin{array}{r} 51 \\ -\ 28 \\ \hline \end{array}
\longrightarrow
\begin{array}{l}\text{(add 2 to both the minuend and} \\ \text{the subtrahend, and the problem} \\ \text{becomes)} \end{array}
\longrightarrow
\begin{array}{r} 53 \\ -\ 30 \\ \hline 23 \end{array}
$$

There was no magic here, only the use of one of the laws of subtraction. By knowing the various laws or properties that govern an operation, students often will have a much wider choice of ways to solve their problems. In the preceding problem, any number could have been added to both terms, but 2 was chosen in order to change the 28 to 30 so that the subtrahend would be a multiple of 10. Subtracting 10, or a multiple of 10, from a number is one of the easier subtractions.

There is still another method of subtraction that involves the concept of equal additions to both the minuend and subtrahend. This method was used to some extent in the 1920s, but it is a bit more difficult to explain and understand. This possibly accounts for the reason it is seldom taught anymore as the basic method of subtraction. Children in the upper intermediate grades, however, are often intrigued with the idea of adding to solve a subtraction problem. In this method, we will be adding the same value to both the minuend and subtrahend, but the way it is added to each term will take a slightly different form, as can be seen in the following example:

$$
\begin{array}{r} 714 \\ -\ 368 \\ \hline \end{array}
\equiv
\begin{array}{r} 700 + 10 + 4 \\ -(300 + 60 + 8) \\ \hline \end{array}
$$

When we examine the problem, we see that we cannot subtract 8 from 4. In order to subtract, we must change the minuend in the units' column to be greater than the subtrahend. To do this, we will add 10 ones to the minuend in the units' column and we will also add an equal value (but in a different form) of 1 ten to the subtrahend in the tens' column. Thus, we have added the same amount to both the minuend and the subtrahend. If we added the value of ten to both numbers in the units' column, we still would be unable to subtract, because the subtrahend would still be the largest term. The same process is repeated in each column where the subtrahend is the largest term so that a solution may be reached, like this:

$$714 \quad\quad 700 + 10 + {}^{1}4$$
$$\quad\quad\quad\quad\quad 70$$
$$- 368 \equiv - (300 + \cancel{60} + 8)$$

Step 1:
Add 10 ones to the units' column of the minuend.
Add 1 ten (an equal amount) to the tens' column of the subtrahend.

After the subtraction is performed in the units' column, the next step would involve the tens' and hundreds' columns.

$$714 \quad\quad 700 + {}^{1}10 + {}^{1}4$$
$$\quad\quad 400 \quad\quad 70$$
$$- 368 \equiv - (\cancel{300} + \cancel{60} + 8)$$
$$\quad\quad\quad\quad\quad\quad\quad\quad 6$$

Step 2:
Add 10 tens to tens' column of the minuend.
Add 1 hundred (an equal amount) to the hundreds' column of the subtrahend.

Following the subtraction in the tens' column, the last step would be performed in the hundreds' column.

$$714 \quad\quad 700 + {}^{1}10 + {}^{1}4$$
$$\quad\quad 400 \quad\quad 70$$
$$- 368 \equiv - (\cancel{300} + \cancel{60} + 8)$$
$$\quad\quad\quad\quad\quad\quad 40 + 6$$

Step 3:
Since the minuend in the hundreds column (700) is greater than the subtrahend (400) no equal additions are necessary and regular subtraction is performed.

The finished problem would look like this:

$$714 \quad\quad 700 + {}^{1}10 + {}^{1}4$$
$$\quad\quad 400 \quad\quad 70$$
$$- 368 \equiv - (\cancel{300} + \cancel{60} + 8)$$
$$\quad\quad\quad\quad\quad 300 + 40 + 6 = 346$$

Another example of the equal-additions method of subtraction would be as follows.

$$537 \quad\quad 500 + 30 + {}^{1}7$$
$$\quad\quad\quad\quad\quad 100$$
$$- 298 \equiv - (200 + \cancel{90} + 8)$$
$$\quad\quad\quad\quad\quad\quad\quad\quad 9$$

Step 1:
Add 10 ones.
Add 1 ten (equal amount).

$$537 \equiv 500 + 1\overset{\curvearrowright}{3}0 + 1 7$$
$$300 \overset{\leftarrow}{} 100$$
$$- 298 \equiv - (\cancel{200} + \cancel{90} + 8)$$
$$\underline{} 30 + 9$$

Step 2:
Add 10 tens.
Add 1 hundred (equal amount).

$$537 \equiv 500 + 1 30 + 1 7$$
$$300 \quad 100$$
$$- 298 \equiv - (\cancel{200} + \cancel{90} + 8)$$
$$\underline{200 + 30 + 9} = 239$$

Step 3:
Regular subtraction in hundreds' column.

Another variation of this equal additions method utilizes adding a value to the minuend number, but it does not add an equal value to the subtrahend number as we did in the preceding examples. Instead, the value is subtracted from the minuend number of the next larger place-value position. The value that is added is known as the complement of ten and is determined by the amount necessary to make the subtrahend number complementary to ten (that is, subtrahend number + complement number = 10). This method of subtraction, sometimes known as the complement method, originated in ancient times and is generally used when computing with an abacus in a situation requiring "borrowing." The principle on which this method is based is also used in some calculating machines today. It is possible that the "borrowing" method of subtraction evolved as a modification of the complement method.

As previously indicated, this method utilizes adding a value to the minuend number that is the complement of the subtrahend number and it also requires subtracting a value of ten from the next larger place-value column. For example, suppose the subtrahend number was 6. In this case 4 would be the complement of ten number or value (that is, 6 + ☐4 = 10) and instead of subtracting 6, we would add 4 to the minuend and subtract 10, which gives the same answer. When the 4 is added, it is added in one column while the 10 is subtracted from the next larger place-value column. This concept of adding the number which is the complement of ten and then subtracting ten is used in several instances in higher mathematics. The teacher must be certain that the children understand that by adding the complement-of-ten number and subtracting ten they have used exactly the same value as the original subtrahend number. A subtraction problem solved by the complement method would be:

$$
\begin{array}{r}
300 \quad30 \\
445 \qquad \cancel{400} + \cancel{40} + 5 \\
-\,276 \qquad -\,(200 + 70 + 6) \\
\hline
100 + 60 + 9 \;=\; 169
\end{array}
$$

Units' Column: We see that we cannot subtract 6 from 5. Since 4 is the complement of 6, it is added to the minuend number, 5, (5 + 4 = 9). Now 10 is subtracted from the minuend number in the tens' column (40 − 10 = 30).

Tens' Column: Again we observe that we cannot make the indicated subtraction. 3 tens are the complement of 7 tens, so they are added to the minuend number, 30, (30 + 30 = 60). Now, 10 tens are subtracted from the hundreds' column (400 − 100 = 300).

Hundreds' Column: Regular subtraction, since 200 can be subtracted from 300.

It will be noticed that when the minuend is greater than the subtrahend, regular subtraction is used. An additional example of subtraction using the complement method would be worked like this:

$$
\begin{array}{r}
400 \quad20 \\
534 \qquad \cancel{500} + \cancel{30} + 4 \\
-\,198 \qquad -\,(100 + 90 + 8) \\
\hline
300 + 30 + 6 \;=\; 336
\end{array}
$$

Units' Column: Since we cannot make the indicated subtraction, the complement of 8, 2, is added to the minuend, 4, and 10 is subtracted from the minuend in the tens' column.

Tens' Column: Again we cannot make the indicated subtraction, so the complement of 9 tens, 1 ten, is added to the minuend, 20, and 10 tens are subtracted from the hundreds' column.

Hundreds' Column: Regular subtraction.

Russian Peasant Multiplication

This method of multiplication dates back at least as far as the Egyptian civilization, but in more recent books it has been described as the type of multiplication used to a great extent by the Russian peasant. Hence, it was given this name to distinguish it from other types of multiplication, not because the Russians invented it. The property on which this type of multiplication is based can be observed in the following examples:

$$\text{Example A:} \quad 8 \times 4 = 32$$

$$\text{Example B:} \quad 16 \times 2 = 32$$

The products of both of these multiplications are the same and if we compare the factors of one example with its counterpart in the other example an interesting relationship can be observed. The first factor in A is one-half the first factor in B, but the second factor in A is twice the second factor in B. This means that we could change example A to example B by multiplying the first factor by 2 and dividing the second factor by the same number, 2, and the product would remain the same. Stated in more general terms, this multiplication property would be: If one factor is divided by a number, the other factor must be multiplied by the same number in order for the product to remain unchanged. The objective of Russian peasant multiplication is to successively repeat the procedure of increasing one factor while decreasing the other factor until it is reduced to 1, the identity element of multiplication. When one factor is thus reduced to 1, the other factor must be the product sought, because the product has remained unchanged by the successive multiplying and dividing. To illustrate Russian peasant multiplication, we will first use a relatively simple problem, find the product of 5×4:

Multiply this side		Divide this side by the same number
5	X	4 (original problem)
10	X	2 (left side multiplied by 2, while the right side is divided by 2)
20	X	1 (left side times 2, right side divided by 2. Factor on the right is now identity element)

The product, 5×4 is 20

It makes no difference which factor is chosen to be divided or which is chosen to be multiplied, if it is possible to factor one term as easily as the other term. If one term will factor easier than the other (in the preceding problem, 4 will factor easier than 5), it is usually best to divide it and to multiply the other term. In the next example (24 × 26), we will divide the left factor and multiply the right:

Divide this side		Multiply this side by the same number
24	X	26 (original problem)
12	X	52 (left side divided by 2, right side multiplied by 2)
6	X	104 (second successive division and multiplication by 2)
3	X	208 (third successive division and multiplication by 2)
1	X	624 (left side divided by 3, right side multiplied by 3. The left side is now the identity element).

The product, 24 × 26 is 624.

It probably is fairly apparent that Russian peasant multiplication has some rather severe limitations. It is not feasible to use it in every situation calling for multiplication. It is only practical to use this method when the factors are not too large and when at least one of the factors can be reduced to one in fairly easy successive divisions. Although Russian peasant multiplication has limitations, it can be quite useful in certain mental calculations.

Lattice Multiplication

The next method of multiplication is a method that was used fairly extensively about 250 years ago. It was the idea on which one of man's earlier attempts to devise a mechanical means of computation was based. This mechanical device was known as Napier's Bones and consisted of a set of rectangular, rod-shaped pieces of ivory (hence the term "bones") on which were carved the multiplication facts. By arranging these ivory rods in a certain way, the product of a multiplication problem could be read from the bones. The inventor of the bones was John Napier, a famous seventeenth-century Scottish mathematician who made many noteworthy mathematical contributions, including the discovery of logarithms. The lattice method of multiplication uses a rectangular lattice, or grid as shown in Figure 15.2. The multiplier or mul-

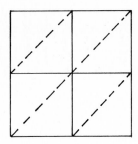

Figure 15.2

tiplicand is placed along the top edge, while the other term is placed along the right edge. For example, if we were preparing to work 24 X 26, we would place the multiplier, 24, along the top edge and the multiplicand, 26, along the right edge. (Since multiplication is commutative, we could reverse this placement of terms.) The setup for this problem (24 X 26) is shown in Figure 15.3.

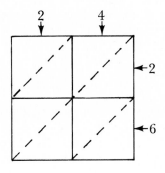

Figure 15.3

The solution would be obtained in the manner shown in Figure 15.4.

Step 1: Each partial product is obtained by multiplying each digit of the multiplicand by each digit of the multiplier. This product is then placed in the cell that is opposite and below each term respectively.

(The product of 2 × 4 is placed in upper right cell.
The product of 6 × 4 is placed in the lower right cell.
The product of 2 × 2 is placed in upper left cell.
The product of 6 × 2 is placed in lower left cell.)

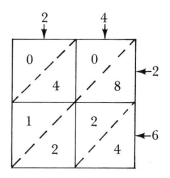

Step 2: After all cells contain the appropriate partial product, the final product is obtained by starting at the lower right, then adding down and along the entire length of each diagonal in the direction shown by the arrows.

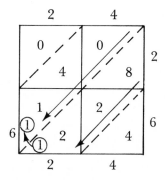

Answer: 24 × 26 = 624.

Figure 15.4

Each partial product is placed in the cell opposite and beneath the two numbers used to get that partial product. For instance, the partial product derived from 6 × 4 is placed in the lower right-hand cell because it is the cell opposite the 6 and also beneath the 4. The dotted diagonals that divide each cell have two functions: (1) the upper half is used for tens (when a partial product is ten or greater), while the lower half contains the units of the partial product; and (2) the answer is obtained by starting at the right and adding diagonally down and along the entire length of each diagonal. When a sum along a diagonal is 10 or more, we bridge or carry to the next diagonal, just as we ordinarily would in regular addition. With the lattice method, the partial products may be obtained in any order without affecting the final product. When each cell in the lattice contains a partial product, we are then ready to add down and along the diagonals to obtain the final product. Starting at the upper left, the answer is ready down and around to the lower right-hand corner. In the event that the first number at the upper left is zero, the zero is not written as part of the answer in this instance.

The next example (Fig. 15.5) will utilize a three-digit number.

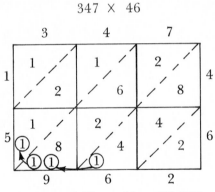

347 × 46

Answer: 347 × 46 = 15,962

Figure 15.5

When we multiplied a two-digit number times a two-digit number, we used a 2 by 2 lattice. For the product of a three-digit number and a two-digit number, we use a 3 by 2 lattice. If we had a three-digit number times a three-digit number, we would use a 3 by 3 lattice, and so on. After the students have had considerable experience working similar problems, variations can be introduced which cause the students to utilize their previous experience and learning. Some examples are shown in Figure 15.6. The teacher might develop other variations.

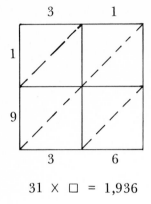

31 × □ = 1,936

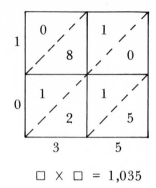

□ × □ = 1,035

Figure 15.6

Multiplication Distributes Over Subtraction

The fact that multiplication distributes over addition has been discussed in preceding chapters and can be shown in the following manner:

$$34 \times 52$$
$$34 \times (50 + 2)$$
$$(34 \times 50) + (34 \times 2)$$
$$1700 \quad + \quad 68 \quad = \quad 1768$$

This idea is developed in most arithmetic textbooks, and justly so, because our conventional algorism for multiplication is based on this fact. However, a fact that many textbooks do not mention (and possibly they are justified in not mentioning it) is that multiplication is also distributive with respect to subtraction. Not all children need or should be introduced to this idea, but there are many children in the upper intermediate grades who would enjoy and profit from working with this type of activity for enrichment. A problem using multiplication distributing over subtraction would be worked very similarly to the way the preceding problem was worked with addition. For instance, 26 × 38 could be worked like this:

26 $\times$ 38   (38 is renamed as 40 − 2)

26 $\times$ (40 − 2)

(26 $\times$ 40) − (26 $\times$ 2)   (Multiplication distributes over subtraction. Note the minus sign between the two sets of parentheses.)

1040 − 52 = 988

Here is another example:

47 $\times$ 69

47 $\times$ (70 − 1)

(47 $\times$ 70) − (47 $\times$ 1)

3290 − 47 = 3242

It is possible to rename both terms and then distribute multiplication over addition, like this:

34 $\times$ 52

(30 + 4) $\times$ (50 + 2)

(30 $\times$ 50) + (30 $\times$ 2) + (4 $\times$ 50) + (4 $\times$ 2)

1500 + 60 + 200 + 8 = 1768

It is also possible to rename both terms and distribute multiplication over subtraction, but in doing so we get into a situation that requires knowledge of multiplication of negative numbers, as shown below:

39 $\times$ 49

(40 − 1) $\times$ (50 − 1)

(40 $\times$ 50) − (40 $\times$ 1) − (1 $\times$ 50) + (1 $\times$ 1)

2000 − 40 − 50 + 1 = 1911

Since renaming both terms may cause students some confusion, it would probably be best not to introduce multiplication distributing over subtraction in which both terms were renamed.

Ancient Egyptian Division

There is one method of division that is quite different from the conventional method. This method has been found in some of the ancient Egyptian writings and documents. They used somewhat similar approaches to both multiplication and division. The method the Egyptians used for division was a kind of inverse of Russian peasant multiplication. The Egyptians started with one and doubled it (see Fig. 15.7) until they reached or came close to the divisor. In a second column, they placed the divisor (in this case, 34) and doubled it each time they doubled the number in the first column.

$$34 \overline{\smash{\big)}\ 1768}$$

1	34		
2	68		
4	136	1632 + 136 = 1768 = dividend	
8	272	1632 + 272 = 1904 (omit)	
16	544	1088 + 544 = 1632	
32	1088		

∴ 32 + 16 + 4 = 52 = quotient

Figure 15.7

The doubling process stops when we obtain the nearest number we can to the divisor without exceeding it (that is, if we doubled the left-hand number one more time, we would exceed the divisor, 34). Now we start with the bottom number in the second column and work upward, adding it to all those numbers above it which will yield a sum less than or equal to the dividend. In this example we start at the bottom and work upward by adding 1088 + 544 = 1632 (which is less than the dividend). Then we add the next number (272) to 1632 and find this sum is 1904, which exceeds the dividend. Therefore, 272 is omitted and the next number above it, which is 136, is added in (1632 + 136 = 1768). With this addition, we have reached the dividend, so it now becomes necessary to determine how many 34s were used to reach 1768. We find that we added 32 plus 16 plus 4 groups of 34. Altogether, we find that it takes 52 groups of 34 to make 1768. The solution is 1768 ÷ 34 = 52.

Another example of this method of division is shown in Figure 15.8.

$$69 \overline{\smash{\big)}\,5796}$$

1	69
2	138
4	276 5520 + 276 - 5796 = dividend
8	552 5520 + 552 = 6072 (omit)
16	1104 4416 + 1104 - 5520
32	2208 4416 + 2208 - 6624 (omit)
64	4416

∴ 64 + 16 + 4 = 84 = quotient

Figure 15.8

Starting with the bottom number and adding up 4416 + 2208 = 6624, yields a sum greather than the dividend, so the 2208 is omitted. The next addition, 4416 + 1104 = 5520, produces a sum less than the dividend, so it is kept. Proceeding upward, the next addition, 5520 + 552 = 6072, produces a sum greater than the dividend and the 552 is omitted. The next addition, 5520 + 276 = 5796, yields a sum which is exactly the same as the dividend. We find that we have added 64, 16, and 4 groups of 69 to reach the dividend of 5796, or a total of 84 groups of 69. The solution to this problem is 5796 ÷ 69 = 84.

Distributive Property of Division

Although it should not come as too much of a surprise to the children, many of them will not have anticipated that division also distributes over addition and subtraction. In many instances, they will be aware that division does not behave exactly like multiplication and this will also be true with the distributive property of division. With multiplication, it did not matter if we renamed either term or both. With division, we do not have this freedom, as will be shown in the next two examples.

$$36 \div 6 \qquad \text{(36 renamed as 24 + 12)}$$
$$(24 + 12) \div 6$$
$$(24 \div 6) + (12 \div 6) \qquad \text{(division distributes over addition)}$$
$$4 + 2 = 6; \text{thus}, 36 \div 6 = 6$$

In this example we renamed the dividend and then applied the distributive property and it worked very similarly to what we did in multiplication. Now observe what happens when we rename the divisor, like this:

$$36 \div 6$$
$$36 \div (4 + 2) \qquad (6 \text{ renamed as } 4 + 2)$$
$$(36 \div 4) + (36 \div 2)$$
$$9 \quad + \quad 18 \quad = 27; \text{however, } 36 \div 6 \neq 27.$$

When the divisor is renamed it does not yield the correct answer, so must specify that division is only distributive when the dividend is renamed. Here is another example of the distributive property:

$$54 \div 9$$
$$(36 + 18) \div 9$$
$$(36 \div 9) + (18 \div 9)$$
$$4 \quad + \quad 2 \quad = 6; \text{thus, } 54 \div 9 = 6.$$

In the preceding examples, the dividends were renamed so that a complete division could be made. It is possible, however, to rename the dividend any way we want to and it will still work. The only difference is that instead of having whole numbers to work with, we may have fractions and mixed numbers. For example, if we had chosen to rename 54 as 47 + 7, we would have had a mixed number and a fraction to add, but we still would have gotten 6 as the quotient.

The Check of Nines

It has become almost traditional for teachers to require that students check their computation when doing homework, practicing exercises, and the like. This is but one of several ways in which students are encouraged to try to eliminate errors in their computation. The more conventional methods of checking computation for errors will not be presented in this discussion because they can be found in almost any student textbook. Rather, the methods presented at this time will center around the mathematical process known as the check of nines.

The number nine has many unique and interesting characteristics that are not found in or shared with any other number. In the past

some people, and even some cultures, have believed that certain numbers contained some mystic power. Even today many people think that
the number 13 is unlucky. We know, however, that numbers do not
contain any mystic power. The unique characteristics of the number
nine arise from the structure of our system of numeration and not from
any mystic source. The main factor contributing to its uniqueness is
that nine is the largest whole number below our chosen base of ten.
This means that it is the largest single digit that we can write; in order
to write a larger whole number, we must start combining single digits in
our place-value scheme.

Now a property of modular arithmetic becomes meaningful because
any number is equivalent (or congruent) to the sum of its digits in
modulo 9. (Modular arithmetic is discussed in Chap. 16.) This property
could be illustrated as follows:

$$365 = (3 \times 10^2) + (6 \times 10^1) + (5 \times 10^0)$$

However, since $10 \equiv 1 \pmod 9$, we can rewrite the above in the following way in modulo 9.)

$$365 \equiv (3 \times 1^2) + (6 \times 1^1) + (5 \times 1^0)$$

$$= 3 + 6 + 5 = 14 \equiv 5 \pmod 9.$$

This shows that the digits of a number may be added, until a single digit
is obtained, to be expressed in modulo 9. When this idea is applied to
checking addition, we would add the digits of each addend until a single
digit is obtained. The modulo 9 sums are obtained from each addend
and are then added until a single digit is obtained once again. This
number is then compared to the modulo 9 sum of the answer, like this:

(check for addition)

$$
\begin{array}{lll}
324 & 3+2+4=\ 9 \equiv 0 & \\
 & & \quad 0 + 4 = ④ \text{(modulo 9 sum of} \\
 & & \qquad \text{the addends)} \\
+\ 472 & 4+7+2=13 \equiv 4 & \\
\hline
796 & 7+9+6=22 \equiv ④ & \text{(modulo 9 sum of} \\
 & & \quad \text{the answer)}
\end{array}
$$

When the modulo 9 sum of the answer corresponds to the obtained
modulo 9 sum of the addends, this indicates that there probably has
been no error made in computation. If the two modulo 9 sums do not

equal, this indicates an error has been made, but it does not indicate the kind of error nor the location of the error. When using this method of checking, we customarily do not write the modulo 9 to designate the number sums. The following example illustrates this checking process when an error has been made:

$$214 = 2 + 1 + 4 = 7$$
$$+ \ 326 = 3 + 2 + 6 = 11 \equiv 2 \qquad 7 + 2 + 4 = 13 \equiv ④ \text{(modulo 9 sum}$$
$$+ \ 157 = 1 + 5 + 7 = 13 \equiv 4 \qquad \qquad \text{of the addends)}$$
$$687 = 6 + 8 + 7 = 21 \equiv ③ \qquad \text{(modulo sum of the answer)}$$

It can be seen from this example that the two modulo 9 sums are different, therefore, an error has occurred. The reason or location is not revealed when this method is used, so the problem must be reworked to find the error.

The check of nines may also be used to check subtraction. In this case, we subtract the modulo 9 sum of the subtrahend from the modulo 9 sum of the minuend, and compare this difference to the modulo 9 sum of the digits in the answer, like this:

(check for subtraction)

$$563 = 5 + 6 + 3 = 14 \equiv 5$$
$$5 - 2 = ③ \text{(difference of modulo}$$
$$- \ 236 = 2 + 3 + 6 = 11 \equiv 2 \qquad \qquad 9 \text{ sums)}$$
$$327 = 3 + 2 + 7 = 12 \equiv ③ \qquad \text{(modulo 9 sum of the answer)}$$

In the event that the modulo 9 sum of the minuend is less than the corresponding sum of the subtrahend, we add 9 to the sum of the minuend and then subtract. It is possible to add 9 to a number in modulo 9 without changing the value of the number, because all two-digit numbers, or larger, are congruent to one of the single-digit numbers of modulo 9 (for example, in modulo 9, 1 is congruent to 10, 19, 28 . . . ; 2 is congruent to 11, 20, 29 . . . ; and so on). By doing this in checking subtraction, it is possible to avoid the use of negative numbers.

Multiplication may also be checked with the check-of-nines method. In this instance, we would multiply the modulo 9 sums of the multiplicand and multiplier, and then compare this product with the modulo sum of the digits in the answer, like this:

(check for multiplication)

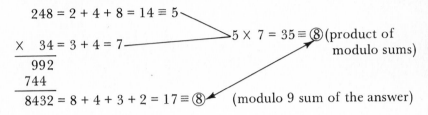

$248 = 2 + 4 + 8 = 14 \equiv 5$

$\times \quad 34 = 3 + 4 = 7$

$5 \times 7 = 35 \equiv \circled8$ (product of modulo sums)

$\underline{992}$

$\underline{744}$

$8432 = 8 + 4 + 3 + 2 = 17 \equiv \circled8$ (modulo 9 sum of the answer)

Multiplication can also reveal another interesting characteristic of the number nine. Examine the following basic multiplication facts:

1 × 9 = 9	4 × 9 = 36	7 × 9 = 63
2 × 9 = 18	5 × 9 = 45	8 × 9 = 72
3 × 9 = 27	6 × 9 = 54	9 × 9 = 81

If the digit sums of these products are observed, it can be seen that they all add up to nine. Later, this idea can be extended to include the product of any counting number and 9; the product will also have a digit sum of 9. This discovery can be helpful to students in learning their multiplication facts as well as when they check a product in which 9 is a factor.

It is also possible to check division by the check-of-nines method, but it is a much more complicated process and under certain conditions it does not work at all. For this reason, checking division by this method will not be presented.

CHAPTER 16

ADVANCED CONCEPTS AND NEW FIELDS

Curriculum changes and innovations have resulted in the introduction of many interesting topics which are new to elementary school mathematics. These can be enjoyable and profitable to both teachers and students. At this time there appears to be little agreement on which of these topics should be included in an elementary school mathematics program. Therefore, this chapter is going to present several topics that are not generally included in most elementary school mathematics books. By including these topics in a methods book for elementary school mathematics, the authors are not implying that they should be an integral part of the mathematics program nor should every pupil be exposed to and/or be expected to master these activities. Because of the nature of these topics, they will not be introduced until the intermediate grades after pupils have gained reasonable mastery and understanding of basic operations. Each teacher will have to determine the extent to which these topics will be of value for the students in his class. It may be that the teacher will involve the entire class in one topic and then involve only certain students in another topic.

Ratio and Proportion

A large part of the mathematics presented up to this point has involved comparing (in some way) one quantity with another quantity. In Chapter 8, fractional numbers were presented both as a comparison of quantities (compared by division) and as a ratio. Ratio is also a comparison of one quantity with another and this relationship is expressed in the form, 1:3. It should be noted that ratio can be expressed in ratio form such as 1:3, or in fractional form such as $\frac{1}{3}$, both of which express exactly the same relationship.

Some textbook authors suggest teaching all rational numbers as ratio rather than as fractional numbers. We believe that it is best to teach rational numbers as fractions (as presented in Chap. 8), and then at a later time, when the students have achieved reasonable mastery of fractions, ratio can be presented as another application of previously mastered skills. This section will present a brief discussion of ratio, followed by the development of a related concept, proportion.

RATIONALE FOR RATIO AND PROPORTION

The idea of ratio and proportion, and its usefulness in mathematics was known as early as the Egyptian and Babylonian civilizations, and possibly earlier. Down through the ages, civilizations have known and made use of this mathematical relationship; from this knowledge sometimes came other mathematical developments. At one time in our nation's history, ratio and proportion were considered to be vital to problem-solving ability. Consequently, they received great emphasis in the mathematics programs of the late 1800s and were taught as the *only* way to solve problems. By about 1910, a reform movement caused ratio and proportion to be all but eliminated from the elementary school program. In the late 1950s, the use of ratio and proportion was revived in the elementary school program as a result of the so-called revolution in school mathematics and received further impetus from the recommendations of the School Mathematics Study Group (SMSG). Although the idea has been revived, as most mathematicians and educators agree that it should have been, there is currently little agreement on the extent to which ratio and proportion should be included in an elementary school mathematics program.

The ratio idea is the more basic of the two, but by itself ratio is of little value in the elementary school mathematics program. It is only after the idea of proportion is developed and linked to it as an extension that the usefulness of ratio as a mathematical tool is realized. Students would probably not be introduced to this topic until about the fourth grade, and even then only the most fundamental aspects would be investigated. Each time that the topic is revisited, however, it can be explored in more depth.

DEVELOPING CONCEPTS OF RATIO

Ratio can be described as the numerical relationship that exists between two sets, while *proportion* is two or more equivalent ratios. Ratio can have two interpretations or meanings: one is that of *rate*, while the other is *comparison*. Rate can be thought of as a fixed ratio between two changeable sets, such as this example: if three objects cost 12¢, six objects would cost 24¢, and so on; or the rate would be 4¢ per object. Comparison can be thought of as a fixed ratio between two unchanging sets, such as this example: Buddy has 12 golf balls and Kelly has 6 golf balls, or Buddy has 2 golf balls for every 1 ball that Kelly has. Ratio can involve matching sets in a one-to-one, one-to-many, many-to-one, or a many-to-many correspondence.

Ratio, as presented in Chapter 8, makes possible certain comparisons. For example, if we wanted to compare the numbers of boxes of cookies sold by two girls, the amount (or number of boxes) sold by one of the girls would have to be chosen as the reference point, and then the other girl's sales could be compared to the point of reference. Let us say that Ann sold two boxes and Sue sold six boxes. If we compare the number of boxes sold by Ann with the number sold by Sue, we could say: Ann sold $\frac{1}{3}$ (or $\frac{2}{6}$) as many boxes as Sue; or we could say that Ann sold one box for every three boxes Sue sold. This comparison with Sue as the point of reference could be expressed in fractional form as $\frac{1}{3}$ or, in ratio form, as 1:3 (or 2:6). Another way to make a comparison of the same two girls' sales would be to use Ann as the point of reference: Sue sold three boxes for every one that Ann sold. From this point of reference, expressed in fractional form, the comparison would be $\frac{3}{1}$ (or $\frac{6}{2}$) and in ratio form it would be 3:1 (or 6:2).

The children should be helped to discover the relationships between the fractional form and ratio form. In beginning to guide this discovery, it should be emphasized that rational numbers are just another name for fractions and that ratio is the root word in rational. By skillful questioning, the teacher can guide the comparison of the way the same number is expressed in both forms, like this:

$$\frac{1 - - \to 1 : 3}{3 - - - - - \nearrow}$$

The students would then verbalize this relationship something like this: The first number in the ratio form is the same as the numerator in fraction form; the second number in the ratio form is the same as the denominator (and also the point of reference in both forms) in fractional form; and the two dots in the ratio form is the same as the line separating the two numbers in fractional form.

Some text authors believe that percent should be taught by utilizing the concept of ratio. We believe that percent is learned better and is less inhibiting to future learning if it is taught as a special form of decimal fractions (as presented in Chap. 10). However, after development of the concept of decimals and percent, the latter may be related to ratio as one of the many uses of ratio. For example, if we are considering a percent, such as 50%, we are comparing 50 to 100. We have already discussed that 50% is another name for $\frac{50}{100}$. From the study of equivalent fractions, we know that $\frac{50}{100} = \frac{1}{2}$ or 1:2.

DEVELOPING CONCEPTS OF PROPORTION

At this point we can develop another very important and practical use of equivalent fractions. This will involve using equivalent ratios and is known as *proportion*. Mathematicians have utilized the concept of proportion in much of higher mathematics, and this concept can also be very useful in arithmetic. *A proportion is two equivalent ratios,* or two equivalent fractions. If we were to use the previous example of 50%, it could be expressed like this:

(equivalent ratios)   (equivalent fractions)

$$50:100 = 1:2 \qquad\qquad \frac{50}{100} = \frac{1}{2}$$

The teacher can prepare students for proportion by giving them experiences first with equivalent fractions. For example:

$$\frac{1}{2} = \frac{2}{4} = \frac{3}{6} = \frac{4}{8} \cdots$$

$$\frac{1}{3} = \frac{2}{6} = \frac{3}{9} = \frac{4}{12} \cdots$$

$$\frac{1}{4} = \frac{2}{8} = \frac{3}{12} = \frac{4}{16} \cdots$$

$$\frac{1}{5} = \frac{2}{10} = \frac{3}{15} = \frac{4}{20} \cdots$$

This could be followed by work with equivalent fractions in which one of the terms of one of the fractions is omitted, and the students are asked to determine what number must be used in order to make the fractions equivalent, like this:

$$\frac{2}{3} = \frac{N}{12}$$

(The students are to determine what number must be used for N, so that the fractions will be equivalent.)

Then students are given problems where the missing number could be in either numerator or denominator of either fraction, as in these examples:

$$\frac{N}{3} = \frac{8}{12}, \frac{2}{N} = \frac{8}{12}, \frac{2}{3} = \frac{N}{12}, \text{ or } \frac{2}{3} = \frac{8}{N}.$$

As the pupils gain experience working with these types of equivalent fractions, they can be guided into discovering an important relationship of equivalent fractions, namely, that the product of the numerator of the first fraction and the denominator of the second fraction will equal the product of the denominator of the first fraction and the numerator of the second fraction. You may remember learning this in algebra as the cross-product like this:

$$\frac{2}{3} \times \frac{14}{21}$$ or

(Numerator of first fraction times denominator of second fraction, 2 × 21; and denominator of first fraction times the numerator of the second fraction, 3 × 14. Or this relationship indicates 2 × 21 = 3 × 14)

The teacher is cautioned *not* to give the cross-product method to the pupils, but rather to guide them in discovering this relationship for themselves. After pupils have made this discovery, they can be guided to realize that if we know three of the terms of equivalent fractions, we can find the fourth, or missing term.

Besides the mathematical applications of proportion to be learned in higher grade levels, there are practical uses of proportion in many different fields, such as art, music, architecture, and navigation. Some of the mathematical applications would include indirect measurement, certain phases of geometry, algebra, and other mathematics. There are some people who recommend teaching the solution of percent problems by using proportion, but if solutions to percent problems were introduced in this way, it would likely inhibit future learnings, as well as be very difficult for the students to understand. After reasonable mastery of the method presented in Chapter 10, some students will profit from solving percent problems with proportion. The following examples illustrate how proportion can be used to solve the three types of percent problems:

_____ is 60% of 25.

This problem asks what number, when compared to 25, will have the same value as 60 compared to 100, or

$$\frac{N}{25} = \frac{60}{100}$$

27 is _____ percent of 54.

This problem asks when 27 is compared to 54, what number must be compared to 100 so that the fractions will be equivalent:

$$\frac{27}{54} = \frac{N}{100}$$

28 is 56% of _____.

This problem asks to what number must 28 be compared so that the fraction will be equivalent to the fraction formed by comparing 56 to 100, or

$$\frac{28}{N} = \frac{56}{100}$$

It should be emphasized again that children should not be taught to memorize these problems by types.

This section has presented ratio and proportion. Ratio was described as a method of comparing one quantity with another quantity. Ratio can be written in fractional form, such as $\frac{1}{3}$, but generally it is written in ratio form such as 1:3. Proportion was described as two equivalent ratios. Next was presented a method of determining the missing term of a proportion when the other three terms are known. The section concluded with a discussion of the uses of proportion, including a method of solving percent problems using proportion.

Probability

The topic of probability is becoming an integral part of our daily lives. It is likely that it will also become more and more a part of elementary school mathematics. Probability involves using the available data to determine the likelihood, or chance, that certain events will happen. The probability, or chance, that an event will occur is expressed in numerical terms of a ratio, fraction, or percent. A person who understands some of the basic tenets of probability can utilize this knowledge rather than having to resort to trial and error to solve certain problems. It should be noted, however, that the understanding of even the more elementary aspects of probability requires a considerable amount of abstract thinking. For this reason, probability should not be introduced before about the fifth-grade level.

RATIONALE FOR PROBABILITY

Two seventeenth-century French mathematicians, Blaise Pascal and Pierre Fermat, are credited with developing the theory of probability. They first became interested in probability through games of chance (gambling). They had observed that certain of these games of chance seemed to behave according to a set of principles that were mathematical in nature. From this apparently insignificant beginning came one of the most useful tools that a scientist, statistician, or mathematician employs. Some of the practical uses of probability are in the field of life insurance, research in medicine, education, psychology, and science, advertising, opinion polls, and weather forecasting.

Man now lives in a complex age that often requires decision-making in a very short time. These decisions must often be made in situations that will not yield final, complete answers. Instead, they yield an indication of the probability of an event occurring, and also whether this probability is greater than the expectation would be from pure chance alone. In many situations it is considerably less comfortable to have an indication of probability than to know the outcome with certainty. However, recognizing that probability statements are the best alternative available in these cases, and using the laws of probability together with his past experience and common sense, man has the capability to make relatively accurate predictions on which logical decisions can be based. Probability, then, is a form of mathematical predicition that allows us to face an uncertainty with more assurance than we could get from a random or wild guess. The probability that an event will occur is expressed as a fraction or percent and is derived by comparing the favorable events with the sum total of the favorable and unfavorable events.

As previously indicated, man's ability to recognize the regularity of his universe enabled him to discover certain basic laws or generalizations that seem to govern objects and events. By learning to apply these generalizations at the proper time, man was able to change from a creature limited by and totally dependent on his immediate environmental surroundings to a creature who could use his intellectual powers to become a factor affecting him in his environment.

The fundamental aspects of probability are not beyond the ability of most intermediate students. An exploratory approach should be used in which students experiment with physical objects and analyze the results of their experimentation. With teacher guidance, students can discover basic theoretical concepts of probability and then apply these findings to develop essential understandings.

DEVELOPING CONCEPTS OF PROBABILITY

There are many ways that a need for learning about probability can be created. It may arise from a game situation, or from a project of a work group, or in some other situation. Regardless of how the need is created, it is vital that pupils experiment with concrete objects themselves. From this experimentation, they can be guided inductively to make generalizations about their findings. The preliminary generalizations may not be as sophisticated as desired by the teacher, but they can serve as a basis for building better generalizations at a later time. In guiding school children to an understanding of probability, it is probably best to avoid situations such as rolling dice or tossing coins, in which it might appear that gambling was being taught.

To help students develop their generalizations, it is best to make sure they start with relatively simple situations and then progress to the more complicated. Probably the simplest type of situation involves a problem in which one of two things has an equal chance of happening. For example, using a two-colored disk, one side one color, the other side another color, the children can flip the disk and record the color of each trial. The teacher can then guide the pupils to realize that with a two-colored disk there are only two possible colors that can appear, and of these two, one is as likely to appear as the other. A similar type of problem would be a situation where there were two different colored marbles (say one black and one white) in a sack and one of the marbles is to be drawn out. There are two possibilities, but we can only draw, or choose, one marble, so only one of the possibilities will be realized. Suppose we wanted to determine the probability of drawing a white marble. After establishing that there is one chance out of two of drawing a white marble $\left(\text{written in probability as } \frac{1}{2}\right)$, the teacher's line of questioning might be something like this: "If I were to draw a marble from the sack four times (always returning the marble to the sack after each drawing so that for each drawing there would be two possibilities), would I draw two white marbles?" (Maybe so, maybe not.) "If I were to draw a marble from the sack 20 times, would I get 10 white marbles?" (Not necessarily, but possibly.) As the students perform and record these and similar experiments, they can be guided to generalize that probability could be described as:

$$\text{Probability} = \frac{\text{favorable events}}{\text{favorable events} + \text{unfavorable events}}$$

After establishing a general description of probability, the students can be guided to understand that the probability of something happening can never be greater than one, and that when the probability is zero, the event cannot happen.

After gaining reasonable mastery of simple probability problems, the students can be guided into more complex situations. For example, they could flip two of the two-colored disks (suppose one side of each disk was red and the other side was blue) and see how many possible combinations result. After determining all of the possible combinations, they might be asked to determine the probability that both disks would be the same color after they are flipped. They could also be asked what the probability would be that both disks would be a specific color (both red or both blue) after being flipped or what the probability would be of the disks being a different color? During the pupils' experimentation, the teacher can guide them to realize once more the importance of an orderly, systematic approach to organizing their data. For example, some students will probably realize soon after they start working with two disks that they can make a chart like the one shown in Figure 16.1. When the results can be viewed in an organized arrangement, it is easier to determine probability of future events.

disc A	R	R	B	B
disc B	R	B	R	B

(R = red; B = blue)

Figure 16.1

The students might be asked what they think (or hypothesize) would happen if we used three disks instead of two? After allowing some discussion of what might happen, the students could be given three disks to experiment with. In using three disks the students might develop the chart shown in Figure 16.2. By examining the chart, they should be able to discover that the probability of all red $= \frac{1}{8}$, the

disk A	R	R	R	B	R	B	B	B
disk B	R	R	B	R	B	R	B	B
disk C	R	B	R	R	B	B	R	B

Figure 16.2

probability of two red and one blue $= \frac{3}{8}$, the probability of one red and two blue $= \frac{3}{8}$, and the probability of all blue $= \frac{1}{8}$. The sum of the probabilities would be unity:

$$\frac{1}{8} + \frac{3}{8} + \frac{3}{8} + \frac{1}{8} = 1$$

The students could be guided into discovering Pascal's triangle in the following manner. After working with three disks, they could move on to more disks and determine what effect increasing numbers of disks have on determining probability. Having worked with one disk, two disks, three disks, and four disks, the students could be guided into discovering the relationships shown in Figure 16.3. From this arrangement of combinations, they could be guided to discover a pattern from which they could determine the possibilities when using six disks, seven disks, and other larger numbers. (A more complete discussion of Pascal's Triangle can be found in any encyclopedia or mathematics book.)

Number of disks tossed	Probability of various combinations	Total number of combinations
1	1, 1	2
2	1, 2, 1	4
3	1, 3, 3, 1	8
4	1, 4, 6, 4, 1	16
5	1, 5, 10, 10, 5, 1	32

Figure 16.3

As the students experiment and test their theoretical data, they will probably find that their experiments do not always coincide exactly with their hypothesis. For example if they tossed one disk 10 times, they should, theoretically, get 5 red and 5 blue. They may in fact get 6 red and 4 blue (or 7 blue and 3 red, or any other combination). At this point the teacher needs to guide their understanding very carefully so that an important aspect of probability is not passed over: probability is based on an exceedingly large number of trials and their hypothesis would more likely be true if they tossed their disk 100 times instead of 10 (and would still more likely be true if they tossed it 1,000 times instead of 100, and so on). It is important that children discover and understand that in any one experiment, in which an exceedingly large number of trials are not used, they may or may not achieve the predicted combination. For example, if they were going to toss the disk 100 times, they would likely predict 50 times out of 100 would be red. In actuality they may not achieve this predicted figure, *but* they would probably be closer to the predicted number of 50 than they would be to 100.

It is also important that students be guided to understand that the probability of any one toss of the disk is always $\frac{1}{2}$, regardless of what has occurred in previous trials. If we were going to toss the disk 10 times, and the first 9 trials came up blue, the probability of the disk coming up blue on the tenth trial is still $\frac{1}{2}$. Elementary school students will need careful guidance to understand this aspect of probability.

This section has been concerned with a discussion of probability. Probability involves using all of the available information to guess the likelihood, or chance, that a certain event will happen. Although probability is a guess as to what could happen, it is not a wild guess; it is the best educated guess that we can make under the circumstances. Probability was described as a numerical ratio or fraction that was obtained by dividing the number of favorable events by the total (favorable + unfavorable) events possible. It was emphasized that generalizations about probability should be developed inductively by having students actually experiment with physical objects themselves, communicating their findings verbally after sufficient experimentation. Probability is based on an exceedingly large number of trials and the actual outcome may not always match the theoretical outcome, but the results will usually resemble the predicted outcome more than they will differ from it.

Modular Arithmetic

The topic of modular arithmetic, or "clock arithmetic" as it is sometimes known, is receiving varying degrees of attention in the textbooks used in the elementary schools and in many teacher education programs. The nature and abstractness of modular arithmetic will somewhat limit its use in the elementary school mathematics program, and for this reason teachers should exercise care in selecting it for a topic of study. In some situations however, it can serve quite effectively as an enrichment activity for students of the upper elementary grades. One of the main reasons that this type of activity should not be attempted before the upper elementary grades is that students will need a reasonable mastery of the basic operations with whole numbers before attempting it. If work is attempted in a modular system before reasonable mastery with the basic operations is attained, there is the likelihood that the experience with the modular system will inhibit the learning of the basic operations.

As students learn to tell time, they are learning a modular 12 system, but they are probably not aware of it as such. In learning this system, students probably encountered some differences between the operations possible within it and the basic operations. For example, in the basic operations they found that $11 + 3 = 14$, but when they sought to find what time it would be 3 hours after 11 o'clock ($11 + 3 \equiv 2$ mod 12) they found a different answer (see Fig. 16.4).

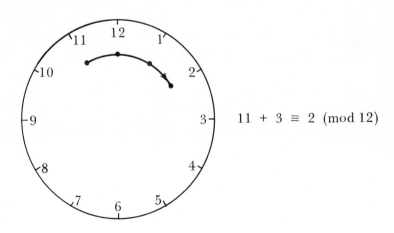

$$11 + 3 \equiv 2 \ (\text{mod } 12)$$

Figure 16.4

Another example of a modular system with which student⌐ are likely to be familiar is the days of the week, a modular 7 sy⌐⌐⌐⌐⌐. If we wanted to determine the fourth day beyond Thursday, we c⌐⌐⌐⌐ do it as shown in Figure 16.5. From these two illustrations, it can b⌐

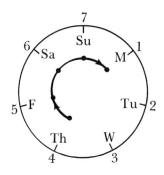

Thursday + 4 days = Monday

or

$$4 + 4 \equiv 1 \ (\text{mod } 7)$$

Figure 16.5

From these two illustrations, it can be seen that modular arithmetic deals with a finite system that never goes beyond a specified or designated limit.

RATIONALE FOR MODULAR ARITHMETIC

The creation of abstract systems such as modular arithmetic makes possible the development and extension of concepts of operations developed in regular arithmetic. It is also possible to adapt these abstract systems to certain other situations and/or interpretations as our past experiences provide us with the insight necessary for such understanding. As children are guided into a study of modular arithmetic, the teacher should seek to make them understand that there are other arithmetics besides the one we customarily use, and that these systems also adhere to a set of basic laws. In many instances, the laws that were discovered in regular arithmetic will also be true in other systems. As a case in point, the laws that govern operations in a modular system are essentially the same laws that govern our familiar arithmetic. From this type of insight, children can gradually grasp the significance of the regularity and consistency of mathematics, and also open for themselves new regions for exploration. A strengthening of the student's ability to process information for patterns and to make generalizations can result from investigations of this type.

ACTIVITIES FOR MODULAR ARITHMETIC

Modular arithmetic has been described as a cyclic arithmetic using a finite set of members. The determination of the finite set depends upon the modulus selected; therefore regardless of the operation performed, the answer will always be one of the members of this finite set. For example, if we wanted to consider the operation of addition in modulo 6, the members of the finite set to be used would be: 0, 1, 2, 3, 4, 5. It may seem, at this point, that modulo 6 is the same thing as $base_6$. Although there are many similarities between modular arithmetic and arithmetic in decimal and nondecimal bases, there is a fundamental difference between them. Modular arithmetic is based on using only the finite members of the selected modulus, while the arithmetic we customarily use is based on an infinite set of members. An illustration of an addition problem is modulo 6 and $base_6$ will serve to clarify this difference:

$$5 \quad + \quad 4 \quad \equiv \quad 3 \ (\text{mod } 6)$$
$$5^6 \quad + \quad 4^6 \quad = \quad 13^6$$

It will probably do no harm if students recognize the similarity between the two systems as long as they also recognize that the two are not exactly the same.

For convenience and clarity, the same modulus will be used throughout each presentation of an operation. To work the same operation, but with a different modulus, the method would remain essentially the same. The only difference would be the result of differences in the moduli themselves. In the discussion of modular addition, modulo 6 will be used. Modulo 5 will be used in discussing subtraction, and modulo 7 in multiplication.

In the initial phase of introducing and working with modular arithmetic, the students and the teacher would perform most of the indicated operations on a linear number line, like this illustration in modulo 6:

```
•  •  •  •  •  •  •  •  •  •  •  •  •  •  •  •  •  •  •  •  •  •  •
◄──────────────────────────────────────────────────────────────►
  0  1  2  3  4  5  0  1  2  3  4  5  0  1  2  3  4  5  0  1  2
```

or, a closed, circular number line, as shown in Figure 16.6.

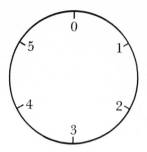

Figure 16.6

Modular Addition. Addition would be taught in a manner very similar to the method in which addition in regular arithmetic was taught. The students initially work the problem on the number line and the teacher symbolizes the operation on the chalkboard or overhead projector, like this example of 3 + 4 in modulo 6:

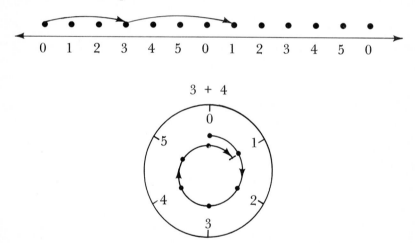

Figure 16.7

Figure 16.7 shows the same problem worked out on a closed, circular number line. The student would start at zero and trace a path along the edge of the number line to 3, then trace an additional path 4 more spaces beyond 3, and arrive at 1. The teacher would symbolize this problem something like this:

$$3 + 4 \equiv 1 \pmod 6$$

This would be read, "Three plus four is equivalent to one, modulo 6," or "Three plus four is congruent to one, modulo 6." The familiar equal sign (=) is not used in modular arithmetic because it could be confused with the way it is customarily used in regular arithmetic. There are other acceptable ways to write this same thing, such as the following:

$$\overset{6}{3 + 4 = 1}$$

$$3 + 4 \longrightarrow 1 \;(\text{mod } 6)$$

Using the equivalent symbol ($\equiv$), however, seems to have the widest acceptance.

After some time is spent working problems and learning to symbolize them, the teacher then guides the students into the development of an addition table for that particular modulus, as shown in Figure 16.8. Dur-

+	0	1	2	3	4	5
0	0	1	2	3	4	5
1	1	2	3	4	5	0
2	2	3	4	5	0	1
3	3	4	5	0	1	2
4	4	5	0	1	2	3
5	5	0	1	2	3	4

Figure 16.8. Addition Table (mod 6)

ing the time that this matrix or table is being developed, the teacher guides students to an awareness of the inherent patterns that exist in it. (Similar patterns were found and studied as we developed the regular addition table.) After the students have developed an addition table, they will probably be ready to formalize the statements concerning the properties of addition. Many of the students will have discovered some of the properties, or know intuitively that they exist from the work done in this system. Since all operations performed in a modular system are binary operations, these properties can be developed inductively in a manner similar to that used in regular arithmetic.

The laws of addition that can be developed for a modular system would be:

1. Closure property: every addition in a modular system produces an answer that will always be one of the members of the designated, finite set.

2. Commutative property: any pair of elements in this system will produce their unique sum when added, regardless of the order of the elements.

3. Associative property: the sum of any three, or more, numbers will be the same in this system regardless of the order in which they are added.

4. Identity element: there exists an element (zero) that can be added to any element of this finite system and their sum produces an answer identical to the original number.

5. Inverse: there is an operation (subtraction) in this system that will undo the operation of addition.

Addition in other moduli can be investigated in much the same manner as was presented for modulo 6. The teacher would guide students in the computation and gradually assist them in uncovering the laws that regulate the operations within the system.

An unusual aspect now starts to become apparent. It can be determined that $15 \equiv 3 \pmod 6$, but so are $3, 9, 21, 27, 33, 39, \ldots$. All of these numbers are equivalent or congruent to 3 (mod 6). A partial explanation of this phenomenon is that modular systems make little or no use of place value, consequently no real attempt is made to group by a chosen base or to keep track of the number of groups possible in that base. In a modular system, when we reach what we customarily would call one group of the base, we start all over again and do not keep count of the number of groups of the base as we would in our regular system. To illustrate this with modulo 6, when we get as much as 6, we start all over again, because $6 \equiv 0 \pmod 6$, or we have come back around to our starting point. If we had 12, we would also be right back at our original starting point because $12 \equiv 0 \pmod 6$. There is no provision in a modular system to distinguish a 3 (mod 6) attained with one revolution from a 3 (mod 6) reached with two or more revolutions.

At this point we can analyze addition of modulo 6 and base 6. In an example used earlier in this section, it was shown that $5 + 4 \equiv 3$ (mod 6) and $5_6 + 4_6 = 13_6$. In modulo 6 we in effect divide out the sixes; this means that if we want to change base$_6$ to modulo 6, we can ignore the base, and simply determine the number that would be placed in the units position of the algorism. This is the same number that would be found in modulo 6.

Modular Subtraction. Subtraction would be developed as the process that undoes, or is the inverse of, addition after the students have achieved reasonable mastery of modular addition. The concepts of take-away subtraction and difference subtraction are not as easily represented in the system of modular arithmetic as they were in regular arithmetic. On the other hand, the concept of subtraction as the inverse of addition can be shown quite easily and, therefore, it will be used for the investigation of the operation of modular subtraction.

In the operation of modular addition, movement on the circular number line was performed in clockwise direction, or left-to-right on the linear number line. The inverse of these movements would be counterclockwise on the circular number line, or right-to-left on the linear number line. Modulo 5 will be used throughout this discussion of modular subtraction. The teacher can start the investigation by comparing the similarities and differences between modular addition and regular addition and then pose the question of how the students think modular subtraction would compare with regular subtraction. From this type of question, a need can be created to try some modular subtraction problems. A typical problem to start with would be 4 – 2,

4 – 2

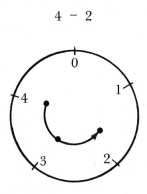

Figure 16.9

as shown in Figure 16.9. This can also be shown on a linear number line, like this:

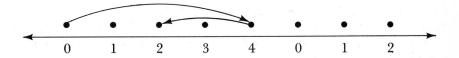

The teacher would symbolize this on the chalkboard or overhead projector like this:

$$4 - 2 \equiv 2 \pmod 5$$

The students will probably observe that this problem is just like regular subtraction.

The introduction of the type of problem where the subtrahend is greater than the minuend, for example $1 - 3$, will serve to illustrate a difference between regular and modular subtraction. Before attempting to work this problem, the students should be asked how they would interpret this subtraction. It should be fairly obvious to them that this type of problem is quite different from regular subtraction. Some students may even believe that this type of problem can have no solution. If none of the students has suggestions to offer, the teacher can offer some suggestions in question form, such as "What do you suppose would happen if we tried _____?" Figure 16.10 shows the problem when worked on the circular number line.

$$1 - 3$$

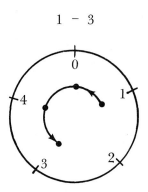

Figure 16.10

On the linear number line, the problem $1 - 3$ would look like this:

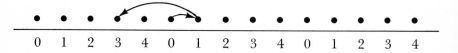

The teacher would symbolize this operation, as follows:

$$1 - 3 \equiv 3 \pmod 5$$

After some time is spent by the students learning the operation and how to write it, the teacher should guide them in the development of a subtraction table for this modulus (Fig. 16.11).

−	0	1	2	3	4
0	0	4	3	2	1
1	1	0	4	3	2
2	2	1	0	4	3
3	3	2	1	0	4
4	4	3	2	1	0

Figure 16.11. Subtraction Table (mod 5)

While this table is being developed, the students should receive teacher guidance in detecting and uncovering patterns. The patterns evident in this table are quite different from those of the addition table and some time can profitably be spent comparing and discussing these differences. At the appropriate time, the properties of modular subtraction can be developed in a more definitive way. These properties are:

1. Closure property: every subtraction in a modular system will produce an answer that will always be one of the members of the finite set of that system. This means that modular subtraction has closure. It will be remembered that regular subtraction does not have closure.

2. Identity element: there exists an element (zero) that also serves as the identity element in modular subtraction.

3. Inverse: there exists an operation (addition) that will undo subtraction.

Modular Multiplication. Modular multiplication should be developed as a special kind of addition that puts together like-size sets in a manner similar to the method that was used in regular multiplication. In performing this modular operation, the students will probably observe

many similarities between this type of multiplication and regular multiplication and they also will probably gain a more comprehensive insight
into the cyclic nature of modular arithmetic. This cyclic nature seems
to become much more apparent in multiplication than in any of the
other operations.

The teacher can start the initial investigation of modular multiplication by reminding the students that they found a great deal of similarity between modular and regular addition, but there were considerable
differences between modular and regular subtraction. He might then
lead the students into a discussion of what they expect to find in
modular multiplication, including how this type of multiplication
would be interpreted. This discussion should precipitate the need to
work some modular multiplication. Figure 16.12 shows the problem
3 X 4 in modulo 7.

3 X 4 = 3 sets of 4

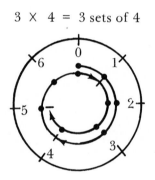

Figure 16.12

The same problem on a linear number line looks like this:

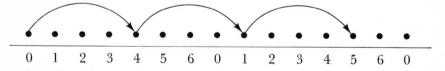

0 1 2 3 4 5 6 0 1 2 3 4 5 6 0

The teacher would symbolize the operation like this:

$$3 \times 4 \equiv (\text{mod } 7)$$

After students have learned to perform the operation and how to
symbolize it, they should then progress to developing a modular

multiplication table (Fig. 16.13). With teacher guidance, the students should recognize that the laws governing modular multiplication will be

X	0	1	2	3	4	5	6
0	0	0	0	0	0	0	0
1	0	1	2	3	4	5	6
2	0	2	4	6	1	3	5
3	0	3	6	2	5	1	4
4	0	4	1	5	2	6	3
5	0	5	3	1	6	4	2
6	0	6	5	4	3	2	1

Figure 16.13. Multiplication Table (mod 7)

very similar to the laws of regular multiplication. The properties of modular multiplication are:

1. Closure property: every product produced in modular multiplication will always be one of the members of the finite set of that modulus.

2. Commutative property: the order of the factors does not affect the product.

3. Associative property: the order of three or more factors will not affect the product.

4. Identity element: there exists an element (one) that serves as the identity element of modular multiplication.

5. Inverse: there exists an operation (division) that will undo this type of multiplication.

Modular Division. Division in modular arithmetic is not as easy to illustrate and work with as were the three preceding operations. This is partially because of the nature of division itself and partially because of the nature of modular arithmetic. In theory, division is possible in a modular system. In practice, not every pair of numbers will produce an integer when divided. When a quotient has a remainder, or is a fractional part of a number, the quotient in that instance is not a member of the designated finite set. Under these conditions, such problems must be considered to have no solution in modular division. Usually the divisions that are possible in a modular system occur only when the divisor is a factor of the dividend. Consequently, division in a modular system is usually not performed unless it is known that a quotient exists for the pair of numbers involved. If a teacher decides to introduce modular division, care should be taken in the selection of problems to be worked so that confusion and uncertainty can be kept at a minimum.

Modular arithmetic, sometimes known as "clock arithmetic," was presented as a cyclic arithmetic that uses a finite set of members. The determination of this finite set depends upon the selection or designation of the modulus. Regardless of the operation performed, the answer will always be one of the members of this finite set. The study of modular systems allows students to experience other arithmetics besides the one that is customarily used. From this study, students can gain insights into the laws that govern other systems, as well as a broader understanding of the regularity and consistency of mathematics. The operations of addition and multiplication were found to be very similar to the corresponding operations in regular arithmetic. Subtraction was found to have some similarities with regular subtraction, but more differences were encountered in this operation than were found in addition and multiplication. The section concluded with a brief discussion of modular division. It will be remembered that modulo 9 was used in the check-of-nines discussed in Chapter 15.

Topology

Most of the geometry presented in Chapter 9 is known as Euclidean geometry because it is based chiefly on the works and assumptions of the famous Greek mathematician, Euclid of Alexandria (about 300 B.C.). This geometry is founded on a basic set of assumptions on which all other reasoning or proof in this system is built. History reveals that this system of geometry has served mankind quite well for most practical purposes. For instance, it seems to be a fairly well-established fact that many of the earlier civilizations, such as the Egyptian and Babylonian, knew and used ideas and concepts that were later listed by Euclid. With the development of reason and logic in mathematics (about 500 B.C.), however, it became necessary and desirable to prove some of the mathematical statements that had long been accepted as true. Probably for this reason, Euclid organized geometry into a single logical system.

Shortly after 1800, some mathematicians working more or less independently of each other began an inquiry into what the results would be if some of Euclid's assumptions, particularly his assumptions about parallel lines, were changed. From these inquiries, other systems of geometry have grown and developed. These different systems have become known as non-Euclidean geometry. One such non-Euclidean system is *topology*. Euclidean geometry is concerned with lengths, straightness, and other metric properties of geometric figures. Topology, on the other hand, is concerned with the study of the properites of geometric figures that remain unchanged when the figures are subjected to distortions so great that they lose their metric and projective properties. For this reason, topology is often referred to as "rubber sheet" geometry.

RATIONALE FOR TOPOLOGY IN ELEMENTARY SCHOOL MATHEMATICS

Most systems of geometry require a rather formal and rigorous proof. In most cases, this formal proof is beyond the level of reasoning achieved by elementary students. Consequently, the geometry program in the elementary school is an informal one designed to develop intuitive ideas about geometric shapes and their relationships. Some of the more fundamental ideas of topology can be developed intuitively without formal proof, even though it is a rather complex geometry. From studying topology, students can add to their intuitive ideas concerning geometric figures. Perhaps the students may even extend the way they view and think about other things.

It should be evident from the nature of topology that this discussion and the suggested activities will be brief and deal with only some of the most elementary ideas. Since there will be only limited experiences in this area, the children will need to understand that the development of generalizations at this time will be on a tentative basis. The teacher will need to use these activities very selectively and not confuse those students who have not yet formed clear ideas about the other aspects of geometry. Thus, this topic seems to be best suited for use in the upper intermediate grades.

SELECTED TOPICS FROM TOPOLOGY

Since topology is chiefly concerned with the properties of geometric figures that do not change even when subjected to distorting or deforming by bending, stretching, shrinking, and the like, shape has little significance. For example, a sphere and a cube, both made from foam rubber, could be molded and distorted until they assumed the same characteristics. This would be true also of such two-dimensional figures as a circle, square, and triangle, drawn on a rubber sheet; they could be stretched and distorted until they approximated each other. Length also has little significance, because of the stretching or shrinking that can take place.

The materials needed for the study of topology are sheets of rubber and pieces of foam rubber from which various solid shapes may be cut. If the teacher cannot find sheets of rubber, large rubber balloons slit so they will lay as flat as possible may be used instead. To introduce the idea of studying figures in a way other than involving the properties of shape, distance, and the like, the teacher can have the students draw a circle, square or triangle on the rubber sheet (Fig. 16.14), and have them observe the similarities and differences of the figure when it is stretched and when it is not.

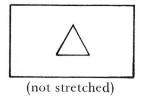
(not stretched)

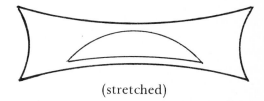
(stretched)

Figure 16.14

After discussing their observations, the students can then draw either an additional figure or a different figure and observe what happens when it is stretched. The teacher should encourage the children to stretch or deform the figure (but not tear it) in as many different ways as they can. These observations could then be discussed and compared to their other observations. During the time of experimenting and observing by the students, the teacher should suggest the use of many geometric figures, so that a distinction can be made between simple closed figures (figures which do not intersect themselves) and simple open figures (that also do not intersect themselves). To study what happens when a figure is shrunk, the rubber sheet can be stretched taut before the geometric figure is drawn on it. Then, after the figure is drawn, the rubber sheet can be allowed to return to its original condition. Gradually from these experiences, the following generalizations will be developed:

1. All lines are referred to as curves in topology.
2. A simple closed figure remains a simple closed figure and a simple

open figure remains an open figure regardless of the distortion (called topological transformation).

3. a. Any point inside a closed figure remains inside the figure.

b. Any point on the figure remains on the figure, and

c. Any point outside the figure remains outside the figure, regardless of the topological transformation (distortion).

4. Any curve (or curves) passing through a point will pass through that point regardless of the topological transformation (distortion). Any curve not passing through a point cannot be made to pass through a point by a topological transformation.

The students could explore the topological properties of solid figures cut from foam rubber. A variety of solid figures, such as cubes, prisms, pyramids, and the like could be worked with by the students. The teacher might need to remind the students that they were seeking to determine as many topological properties of these solids as they can. The students will probably discover that such properties as volume, surface area, and the like will change under certain distortions. They will also probably find that such properties as the number of surfaces (or faces), the numbers of corners (or vertices), and the number of edges do not change. With some teacher assistance in organizing this information, the students may be able to become aware of a pattern that is the basis of an important mathematical formula. The teacher could guide the organization of this information into chart form as shown in Figure 16.15. At first glance, the pattern is not really apparent and very likely the students will need assistance in discovering it. With guidance, however, the students will realize that there is a relationship between the number of edges and the sum of the faces and vertices. The students will probably state it something like this: There are two less edges than the sum of the vertices and faces. This could be translated into a formula, like this:

$$Vertices + Faces = Edges + 2$$

or

$$V + F = E + 2.$$

In Figure 16.15, only a limited number of examples were used, but this was enough to show a trend. The teacher would probably need to include several more examples in the chart used with the children and

Figure	Vertices	Faces	Edges
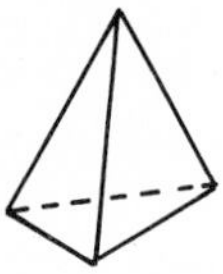	4	4	6
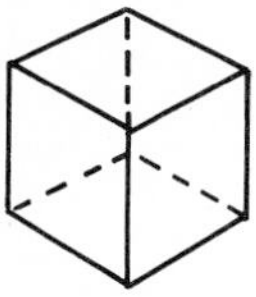	8	6	12
	6	5	9
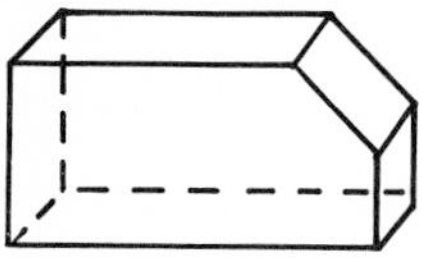	10	7	15

Figure 16.15

also need to caution the children that although they have an intuitive hunch that they have found a pattern, there must be considerably more information and testing before a generalization can be proven. This relationship of the vertices, faces and edges of polyhedra (a polyhedron is a solid which has polygons as all its surfaces) was discovered by Leonhard Euler, a famous nineteenth-century Swiss mathematician, and has been proven to be true for all polyhedra.

Another fascinating idea in topology deals with one-sided surfaces. An ordinary surface has at least two sides. If, for instance, we consider a sheet of paper as a surface, it would have a top and a bottom. A small bug crawling along the top surface of the paper could not reach the other surface without crossing a boundry (or edge) of the paper. A.F. Moebius, a nineteenth-century German mathematician, discovered that there are some surfaces that have only one side. Such a one-sided surface is called a Moebius strip. A bug crawling along the middle of this strip would return to his original starting place on the opposite side (or upside down). Figure 16.16 shows how to make a simple Moebius strip from a long, rectangular strip of paper (about 1 inch wide and 12 to 15 inches long). One end of the strip is twisted or rotated 180 degrees; then the two ends are pasted together.

First, rotate one end of the paper 180 degrees.

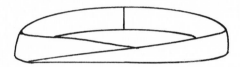

Then paste the two ends together to form this continuous loop.

Figure 16.16

Now a point can be designated marked as the starting point, and the path along the middle of the paper strip that the bug would follow can be traced. After one complete trip, the bug will be back at the starting point, but will be on the opposite side of the paper from which it started.

Another interesting activity with the Moebius strip is to take a pair of scissors and cut along a line drawn down the middle of the strip. Most children will expect to get two circular loops. This is not what happens. Instead, you get one large single loop. A great deal of discussion can follow concerning why. A little later, the students can speculate as to the results that would be obtained from two twists (or rotating one end 360 degrees) before pasting. Or, the students could be given the opportunity to speculate what would happen in the large single loop, obtained from the first cutting of the Moebius strip, were cut again along the middle. Once more the results will probably be unexpected. (The teacher should try these activities himself before introducing them to students.)

The final activity presented in this section will deal with topological curves and vertices, points where they intersect. Most children will already know that an infinite number of lines can pass through a point. This same concept carries over into topology, because an infinite number of curves may pass through a point. The point of intersection, called a vertex, is named by the number of curves passing through it. If an odd number of curves pass through a point, it is known as an *odd vertex;* if an even number of curves pass through a point, it is known as an *even vertex.* Figure 16.17 shows odd and even vertices.

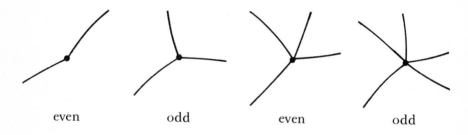

even   odd   even   odd

Figure 16.17

A geometric figure with two or more points connnected by several curves is known as a *network.* Mathematicians observed that some networks can be traced with a pencil without lifting the pencil from the paper and without tracing any of the curves more than once (although it may be necessary to pass through a vertex more than once). Figure 16.18 shows a network that can be traced in this manner. Other   fig-

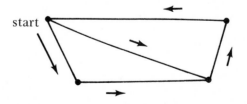

start

Figure 16.18

ures, cannot be traced in this manner; either the pencil has to be lifted or a curve must be traced more than once in order to complete the figure. Figure 16.19 shows a network that cannot be traced in a single path.

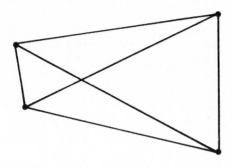

Figure 16.19

Mathematicians were curious to discover why some figures could be traced with one single path while others could not. This activity will allow students to inquire into a problem in much the same way that the mathematicians explored it and very likely arrive at conclusions similar to those reached by the mathematicians. The students will need to try tracing numerous figures with only one path and then should keep a record of their results. The teacher can construct 8 to 10 figures on the chalkboard for the students to use in starting their investigation and encourage them to add some of their own construction. After the students have obtained a reasonable set of data, it would look something like the information shown in Figure 16.20. As the students compile and organize their data, they will observe certain seeming regularities about the number of odd vertices and the number of even vertices. With teacher guidance, these observed patterns can be brought into sharper focus and the less obvious can be made more apparent. Gradually, the students should develop generalizations similar to the following:

1. A figure with two odd vertices can be traced in a single path, but if it has more than two odd vertices, it cannot be traced in a single path.

2. A figure with all even vertices can be traced in a single path.

3. The determining factor whether or not a figure can be traced with one path when it has a combination of odd and even vertices is the number of odd vertices. With only two odd vertices and any number of

Figure	No. of ODD vertices	No. of EVEN vertices	Can it be traced with one path?
1. 	0	2	yes
2. 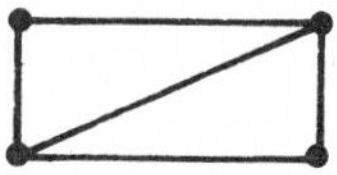	2	2	yes
3. 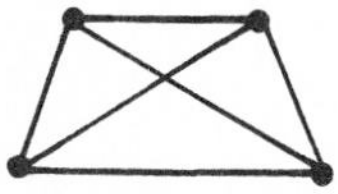	4	0	no
4. 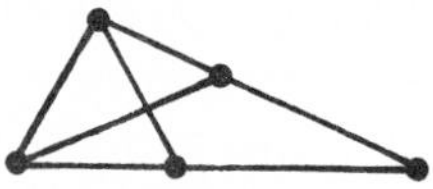	4	1	no
5. 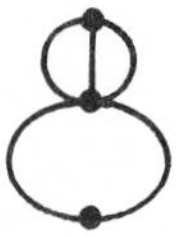	2	1	yes
6. 	0	5	yes
7. 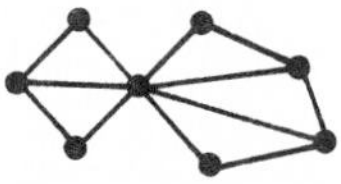	2	7	yes
8. 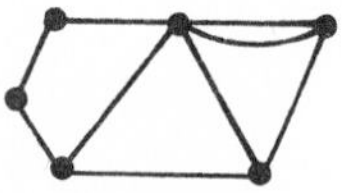	4	2	no
9. 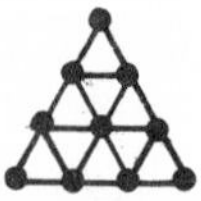	5	5	no
10. 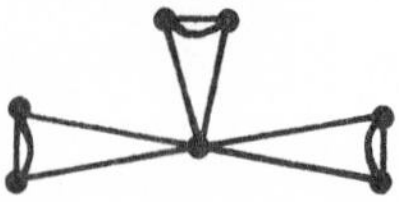	6	1	no

Figure 16.20

even vertices, the figure can be traced with one path. If it has more than two odd vertices, it cannot be traced in one path.

4. The number of even vertices does not seem to be a factor in determining whether or not a figure can be traced in one path.

Topology, then, is concerned with studying the properties of geometric figures that are unchanged by distortions or deformings that affect metric and projective properties of the figures. It is possible to use the topic of topology in an elementary school mathematics program because several of its most basic concepts can be developed intuitively without formal proof. Emphasis should be placed throughout each activity on guiding students in developing intuitive ideas and making tentative generalizations from observed patterns.

CHAPTER 17

SUGGESTED PLACEMENT OF CONTENT BY GRADE LEVEL

The following suggestions are made with the knowledge that it will not be possible for a teacher to stay within these guidelines each year. Some classes will need to go more slowly than the guide suggests while other classes will move more quickly and will go beyond the outline. The following, then, are made as tentative suggestions.

Kindergarten

MATERIALS TO BE USED

1. Cubes (blocks—one-half inch)
2. Cuisenaire rods
3. Number lines without numerals
4. Number lines with numerals
5. Plastic numerals
6. Cardboard squares with numerals on them
7. Peg board and pegs
8. Plane geometric figures (made from cardboard)
9. Solid geometric figures
10. Geo plane
11. Clay

METHOD

The teacher should always take into account the maturity of the child when setting up learning situations. Young children should not be called upon to make algorisms or even to fill in blanks with numerals. They should use the concrete materials and should be encouraged to verbalize their discoveries. There is no certain amount of subject matter that should be taught during the kindergarten year, therefore there should be no pressure on the child. There are many prenumber situations which involve quantitative thinking that are appropriate for kindergarten children. The method should be one of inquiry in which children are guided to make discoveries on their own as much as possible. Appropriate concrete materials should be available for each task.

TOPICS AND ACTIVITIES

1. Make a one-to-one comparison between the elements of two sets using blocks.

2. Select the largest or the smallest of several similar geometric figures (three squares, three circles, and others).

3. Compare the lengths of different Cuisenaire rods: larger, smaller, the same, less than, more than, and equal to.

4. Separate the large blocks from the small blocks.

5. Match the large circle from a group of circles to the large square from a group of squares.

6. Compare the lengths of two lines. (The teacher should make a copy of one line on a transparent sheet. The child can put this over the other line and measure to see if his estimate is correct.)

7. Put pegs in a peg board.

8. Learn to count (see Chap. 6). Reinforce this work with blocks, the number line, and the pegs and peg board.

9. Learn to identify the simple polygons (triangle, square, rectangle, quadrilateral, hexagon).

10. Spend much time classifying materials. Use blocks, rods, and science materials. Listen to the child as he verbalizes what he does.

11. Help child to understand reversibility of action and thought.

12. Stress the ability to correct errors: if one makes mistakes, he can correct them.

13. Learn to identify the circle and ellipse.

14. Compare many objects for more than, less than, equal to.

After children have learned to count using the structured concrete materials, they can use their skill by counting things in their environment. Children can learn something of the conservation of mass through the use of clay. If each child has a ball of clay and each one rolls it out to make a long roll (snake) the teacher should ask, "Which has more clay in it the ball or the long roll?" Usually the children will think that the roll is larger, has more clay in it. A correct answer does not have to be given at once. The teacher may say that he's not sure that the roll is larger. Then the same experiment can be repeated several times. The teacher should ask questions to help children discover that the roll and the ball are made of the same clay, and that therefore they are equal. ("If the roll is larger, where does the extra clay go when you make it into a ball?" would be one of the questions the teacher might ask.) Not every child will arrive at a correct answer, but it is important that every child be challenged often with problems of this nature. With the blocks, rods, number line, and peg board the teacher can help the children count, see relationships between numbers, and understand place value for units and tens. Some children may even learn tens, two tens (or 20) and 50 on to 100. The child is the one who determines how far he can go. Children can compare weights of objects by holding one object in the left hand and another in the right. Crumpled paper can be compared with a piece of clay or a rock about the same size. The child will enjoy estimating such measures as heavier than, longer than, and shorter than. The teacher should see that all estimations are checked (weighed or measured) to find correct answers. The child will refine his judgment through the testing of it.

The kindergarten program is very much one in which the teacher must be aware of quantitative situations so that children can work through them, make intelligent guesses, and check for accuracy. Some children may need to go on to work that is normally done in the first grade. Care should be exercised in crossing over to first-grade work, however, to be sure that the child's accomplishment will be accepted by the first-grade teacher so that he does not have to repeat work he has already learned in kindergarten.

The questions that the teacher asks are very important. Some questions may ask for exact answers (not memory recall), such as, "Which rod is longer?" Some questions should have answers that are matters of judgment, such as "Which line looks longer?" A question such as the

--------------------------------------->   <--

latter calls for measurement for proof; some questions should call for logical reasoning. While many children in kindergarten will not develop logical reasoning, the situations will give them readiness for logical reasoning in the future. An example of this would be that when some children are comparing the unit rod, the white Cuisenaire rod, with the two rod, the red one, they can tell you that it takes two white ones to equal the red rod but cannot conclude that the red rod is a two. Other children will understand this concept at once.

Grade One

MATERIALS TO BE USED

1. Cubes
2. Cuisenaire rods
3. Squares made of heavy paper or cardboard
4. Goemetric shapes made of heavy paper, cardboard, plastic, or wood
5. Three-dimensional models of prisms, pyramids, cylinders, spheres, and cones
6. Number lines
7. Plastic numerals

METHOD

Use a discovery method. The child works with blocks or rods and forms all physical models. The teacher sets up the situation and guides discovery through questions and suggestions, but the child finds all answers for himself. If given the opportunity to manipulate materials in a planned situation, children can discover patterns and answers, and will develop skills through the use of the senses of sight and touch.

CONTENT

1. Counting (see Chap. 6). The teacher will listen for correct responses as each child moves one block at a time and counts aloud.
    a. Counting is tested as children are asked to place different numbers of blocks on a piece of paper.
    b. Divide children into two groups
    (If the total group is so large that the teacher cannot observe each child as he sets up the models).
    c. After children have learned to count and can identify the cardinal number of a group or set, arrange classroom situations so that children can practice the skill of counting chairs, children, books and other things.
2. Comparing groups or sets of objects.
    a. equal groups =
    b. a greater number of objects >
    c. a lesser number of objects <
    d. enlarge the vocabulary to include such words as "more," "less," "greater," "equal," "unequal," "larger," "smaller," and others

e. comparisons made by one-to-one correspondence

3. Sets. Make models and teach children to arrange models to illustrate each concept of sets.

a. Equal sets: A = {X X X}, B = {X X X}. Lead children to define equal sets in as many ways as possible and to describe the sets in a variety of ways.

b. Equivalent sets: A = {X X X}, B = {Y Y Y}. Help children learn to distinguish between equal and equivalent sets and to describe these differenences in several ways.

c. Empty set: A = ∅ or { }. Children in the first grade should recognize symbols such as: >, <, =, and { }, but should not be expected to make the symbols.

d. Finite set: a set whose members can be counted.

e. Infinite set: a set whose members cannot be counted.

4. Numerals.

a. Check at intervals to see if children recognize the numerals. Do this in many ways, with children responding orally.

b. Have periods of practice in writing numerals as children learn to write letters and words. *Do not* have children write numerals in problem situations until the numerals can be written without difficulty.

c. Children should learn to identify numerals in many situations and to be able to select numerals for algorisms and to tell the teacher which numeral to use.

5. Learn to identify different geometric shapes.

Triangles

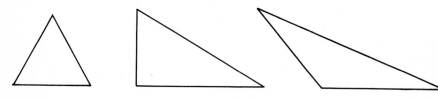

a. How many sides does a triangle have?
b. Are all triangles shaped alike?
c. What else can you find out about triangles?

Squares (A square is an equilateral rectangle)

Rectangles

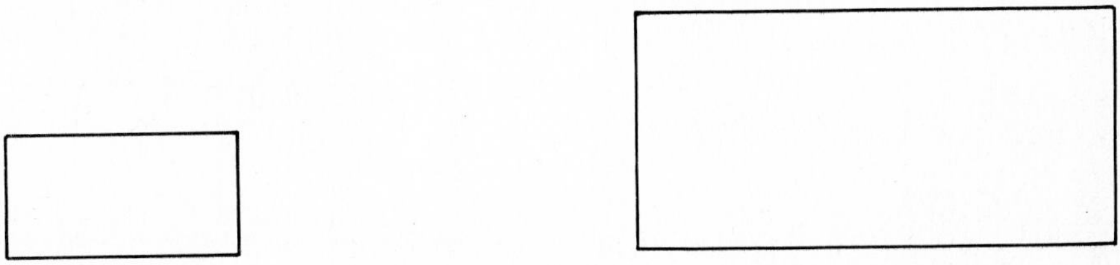

Circles

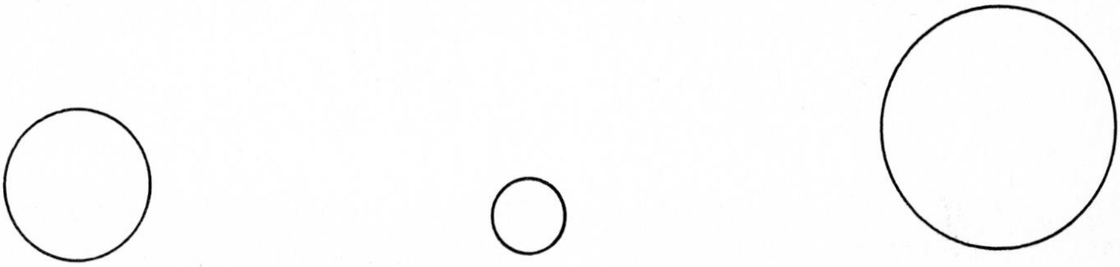

Ask questions about all geometric figures. After children can identify them, ask them to find examples of these figures.

6. Make comparisons of sizes of geometric figures. Have circles,
    squares, triangles, and rectangles cut from heavy paper. Let chil-
    dren compare circle with circle, match the largest circle with the
    largest square, and make other comparisons.

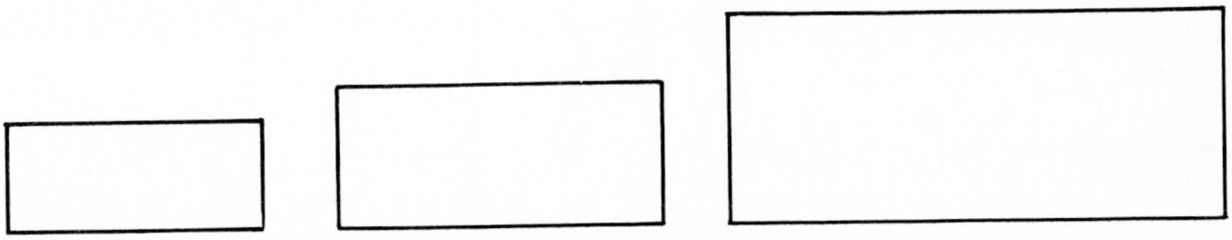

a. Place a 1 on the largest rectangle.
b. Place a 0 on the smallest rectangle.

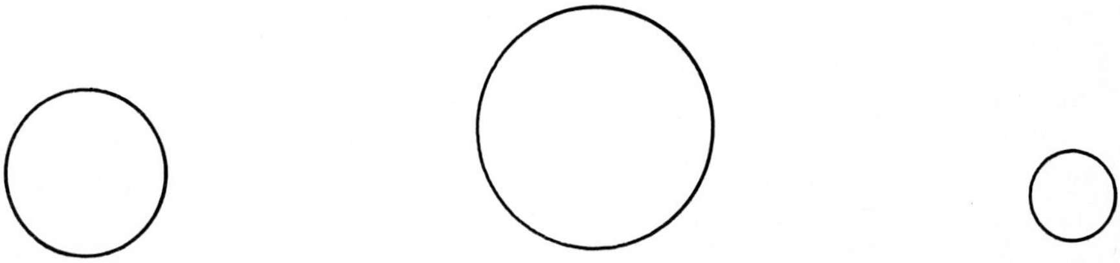

a. Place a 1 on the largest circle.
b. Place a 0 on the smallest circle.

a. Place a 1 on the largest triangle.
b. Place a 0 on the smallest triangle.
   Use the geo plane.

7. Addition.
   a. Use blocks for developing concepts of addition. Children make the physical models and the *teacher* symbolizes the problems; for example, 2 + 3 = 5.
   b. Use the number line for developing the concept of addition. Show how you measure to find sums.
   c. Teach the commutative law of addition.

      3 + 2 = 2 + 3
      XXX + XX = XX + XXX

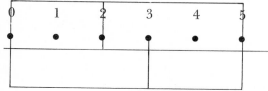

Make models using blocks. Make models using a number line. Some children learn better by using digital (counting) materials, and some learn more easily through the use of analog (measuring) materials. All children should learn to use both types of materials. Number lines should be available at all times and should be placed at a height which is easy for the children to reach.

   d. Make models, discuss, explain and develop understanding of addition facts as far as children are able to learn them. Some children will get sums to 6, some to 10, and some to 18.
   e. Symbolize the algorism for addition in several ways (the teacher does the writing):

      (1)   2 + 3 = 5
            2 + _ = 5
            2 + 3 ≠ 3 + 3
            2 + 3 ≠ 6

(2)   1 + 4
       2 + 3
       3 + 2 >5
       4 + 1

1. Look for patterns.
2. How many combinations do you find?
3. Are there other combinations?

(3)   1 + 5
       2 + 4
       3 + 3 >6
       4 + 2
       5 + 1

1. Look for patterns of odd and even numbers.
2. What kind of combination do you find for 6 that you do not find for 5?
3. How many combinations?

The children set up the physical models using blocks. The *teacher* symbolizes the combinations on the board. The teacher questions and the children discover relationships.

f. Associative property:
    $a + b + c = (a + b) + c = a + (b + c) = (a + c) + b$
    Use this in many situations where the children make the models and the teacher symbolizes them.

g. Identity property:
    By using blocks and a number line, help children to understand that if you add zero to a number you get the same number.

h. Teach that if you add *one* to a number, you count up one; for example, $22 + 1 = 23$.

i. Spend much time in developing the meaning of addition.
    (1) Qualitatively
    (2) Quantitatively

8. Multiplication.
    a. Teach concept of multiplication as addition of equal sets. Make arrays of blocks.
        (1) 3 sets of 2   XX, XX, XX
        (2) 2 sets of 3   XXX, XXX
        (3) Picture the two problems above on a number line.

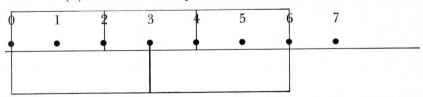

    b. Multiplication is commutative. See diagram above, and make other illustrations.

9. Subtraction.

Teach subtraction only *after* children have learned the concept of addition. For instance, if children have learned to add up to sums of ten (10), they may begin to subtract.

a. Teach subtraction by making a one-to-one correspondence of elements in unequal sets.

A = X X X X X

B = X X X

The remainder set equals 2.

b. Reteach the symbolization of addition for the sum of 8.

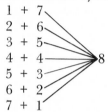

c. Use blocks to make the models.

d. Show that if $1 + 7 = 8$, then $8 - 1 = 7$ and $8 - 7 = 1$.

e. Help children to understand the concept that if either addend is subtracted from the sum, the remainder is the other addend.

10. Division. Division is partition or measure.

a. Teach division as partition. Take 10 blocks, place them into two sets.

b. Divide the 10 blocks into five equal sets.

c. Division is measure. Find point 10 on a number line. Beginning with the 10, measure two units at a time.

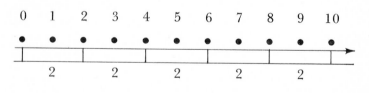

$$10 \div 2 = 5$$

11. Fractions.

a. Teach halves.

(1) Half of one geometric figure.

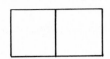

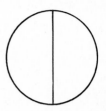

(2) Half of a group of objects.

X X X X | X X X X

X X X X | X X X X

b. Teach fourths—one-fourth of a geometric figure:

1. How many parts?
2. How many parts are colored?
3. How many parts are not colored?
4. How many fourths does it take to make one-half?
5. Is one-fourth > one-half?
6. Is one-half > one-fourth?

12. Addition of numbers greater than 10.

a.
```
        X                   X
      X  X                X  X
    X  X  X             X  X  X
  X  X  X  X         X  X  X  X     XX  Two tens + 2 = 22.
```

b. Tens are added just like ones:

   20 + 30 = 50

   40 + 20 = 60

c. Expanded notation:

   23 + 36 = (20 + 3) + (30 + 6) = (20 + 30) + (3 + 6)

   = 50 + 9 = 59.

Children's knowledge of concepts will usually extend beyond their ability to symbolize. Most children will be able to make simple algorisms, or can place answers on duplicated pages by the end of the *fifth* or *sixth* month of school. If they are required to do so earlier, they often form their numerals incorrectly or fail to advance as they should in concept formation.

Grade Two

MATERIALS TO BE USED

1. Blocks
2. Rods
3. Geometric shapes made from tagboard
4. Rule with simple markings
5. Solid figures
6. Number lines
7. Abacus
8. Felt board materials (cut in shape of geometric figures)

METHOD

1. Discovery. Through the manipulation of concrete materials and through experience with physical models, children will be able to discover structure and order in mathematical situations set up by the teacher.

2. Children will be able to understand simple logic and can understand true statements and false statements, equals and unequals.

3. Verbalization after each concept is understood is a vital part of the approach.

4. Symbolization of number sentences and other algorisms can be developed with second-grade children.

5. Emphasis must be placed upon the use of concrete materials in the development of concepts.

6. As children progress in the learning process, their differences become apparent, and it becomes impossible to have all children in a classroom working at the same place in a textbook.

7. Some time must be taken at the first of the school year to determine how much children know and where the teaching process must begin.

    a. Some children may still have trouble in making the numerals and may not be able to write number sentences and algorisms. If this is the case, special attention must be given to these children on these skills. Other children who are proficient in these skills *must not* be held back; they must go on to new work.

b. Usually children in a classroom may be divided into two groups. This grouping will not make it possible to take care of all differences, but it does permit the teacher to observe how children set up models, how they symbolize their problems, and how they work. With this grouping, the teacher can differentiate assignments and give special help when needed.

CONTENT

1. Reteach content of first grade.
2. Addition.
   a. Commutative property
   b. Identity element
   c. Associative property
   d. Closure for whole numbers
   e. Generalizations about addition of zero and one
   f. Expanded notation
   g. Use set language in many problem situations
3. Multiplication.
   a. Commutative property
   b. Identity element
   c. Multiplication by 0
   d. Distributive property
   e. Multiplication as *addition of equal sets*
   f. Counting by 2
   g. Counting by 5
4. Subtraction.
   a. See grade one
   b. Subtraction of 10s
5. Division.
   a. Partition
   b. Measure
   c. Identity element
6. Sets.
   a. Equal sets
   b. Equivalent sets
   c. Finite sets
   d. Infinite sets
   e. Disjoint sets
   f. Intersecting sets
7. Rational numbers.
   a. Meaning of rational numbers

    b. Fractions
    c. Adding like fractions
    d. Renaming fractions
    e. Adding fractions on a number line

8. System of integers.
    a. Number line introducing positive and negative integers
    b. Direction for addition
    c. Direction for subtraction

9. Geometry.
    a. Identify geometric figures
        (1) square
        (2) rectangle
        (3) circle
        (4) triangle
        (5) hexagon
        (6) perpendicular
        (7) parallel lines
        (8) parallelogram
    b. Compare sizes of similar geometric figures

10. Reteach addition as it was taught in grade one. Use concrete materials and help children relearn skills gained in grade one.
    a. Reteach commutative property
    b. Reteach associative property
    c. Teach the addition of zero as the identity element
    d. Use the number line to help children make generalizations about addition
    e. Teach addition of tens using expanded notation:

$$(1) \quad \begin{aligned} 23 &= 20 + 3 \\ + 54 &= 50 + 4 \\ \hline & 70 + 7 = 77 \end{aligned}$$

$$(2) \quad \begin{aligned} 47 &= 40 + 7 \\ + 25 &= 20 + 5 \\ \hline & 60 + 12 \\ & 60 + 10 + 2 = 70 + 2 = 72 \end{aligned}$$

$$(3) \quad \begin{aligned} 58 &= 50 + 8 \\ + 85 &= 80 + 5 \\ \hline & 130 + 13 = 130 + 10 + 3 = 140 + 3 = 143 \end{aligned}$$

In this process there is no need to think about carrying. After a child has regrouped in this manner for some time, he may begin to do much of the process in his head. *Do not* teach carrying. The child will need to develop real understanding of the process of ten being added to the existing tens. He needs to know that the one which he adds to the next column is one ten. Let the child discover any short cuts for himself. When he is able to explain the process ("The five plus the eight equals one ten and three units, and five tens and eight tens plus the one ten equals fourteen tens. Fourteen tens and three units equal 143"), he no longer needs to symbolize the expanded notation.

    f.   Addition of more than two addends:

$$6 + 5 + 8 = 6 + (4 + 1) + 8 = (6 + 4) + (1 + 8)$$
$$= \quad 10 \quad + \quad 9 = 19$$

It is probably better to symbolize the problem in horizontal form until children are able to find combinations of *ten and how many more* in their heads.

11. Teach multiplication.

    a.   Count by 2s.

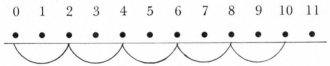

    b.   Show that you are using equal sets of two units each.

    c.   One 2 = 2, two 2s = 4. Work other similar problems.

    d.   Use blocks to make models of the same concept.

    e.   Begin to use the multiplication matrix illustrated on page 145.

X	0	1	2	3	4	5	6	7	8	9
0			0							
1			2							
2	0	2	4	6	8	10	12	14	16	18
3			6							
4			8							
5			10							
6			12							
7			14							
8			16							
9			18							

Use number line (p. 465) to fill in spaces. Note the intersecting sets.

f. Go as far as possible with multiplication, using materials. Do not memorize.

g. Count by 5s.

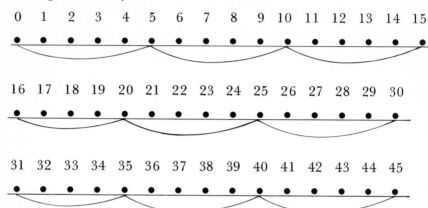

Fill in numerals on the multiplication matrix.

h. Use the number line and blocks to show that multiplying by 4 is the same as 2 twos.

(XX   XX)   (XX   XX)   (XX   XX)   (XX   XX)   (XX   XX)
  XXXX   XXXX   XXXX   XXXX   XXXX

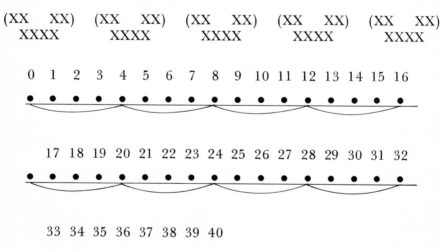

12. Teach division *after* children understand multiplication.

13. Teach subtraction *after* children understand addition. *Do not* teach borrowing: teach *regrouping.*

$$
\begin{array}{rcrcr}
64 - 27 = & & 60 + 4 & = & 50 + 14 \\
& - & (20 + 7) & = & -\ \underline{20\ -\ 7} \\
& & & & 30 + 7 = 37
\end{array}
$$

14. Rational numbers.

   a. $\dfrac{3}{3} = 1$ (any number divided by itself $= 1$)

   b. $\dfrac{3}{1} = 3$ (any number divided by 1 $=$ itself)

      $\dfrac{3}{1}$ is a rational number.

   c. $\dfrac{2}{3}$ is a rational number and is a fraction.

   d.   Use a number line to add fractions.

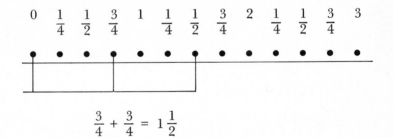

$$\frac{3}{4} + \frac{3}{4} = 1\frac{1}{2}$$

   e.   Teach many names for fractions.

$$\frac{1}{2} = \frac{2}{4} = \frac{3}{6} = \frac{4}{8} = \frac{50}{100}$$

   f.   Use geometric figures and number lines to illustrate all work with fractions:

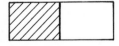 = 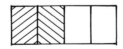 =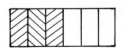

$$\frac{1}{2} \qquad = \qquad \frac{2}{4} \qquad = \qquad \frac{3}{6}$$

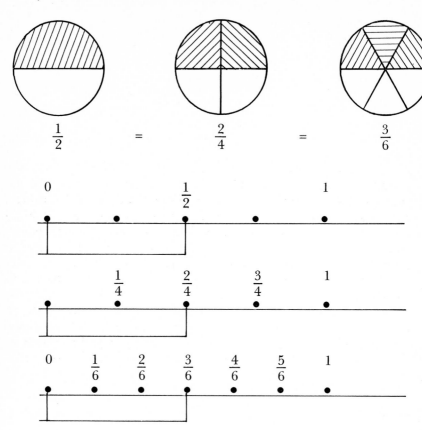

15. Place number lines on the board and make number lines on the floor with masking tape. Show that for every number represented to the right of zero there is a number the same distance from zero at the left of zero. These are negative numbers.

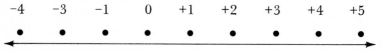

16. Teach the identification and use of different geometric figures. The teacher should:

    a. Draw and cut figures accurately.

    b. Discuss uses of each figure in life situations.

    c. Cut figures of colored paper or felt board materials. Let children make designs using these figures, but let them use only the figures that they can identify.

EXAMPLE:

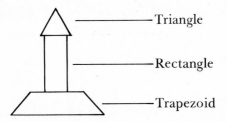

d.   Introduce use of the geo plane.

17. Operate concrete materials. If children are permitted to operate concrete materials to obtain answers for addition, and to use these facts in many problem situations they should know most of the combinations or be able to reason them out easily by the end of second grade. More understanding, not more drill or memory techniques, is needed for those children who do not know all of the combinations.

18. Children will be able to reason to get answers for subtraction facts. If you add 8 and 5 to get 13, then 13 − 8 = 5 and 13 − 5 = 8.

19. An understanding of the meaning of multiplication should be established, *not mere memorization of facts*. Children will memorize many facts while working through the meaning of equal sets as they relate to multiplication, but the emphasis should be placed upon meaning.

Grade Three

MATERIALS TO BE USED

1.   Counters, blocks, and/or rods
2.   Number lines
    a.   Integers
    b.   Fractions
3.   Geometric figures
4.   Charts
5.   Flannel board materials
6.   Abacus

CONTENT

1. Reteach material from grades one and two and teach material that children have not learned previously.

a. Addition—laws and properties (see Grade 2).
b. Multiplication.
   (1) Laws and properties
   (2) Make arrays of counters
   (3) Use number line
   (4) Fill in matrices

X	0	1	2	3	4	5	6	7	8	9
0	0	0	0	0	0	0	0	0	0	0
1	0		2			5				
2	0	2	4	6	8	10	12	14	16	18
3	0		6			15				
4	0		8			20				
5	0	5	10	15	20	25	30	35	40	45
6	0		12			30				
7	0		14			35				
8	0		16			40				
9	0		18			45				

0 times any number = 0

Have children explain each line of numerals that they fill in.
c. Make use of multiplication facts in problem-solving.
d. Use the distributive property as well as counting to fill in spaces in the matrix.
   EXAMPLE:

$$3 \times 8 = 3(2 + 2 + 2 + 2)$$
$$= (3 \times 2) + (3 \times 2) + (3 \times 2) + (3 \times 2)$$
$$= 6 + 6 + 6 + 6 = 24$$

$$3 \times 8 = 3(3 + 5) = (3 \times 3) + (3 \times 5) = 9 + 15 = 24$$

e. Ask many questions in order to develop the knowledge of facts in many different ways.
f. Develop the multiplication facts over a long period of time; teach, come back after a few weeks and reteach. Teach some new facts each time. The children *who are on grade*

level or above should be able to develop the facts to fill in the total matrix by the end of the third grade and should have many of them memorized.

2. Reteach subtraction; stress meaning, use concrete materials where needed, and stress regrouping.

   a. $17 - 7 =$ _____

   b. $12 - 2 =$ _____

   c. $(13 - 3) - 2 = 10 - 2 =$ _____

   d. $8 + 7 = 15$

      $15 - 8 = 7$

      $15 - 7 = 8$

   e. _____ $+ 8 = 13$

      $13 -$ _____ $= 8$

      $13 - 8 =$ _____

   f. Make many stated problems that can be symbolized in number sentences similar to the ones listed above. Use set language in many problems. Use blocks or counters to find answers when needed. See that each child is able to reason out each type of problem.

   g. Find the difference, using expanded notation when needed.

$$(1) \quad \begin{array}{r} 27 \\ -\ 8 \\ \hline \end{array} = \begin{array}{r} 20 + 7 \\ -\ 8 \\ \hline \end{array} = \begin{array}{r} 10 + 17 \\ -\ 8 \\ \hline 10 + 9 = 19 \end{array}$$

     (2) See if children can develop an intuitive sense about subtraction.

$$\begin{array}{r} 27 \\ -\ 6 \\ \hline 21 \end{array} \quad \begin{array}{r} 27 \\ -\ 7 \\ \hline 20 \end{array} \quad \begin{array}{r} 27 \\ -\ 8 \\ \hline 19 \end{array} \quad \begin{array}{r} 27 \\ -\ 9 \\ \hline \end{array} \quad \begin{array}{r} 27 \\ -\ 19 \\ \hline \end{array}$$

     What pattern did you find?

     (3) Work many exercises and stated problems that involve the principles used above. Have children discuss how they worked problems.

3. Reteach division; teach meaning.

   a. Partition into equal sets—use blocks.

   b. Measurement into equal sets—use number line.

   c. Use blocks and number lines to illustrate principles and to find answers.

    d. Use the multiplication matrix to show that division is the reverse of multiplication:

$$6 \times 8 = 48 \qquad 48 \div 6 = 8 \qquad 48 \div 8 = 6$$

4. Symbolize division in several ways:

    a. $6 \div 2 = 3$

    b. $\dfrac{6}{2} = 3$

    c. $2\overline{)6}$ with quotient 3

    d.

25 ⟌ 6000	
250	10
5750	
2500	100
3250	
2500	100
750	
250	10
500	
500	20
	240

    e. Work as many examples as necessary to illustrate the above principles. Children will do better if practice on any skill is spaced; when they gain some understanding, go on to another type of work, and come back for more practice and deeper understanding. The teacher must have great perception in order to stop practice on a skill *just before* the children become bored with the task.

    f. Use simple examples that will have answers with no remainders for teaching division. After children have gained confidence in finding how many equal sets and how much remains with concrete materials, examples of this nature may be symbolized. "Make haste slowly," is a good motto with third-grade children.

5. Learn to compare numbers. Use a number line. A number is equal to, greater than, or less than another number.

    a. $246 < 286$

    b. $470 = 470$

    c. $531 > 529$

0   50   100 150 200 250 300 350 400 450 500 550 600 650 700 750

•   •   •   •   •   •   •   •   •   •   •   •   •   •   •   •

Using the same number line, teach the rounding off of numbers. Is 246 nearer 200 or 250? Is 286 nearer 250 or 300?

6. Teach sets.
   a. Finite sets
   b. Infinite sets
   c. Empty sets
   d. Disjoint sets
   e. Equal sets
   f. Equivalent sets
   g. Intersecting sets
   h. Elements of a set
   i. Subsets of a set
   Use concrete materials, diagrams, and symbols to illustrate the concepts to be taught. *After* children understand a concept make use of it in problem situations using examples from the environment.

7. Work with fractions (see Grade 2).
   a. Use geometric shapes
   b. Use number lines. (Make number lines on heavy paper or sentence strip material. You will probably need a new number line for each new concept.)
   c. Add fractions—measure on a number line.
   d. Compare fractions—measure on a number line.
   e. The teacher symbolizes the problems on the board, the children tell the teacher what to write. As children are able, they will begin writing the number sentences. Stress should be placed on *reading and understanding* the number sentences involving fractions, *not* on writing them.

8. Geometric figures
Identify:
   a. Right triangles
   b. Squares
   c. Rectangles
   d. Parallelograms
   e. Intersecting lines
   f. Parallel lines
   g. Perpendicular lines
   h. Trapezoids

    i. Circles
       (1) diameter
       (2) radius
       (3) circumference

    j. Parts of a figure, such as $\frac{1}{2}$ of a square.

9. There is much to be learned in the third grade. Not all children will be able to learn all of the material in this outline, though some children may need more advanced work. Children who are unable to learn all of the content should not be forced to go through material they do not understand. Children who grasp ideas more quickly can be given more experience in problem-solving using the various concepts and may be taught concepts from a higher grade level.

10. Use material from earlier chapters in this unit:
    a. To extend the thinking of faster pupils
    b. To interest slower students through some of the game situations

Grade Four

MATERIALS TO BE USED

1. Blocks
2. Number lines
    a. Integers
    b. Fractions
3. Geometric figures
4. Compass and rule
5. Charts
6. Abacus

CONTENT

1. Reteach addition.
    a. Use commutative property with larger numbers.
    b. Use associative property with larger numbers. Go into expanded notation to show meanings and to make addition easier.
    c. Stress closure for whole numbers.

2. Reteach multiplication.
    a.   Go back to Grade two for reteaching.
    b.   Complete matrix.
    c.   Spend some time in the use of multiplication facts.
    d.   Teach to mastery if possible.
    e.   Stress the distributive property.
3. Subtraction.
    a.   Reteach from Grades two and three.
    b.   Check for understanding of regrouping; teach if necessary.
4. Division.
    a.   Reteach meaning of division.
    b.   Spend time at spaced intervals on division by two-digit divisors.

(1) 12 | 168 | 10
          120
           48 | 2
           24
           24 | 2
           24
             | 14

(2) 23 | 545 | 10
          230
          315 | 10
          230
           85 | 2
           46
           39 | 1
           23
           16 | 23 r 16

(3) 21 | 460 | 10
          210
          250 | 10
          210
           40 | 1
           21
           19 | 21 r 19

(4) 37 | 1638 | 10
          370
        1268 | 20
         740
         528 | 10
         370
         158 | 4
         148
          10 | 44 r 10

5. Teach the addition and subtraction of common fractions.
    a.   Like denominators—make many problems and many demonstrations.

$$\frac{3}{4} + \frac{1}{4} = \frac{4}{4} = 1.$$

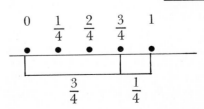

b. Unlike denominators—again use a number line and physical models.

$$\frac{1}{2} + \frac{1}{4} = \frac{2}{4} + \frac{1}{4} = \frac{3}{4}.$$

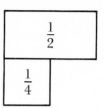

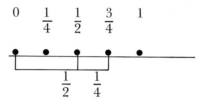

6. Teach prime numbers to 50.
   a. What is a prime number?
   b. What is a composite number?
   c. Find all of the prime numbers less than 50.
7. Learn to find prime factors—find the prime factors of many numbers.

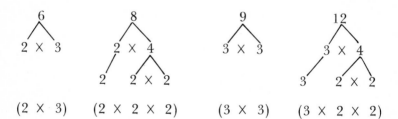

8. Use prime factors in determining the least common denominator.

   a. $\dfrac{3}{8} + \dfrac{7}{12} = \dfrac{3}{2 \times 2 \times 2} + \dfrac{7}{2 \times 2 \times 3}$

   Set A = {2 × 2 × 2} and Set B = {2 × 2 × 3}. The union of set A and set B is a new set which contains all of the factors.

   Thus, set C = {2 × 2 × 2 × 3}. Now find the intersections of sets A and B with set C, and the remainders:

$\{2 \times 2 \times 2\}$ intersects $\{2 \times 2 \times 2 \times 3\}$ at $\{2 \times 2 \times 2\}$ and the remainder element is 3. $\{2 \times 2 \times 3\}$ intersects $\{2 \times 2 \times 2 \times 3\}$ at $\{2 \times 2 \times 3\}$, the remainder element is 2. Thus:

$$\frac{3}{2 \times 2 \times 2} + \frac{7}{2 \times 2 \times 3} = \frac{3(3) + 7(2)}{2 \times 2 \times 2 \times 3} = \frac{9 + 14}{24} = \frac{23}{24}.$$

b. $\dfrac{5}{12} + \dfrac{7}{18} = \dfrac{5}{2 \times 2 \times 3} + \dfrac{7}{2 \times 3 \times 3} = \dfrac{5(3) + 7(2)}{2 \times 2 \times 3 \times 3}$

$$= \frac{15 + 14}{36} = \frac{29}{36}.$$

    c. Use many examples of determining the least common denominator. Point out the use of union of sets (which contain all of the elements of the two original sets) and intersection of sets.

9. Teach bases other than ten.
    a. Teach grouping into 10s, 8s, 4s, 5s.
    b. Change numbers from bases other than base ten to base ten. (see place-value grid on page 101.)
    c. Teach the making of place-value grids.
    d. Teach expanded notation in different bases.

10. Teach that number sentences may be $\neq$ as well as $=$.
    a. Fill in the blanks with the symbol $=$ or $\neq$.

        46 +   18 _____ 64
        303 +   235 _____ 538
        534 −   273 _____ 271
        1962 − 1549 _____ 313

    b. Make stated problems that may be symbolized by $=$ or $\neq$.

11. Identify the property used in each of the following number sentences:
    a. 320 × 7 = (300 × 7) + (20 × 7)   ⟶ Distributive
    b. 643 × 29 = 29 × 643   ⟶
    c. 287 ÷ 7 = (280 ÷ 7) + (7 ÷ 7)   ⟶
    d. 381 + (546 + 9) = (381 + 9) + 546 ⟶
    e. 250 ÷ 5 = (200 ÷ 5) + (50 ÷ 5)   ⟶
    f. 37 + 504 = 504 + 37   ⟶
    g. 46 × 6 = (40 × 6) + (6 × 6)   ⟶
    h. Make many other examples.

12. Study geometry.
    a. Identify square, triangle, rectangle, polygon, regular polygon.

b. Using physical models, identify polygons with:
    (1) six sides   (4) three sides
    (2) four sides   (5) five sides
    (3) eight sides   (6) ten sides
c. Make polygons on the geo plane.
d. Identify angles by size: acute, right, obtuse.

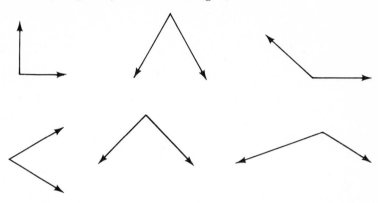

    (1) The sides of the angles are formed by rays.
    (2) The intersection of two rays forms an angle.
e. Identify points, lines, line segments, curved lines, planes, line intersections, and plane intersections.

13. Make use of unknowns to solve problems.

$$n + 4 = 18$$
$$2n = 18$$
$$2n + 4 = 18$$

Make many problems using different letters of the alphabet as the unknown. Faster pupils may even get into such problems as $n - 4 = 18$. Use a number line and explain very carefully.

14. Use physical models to develop understanding of all new processes.

Let the child decide when he needs to use the physical model and when he understands a process well enough to work without the model.

15. Teach children to read line and bar graphs and to make simple ones.

16. Use material from preceding chapters in this unit.

Grade Five

MATERIALS TO BE USED

1. Compass and rule
2. Number lines
   a. Integers
   b. Rational numbers
3. Geometric figures
4. Materials for making graphs

CONTENT

1. Reteach operations with whole numbers, using all laws and principles.
   a. Addition
   b. Subtraction
   c. Multiplication
   d. Division

2. Addition and subtraction of rational numbers. Teach laws and principles.

a. $\dfrac{3}{8} + \dfrac{5}{8} = \dfrac{8}{8} = 1$

b. $\dfrac{3}{8} + \dfrac{5}{12} = \dfrac{3}{2 \times 2 \times 2} + \dfrac{5}{2 \times 2 \times 3} = \dfrac{3(3) + 5(2)}{2 \times 2 \times 2 \times 3}$

$= \dfrac{9 + 10}{24} = \dfrac{19}{24}$

c. $\dfrac{5}{8} - \dfrac{3}{8} = \dfrac{2}{8}$ or $\dfrac{1}{4}$

d. $\dfrac{5}{12} - \dfrac{3}{8} = \dfrac{5}{2 \times 2 \times 3} - \dfrac{3}{2 \times 2 \times 2} = \dfrac{5(2) - 3(3)}{2 \times 2 \times 2 \times 3}$

$= \dfrac{10 - 9}{24} = \dfrac{1}{24}$

e. Commutative property—illustrate also on a number line.

$\dfrac{3}{8} + \dfrac{5}{12} = \dfrac{5}{12} + \dfrac{3}{8}$

f. Associative property

$$\left(\frac{3}{8} + \frac{5}{12}\right) + \frac{1}{6} = \left(\frac{1}{6} + \frac{5}{12}\right) + \frac{3}{8}$$

3. Multiplication and division of common fractions.

a. $\frac{1}{2} \times \frac{1}{6} = \frac{1}{12}$

$$R = \left\{\begin{array}{c}\end{array}\right.$$

A	B	C	D	E	F
1	2	3	4	5	6
7	8	9	10	11	12

$A = \frac{1}{6}$ of R $\frac{1}{2}$ of $\frac{1}{6} = \frac{1}{12}$

b. $\frac{1}{2} \div \frac{1}{6}$ may be written $\dfrac{\frac{1}{2}}{\frac{1}{6}}$

If you multiply the denominator by a number, you must multiply the numerator by the same thing.

$$\frac{6}{1} = \text{multiplicative inverse of } \frac{1}{6}$$

$$\frac{\frac{1}{2}}{\frac{1}{6}} = \frac{\frac{1}{2} \times \frac{6}{1}}{\frac{1}{6} \times \frac{6}{1}} = \frac{\frac{6}{2}}{\frac{6}{6}} = \frac{3}{1} \text{ or } 3$$

	$\frac{1}{2}$			$\frac{1}{2}$	
$\frac{1}{6}$	$\frac{1}{6}$	$\frac{1}{6}$	$\frac{1}{6}$	$\frac{1}{6}$	$\frac{1}{6}$

$\frac{1}{2} = (3)\frac{1}{6}$

c. $\dfrac{2}{3} \div \dfrac{5}{6}$

$$\dfrac{\dfrac{2}{3} \times \dfrac{6}{5}}{\dfrac{5}{6} \times \dfrac{6}{5}}$$

$$\dfrac{\dfrac{12}{15}}{\dfrac{30}{30}} = \dfrac{\dfrac{12}{15}}{1} = \dfrac{12}{15} \text{ or } \dfrac{4}{5}$$

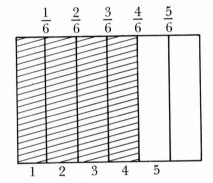

$\dfrac{2}{3}$ represented by shaded portion

$\dfrac{5}{6}$ represented by 5 (bottom numerals) of the six equal parts

$\dfrac{2}{3}$ is $\dfrac{4}{5}$ of $\dfrac{5}{6}$

4. Decimal fractions.

a. $\dfrac{1}{10} = .1$ $\qquad\qquad\qquad$ $1\dfrac{1}{10} = 1.1$

$\dfrac{1}{100} = .01$ $\qquad\qquad\qquad$ $1\dfrac{1}{100} = 1.01$

$\dfrac{1}{1000} = .001$ $\qquad\qquad\qquad$ $1\dfrac{1}{1000} = 1.001$

b. Add decimal fractions

2.5	You keep the decimal points in a
3.14	straight line in order to add units
2.236	to units, and tenths to tenths.
7.876	

c. Addition is commutative

$$2.5 + 3.14 = 3.14 + 2.5$$

d. Addition is associative

$$(2.5 + 3.14) + 2.236 = (2.236 + 3.14) + 2.5$$

e. Multiply decimal fractions

$$.2 \times .3 = .06; \quad \frac{2}{10} \times \frac{3}{10} = \frac{6}{100}$$

(Tenths $\times$ tenths = hundredths.)

f. Divide decimal fractions

$$2.5 \div .5 = 5; \quad 2\frac{5}{10} \div \frac{5}{10} = \frac{25}{10} \div \frac{5}{10} = 25 \div 5 = 5$$

(Tenths divided by tenths = one or units. Any number divided by itself equals one.)

5. Distributive property as it relates to multiplication.

a. $28(532) = 28(500) + 28(30) + 28(2)$
$= 14,000 + 840 + 56$
$= 14,896$

b. $49(500) = 50(500) - 500 =$
$= 25,000 - 500 = 24,500 \ or$
$49(500) = 40(500) + 9(500)$
$= 20,000 + 4,500$
$= 24,500$

6. Teach bases other than ten (see Chap. 5).
   a. Addition
      (1) Commutative property
      (2) Associative property
      (3) Additive inverse
   b. Multiplication
      (1) Fill in matrix
      (2) Commutative property

(3) Associative property
(4) Distributive property

Children need to learn that the laws of addition and multiplication operate for common fractions, decimal fractions, and bases other than ten as well as for whole numbers in base ten.

   c. Change numbers from another base to base ten and vice versa.

EXAMPLE:

Change 547_{eight} to ——————— ten

8^2	8^1	8^0
64	8	1

$7 = 7 \times 1 = 7$
$4 = 4 \times 8 = 32$
$5 = 5 \times 64 = 320$
$\overline{\quad\quad 359}_{ten}$

Change 359_{ten} to ——————— eight

64 | 359 | 5
320
8 | 39 | 4
32
1 | 7 | 7
7

$359_{ten} = 547_{eight}$

   d. Change many numbers from base ten to other bases.
   e. Change many numbers from other bases to base ten (note the special use of expanded notation).
   f. Add and multiply in other bases. Test the commutative, associative, and distributive properties in several bases.
   g. Subtract and divide in several bases.
   h. Fill in multiplication matrices in other bases.

Base Five

X	0	1	2	3	4
0	0	0	0	0	0
1	0	1	2	3	4
2	0	2	4	11	13
3	0	3	11	14	22
4	0	4	13	22	31

Zero X any number = 0
one X any number = that number

What patterns do you see?

0 1 2 3 4 10 11 12 13 14 20 21 22 23 24 30 31 32 33 34 40 41 42 43 44 100 101 102

$(20 - 14)_{\text{five}} = 1_{\text{five}}$

  i. Help the children to appreciate the use of a number line in addition, subtraction, multiplication, and division.

  j. Call attention to various differences between a number line for base$_{\text{five}}$ and a number line for base$_{\text{ten}}$.

 7. Geometry.

  a. Construct perpendicular lines in several ways.

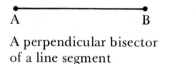

A   B

A perpendicular bisector
of a line segment

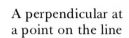

A perpendicular at
a point on the line

A perpendicular from
a point not on the line

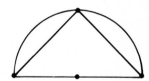

An angle inscribed in
a semicircle

  b. Construct a square.

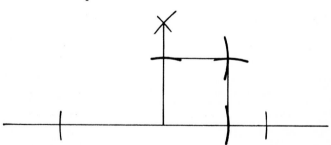

  c. Construct a rectangle.

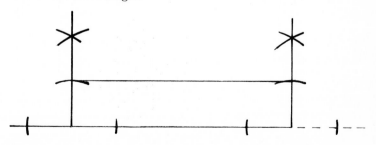

d. Construct a regular hexagon.

e. Construct an equilateral △ in two ways.

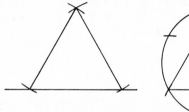

f. Bisect an angle.

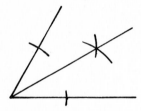

g. Construct an angle equal to a given angle.

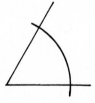 

h. Draw as many lines as possible through one point. Would they all be in one plane?

i. Draw as many lines as possible through two points. How many would be straight lines?

j. How many planes can you draw through *two* points?

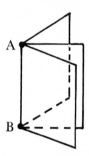

k. How many planes can you draw through three points?

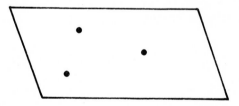

l. Draw and color a design that approximately fills a piece of regulation-size typing paper. Make every line with compass or rule.

m. Ask many questions about lines, points, planes, rays, and geometric figures.

n. Find problems that students can solve from inspection or experimentation.

o. Furnish many physical models and help students make others.

p. Use the geo plane.

8. Sets.
   a. Add the elements of disjoint sets, rename answer.
      Set A = {boys in classroom}
      Set B = {girls in classroom}
      Set C = {children in classroom}
   b. Join intersecting sets.
      John, Jane, Rob, and Mary brought candy to the party. Joe, Mike, Jane, and Jim brought cookies. How many children brought food?
      Set A = { John, Jane, Rob, Mary}
      Set B = { Joe, Mike, Jane, Jim }
      Set C = { John, Jane, Rob, Mary, Joe, Mike, Jim }
      The sets intersect with Jane.
      The number of children is 7.
   c. Use intersecting sets of prime factors to determine least common denominators (see Grade four).
   d. Identify sets as finite, infinite, empty, equal, equivalent, or intersecting.
   e. Reteach symbols, vocabulary, and concepts of sets.
9. Teach percent.
10. Spend time in interpreting graphs of different types.
11. Make graphs.
   a. Collect data.
   b. Organize data.
   c. Decide on the type of graph that would depict the data to the best advantage.
   d. Discuss tendencies indicated by graph.
   e. Discuss the steps in Bloom's Taxonomy of Concept Formation and decide whether or not all steps have been used.

Grade Six

MATERIALS TO BE USED

1. Diagrams
2. Abacus
3. Number line
4. Geometric models
5. Matrices
6. Compass
7. Rule
8. Charts

CONTENT

1. Structure of the number system.

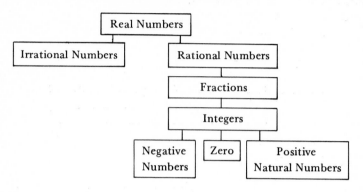

2. Directed Numbers (Signed Numbers)
   a. Within the system of integers, there are integers to the right of zero. These are called natural numbers or natural, positive integers. They are written 3 or $^+3$.
   b. Within the system of integers, the integers to the left of zero are called negative integers. They are written $^-3$. (If a numeral is not marked, it is considered to be positive).
   c. Within the system of fractions, the ones to the right of zero are positive and are written $\frac{1}{4}$ or $\frac{^+1}{4}$. The ones to the left of zero are negative and are written $\frac{^-1}{4}$.
   d. Numbers are said to be directed numbers if the sign of $^+$ or $-$ is placed before them or if the positive sign is taken for granted. In speaking of directed numbers, $^+$ is read "positive" and is usually placed to the upper left of the numeral, $^+4$. When + is placed between two numerals (3 + 4), or low to the left of the bottom numeral, it is read "plus" or "add." The other symbol $(-)$ is read negative or sometimes opposite when it is placed high before a numeral, $^-3$, and it is read "take away," " subtract," or "minus" when placed between two numerals $(4 - 3)$ or low before the last numeral, $\frac{4}{-3}$.

3. Learn to add directed numbers. Use a number line including the positive and negative numbers. (It will probably be helpful to think of the negative sign as "opposite" and two negatives, $4 - (^-3)$, can be

thought of as opposite an opposite, which would be a positive.) Illustrate with directions: north is opposite south; opposite north is opposite opposite south which is south.

    a. $4 + (^-3) = ^+1$
        $4 + (^-7) = ^-3$

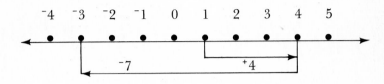

    b. $4 - (^-3) = ?$

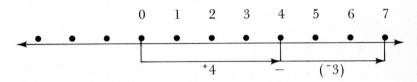

        (1) The negative 3 would make the direction toward the left, but
        (2) The negative before the negative 3 would make it opposite the negative, which would be positive; and the direction would continue toward the right.

    c. The student should be able to discover:
        (1) Positive + positive goes to right on number line. $(^+3) + (^+4) = (^+7)$
        (2) Positive + negative goes right first, then left. The answer may be positive or negative. $(^+4) + (^-3) = (^+1); (^+4) + (^-6) = (^-2)$
        (3) Positive minus a negative is the opposite of an opposite and is positive. $^+4 - (^-3) = (^+7)$
        (4) A negative minus a negative may be either to the right or left of zero.
           (a) $^-4 - (^-7) = ^-4 + 7 = (^+3)$
           (b) $^-4 - (^-3) = ^-4 + 3 = (^-1)$

4. Multiplication of directed numbers.
    a. $(^+3) \times (^+4) = (^+12)$
    b. $(^-3) \times (^+4) = (^-12)$

    c. $(^-3) \times (^-4) = (^+12)$

Let students make their own generalizations about positive $\times$ positive, positive $\times$ negative, and negative $\times$ negative.

5. Comparison of rational numbers.

    a. $\dfrac{3}{1} > \dfrac{3}{2}$

    b. $\dfrac{3}{2} > \dfrac{3}{3}$

    c. $\dfrac{3}{4} > \dfrac{3}{8}$

Students should discover that no matter how small the rational number, there is always another that can be placed between it and zero or between it and the whole number just before it.

The representation of rational numbers on a number line is said to be dense.

6. Addition of rational numbers and fractions.

    a. Like fractions: $\dfrac{1}{6} + \dfrac{5}{6} = \dfrac{6}{6}$ or 1.

    b. Unlike fractions with prime numbers for denominators:

$$\frac{1}{2} + \frac{2}{3} = \frac{1(3) + 2(2)}{2 \times 3} = \frac{3 + 4}{6} = \frac{7}{6} \text{ or } 1\frac{1}{6}$$

    c. Unlike fractions with composite numbers for denominators:

$$\frac{5}{24} + \frac{7}{18} = \frac{5}{2 \times 3 \times 4} + \frac{7}{2 \times 9} = \frac{5}{2 \times 3 \times 2 \times 2} + \frac{7}{2 \times 3 \times 3}$$

$$= \frac{?}{2 \times 2 \times 2 \times 3 \times 3}$$

The union of these two sets is $2 \times 2 \times 2 \times 3 \times 3$.

The denominator of 5 intersects this union with a remainder set of 3.

The denominator of 7 intersects the union with a remainder set of 2 × 2.

$$\therefore \frac{5}{2 \times 3 \times 2 \times 2} + \frac{7}{2 \times 3 \times 3} = \frac{5(3) + 7(2 \times 2)}{2 \times 2 \times 2 \times 3 \times 3} = \frac{15 + 28}{72} = \frac{43}{72}.$$

7. Subtraction of rational numbers is carried on in the same way as addition insofar as common denominators are concerned.

8. Multiplication of rational numbers.

$$\frac{7}{8} \times \frac{5}{7} = \frac{35}{56}$$

9. Division.

$$\frac{2}{3} \div \frac{4}{5} = \frac{\dfrac{2}{3}}{\dfrac{4}{5}}$$

In order to simplify the fraction, one must change the denominator to equal one.

Multiply $\frac{4}{5}$ by its multiplicative inverse $\frac{5}{4}$ and multiply the numerator, $\frac{2}{3}$, by the same fraction:

$$\frac{\dfrac{2}{3} \times \dfrac{5}{4}}{\dfrac{4}{5} \times \dfrac{5}{4}} = \frac{\dfrac{10}{12}}{1} \text{ or } \frac{10}{12} = \frac{5}{6}$$

10. The properties of addition and multiplication apply to rational numbers as they do to whole numbers.

11. Exponents.
   a. $a^2 = a \times a$
   b. $3^2 = 3 \times 3$
   c. $a^3 = a \times a \times a$
   d. $3^3 = 3 \times 3 \times 3$
   e. An exponent is a symbol written above a numeral to the right showing how many times the numeral is repeated as a factor. Use in place-value charts for different bases.

Base 10			Base 5		
10^2	10^1	10^0	5^2	5^1	5^0
$(10 \times 10) = 100$	10	1	$(5 \times 5) = 25$	5	1

12. Coordinate system. Reteach material on graphs from Grade five. Make as much use of graphs as children are able to understand.

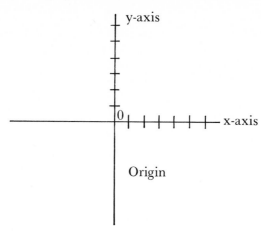

a. Coordinate axes include the x-axis or horizontal axis and the y-axis or vertical axis. O is the origin.

b. There is a one-to-one correspondence between the set of all points in the plane and the set of all ordered pairs of real numbers.

c. Each point, P, of the plane will have corresponding to it a single pair of real numbers, a first and a second (ordered). Each ordered pair of numbers will have just one point in the plane to which it corresponds.

d. The two numbers corresponding to P are called the coordinates of P, the first is the x-coordinate or abscissa, the second is the y-coordinate or ordinate.

Example: Plot $(^-2, 3)$

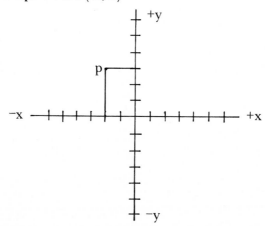

Examples: Locate the following ordered pairs on one set of axis: $(1, 5), (^-3, 2), (5, ^-3), (^-2, ^-4), (3, 2)$

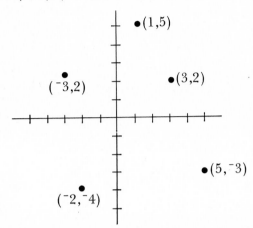

In the elementary school, the chief use that is made of coordinates is in making graphs. The first quadrant $(^+x, ^+y)$ is used most often.

13. Geometry.
   a. Reteach geometric figures studied earlier. Bring out the fact that the circle is the circumference. The inside of the curve is the circular region.
   b. The lines that enclose square regions, rectangular regions, and other plane figures are called perimeters.
   c. Use physical models and pictures of physical models. Students should learn to draw figures and to make reasonable constructions.
   d. Plane figures (use this geo plane).

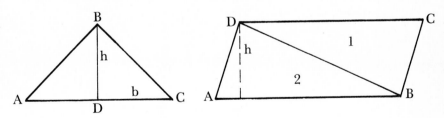

   (1) Find similarities of triangles.
   (2) What triangles make up the parallelogram?

   (3) Find the areas of triangles: $A = \frac{1}{2}$ (height $\times$ base).

14. Percent.
15. Use enrichment material from preceding chapters in this unit.
16. Study geometry in three dimensions.

GLOSSARY

A

Addend. One of two or more numbers to be added together.

Addition. A binary operation governed by a set of laws or rules that can be thought of as:

  a. a putting together process, or

  b. a quick way of counting forward.

Algorism (Algorithm). A written scheme or plan for computing.

EXAMPLE:

Addition Algorisms	Subtraction Algorisms	Multiplication Algorisms	Division Algorisms
$4 + 8 = \square$	$7 - 5 = \square$	$6 \times 10 = \square$	$56 \div 8 = \square$

$$\begin{array}{r} 4 \\ +8 \\ \hline 12 \end{array} \qquad \begin{array}{r} 7 \\ -5 \\ \hline 2 \end{array} \qquad \begin{array}{r} 10 \\ \times\ 6 \\ \hline 60 \end{array} \qquad 8\overline{)56}\ ^{7}$$

Analog. The characteristic of materials that enables them to be measured.

Angle. The union of two rays which have the same end-point but do not lie in the same line.

EXAMPLE:

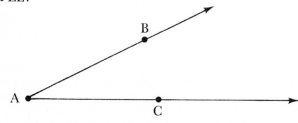

Associative property (grouping property). This can be thought of as an extension of the commutative property, but involves three or more numbers.

    a. When adding three or more numbers, the order in which the addends are added does not affect the final sum.

    b. When multiplying three or more numbers, the order in which the factors are multiplied does not affect the final product.

    c. Subtraction and division are not associative.

    EXAMPLES:

Addition	Multiplication
$(7 + 8) + 9 = 24$	$(2 \times 3) \times 4 = 24$
$7 + (8 + 9) = 24$	$2 \times (3 \times 4) = 24$
$(7 + 9) + 8 = 24$	$(2 \times 4) \times 3 = 24$

B

Base. A consistent method of grouping in a system of numeration. The method of grouping used most frequently is probably base 10, which means we group by tens or powers of ten (tens, hundreds, thousands, ten thousands, and so forth.)

Basic facts (combinations). Those facts or combinations that are considered necessary for reasonable mastery in computation.

    a. The basic addition facts are all possible combinations of a single digit added to a single digit. We teach all combinations up to and including the sum of 10. Tens are added like units (ones).
$8 + 7$ is the same as $8 + (2 + 5)$; $(8 + 2) + 5 = 10 + 5 = 15$.

    b. The basic subtraction facts are all those combinations where a single digit is subtracted from either a single or double digit with the resulting answer always being a single digit.

    c. The basic multiplication facts are all possible combinations of digits 10 or less multiplied by digits 10 or less.

    d. The basic division facts are all possible division combinations of digits 10 or less divided into a number so that the resulting quotient is always a whole number of 10 or less.

Basic operations. Generally refers to the operations of addition, subtraction, multiplication, and division.

Binary operation. An operation that is performed on only two things at a time. Most operations on sets are binary operations because only two sets are worked with at one time. The basic operations with numbers (addition, subtraction, multiplication, and division) are binary operations because they are worked with two at a time regardless of how many numbers are involved.

Bridging (carrying). A term used primarily in addition to indicate that the addend(s) have caused us to bridge over into the next higher place-value position or decade.

C

Cardinal number. A number that tells how many.

Cartesian product. This operation with sets is a pairing process so that each member of one set is paired, in turn, with each member of the other set until all possible ordered pairs have been made.

Closure property. An operation is considered to have closure if performing the operation on any two members of a set results in an answer which is also a member of the same set. Addition and multiplication have closure (for example, a counting number added to a counting number will always have another counting number for the answer). Subtraction and division are considered not to have closure.

Commutative property. This property allows the combining of two numbers or elements without regard for their order. Addition is commutative because we can add the first number to the second or, if we want to, the second number can be added to the first. Thus, $3 + 4 = 4 + 3$. Multiplication is also commutative, but subtraction and division are not.

Concrete materials. Those materials, such as counting blocks, which have substance or physical properties, as opposed to abstract qualities, such as number.

Counting. The process of determining how many are in a set by naming the members by units.

Counting number. Another name for natural numbers. Those whole numbers normally used in counting, such as: $1, 2, 3, 4, 5, 6, 7, 8, 9, 10, 11, \ldots$.

Crutch. An aid used so much by a student that he becomes dependent on the aid.

Curve. The set of all points in a certain path.

D

Decimal fraction. A special form of fractions in which numerals are used to express the numerator, while the denominator is not written but implied. The denominator is always 10 or a power of 10. (.3 is read "Three tenths." .03 is read "Three hundredths").

Denominator. The namer of the fraction. It tells how many equal parts into which the whole has been divided.

Digital. The characteristic of materials that enables them to be counted.

Direct number (signed number). A number that not only indicates magnitutude but also direction from a point of reference, usually zero.

EXAMPLE: $(^-7)\,(^+4)\,(^+1)\,(^-2)\,(^-5)\ldots$

Discovery method. A method of teaching that emphasizes guiding student learning through planned first-hand or simulated experiences so that the student actually discovers things for himself.

Disjoint sets. Sets having no members in common.

Division. A binary operation that may be thought of as:
a. a taking-apart process that involves separating the whole quantity into a specified number of equal sets (partition division), or separating the whole into equal sets of a specified size or quantity (measurement division), or
b. a special process in which there are repeated, equal subtractions from a total quantity.

E

Empty set (null set). A set containing no members. The null set is a subset of every set. The cardinal number of the empty set is zero.

Equality. Being exactly the same.

Equation. A statement of equality between two or more numbers or quantities.

Equation form. Generally refers to a symbolism which is written in the horizontal form rather than in the vertical or some other form.

Equation form:

$$4 + 8 = \underline{}$$

Vertical form:

$$\begin{array}{r} 4 \\ + 8 \\ \hline \end{array}$$

Equivalent. Being greatly similar by one or more characteristics, but not exactly the same.

Even numbers. The set of all natural (or whole) numbers which includes two and all numbers evenly divisible by two.

Expanded notation. Expressing a number as the sum of the positional values of each digit in a numeral.

EXAMPLE: $478 = 400 + 70 + 8$

F

Factor. One of two or more numbers to be multiplied together for a product.

EXAMPLE: 4 and 3 are factors of 12.

Factorization. Expressing a number as an indicated multiplication of two or more of its factors.

Finite set. A set:
   a. in which the elements can be counted; and
   b. which has a definite beginning and ending.

EXAMPLE: the set of vowels— $\{a, e, i, o, u\}$

Fraction (rational number). A number that can be expressed as a quotient in the form of $\frac{a}{b}$, where a and b are integers and b $\neq$ 0.

G

Geo plane. A plane with nails or pegs placed in regular spacing to form square units. Rubber bands can be attached to it and stretched to make various geometric shapes.

Greenwood division (subtractive method of division). A method of division that emphasizes the subtractive nature of division. The student has the freedom to repeatedly subtract as many or as few equal sets from a total quantity as he desires until the total is completely separated. The total number of equal subtractions is then added together to give the quotient.

EXAMPLE:

$$
\begin{array}{r|l}
13\ \big|\ 156 & \\
\quad 130 & 10 \\
\hline
\quad 26 & \\
\quad 26 & 2 \\
\hline
& 12
\end{array}
\qquad
\begin{array}{r|l}
13\ \big|\ 156 & \\
\quad 65 & 5 \\
\hline
\quad 91 & \\
\quad 65 & 5 \\
\hline
\quad 26 & \\
\quad 26 & 2 \\
\hline
& 12
\end{array}
$$

I

Identity element. A number that does not change or affect the original number after having an operation performed on it. The identity element of addition and subtraction is zero; one is the identity element of multiplication and division.

Inequality. Not the same; unequal.

Infinite set. A set:
   a. so large that it cannot be counted, or
   b. which does not have a definite end.

EXAMPLE:
   $\{1, 2, 3, 4, 5, 6, 7, 8, \ldots\}$

Integer. (whole number)
    a. Any number that can be expressed as the difference of two natural numbers.
    b. The set of integers includes all positive whole numbers, negative whole numbers, and zero.

Intersection of sets. A binary operation on sets that creates a common subset of all members jointly in both sets.

Inverse. Any operation that undoes another operation.

    EXAMPLE: Subtraction is the operation that undoes addition.

J

Joint sets. Sets having at least one member in common.

L

Likeness property.
    a. Things that are not alike must be made alike before they can be added or subtracted. We usually call this renaming.

    EXAMPLE: Boys plus girls equals children.

    b. Multiplication is the putting together of like sets, while division is the taking apart of like sets.

M

Member (element) of a set. Any item which belongs to or is included in a specific set.

Missing addend. A problem in which one of the addends is not given and the student is expected to determine the correct addend for a solution. This type of problem appears to be an addition problem, but its solution is generally reached by subtraction.

    EXAMPLE: $7 + \rule{2cm}{0.15mm} = 12$

Multiplication. A binary operation that may be thought of as:
    a. a special kind of repeated addition that puts together like size sets, or
    b. the inverse of division.

Multiplicative inverse (reciprocal). The number by which to multiply another number so that the product will be one.

    EXAMPLE: The multiplicative inverse of 6 would be $\frac{1}{6}$.

N

Natural numbers (counting numbers). Considered the most basic of all numbers—the numbers generally used in counting; that is, all positive integers.

Nondecimal base (base other than 10). A grouping scheme using some number other than 10 to group by.

Number. An abstract idea of quantity that is associated with all sets.

Numeral.
  a. The language, either verbal or written, used to communicate the idea of number, or
  b. the symbol used to represent a number.

Numerator. The numberer of the fraction, or how many of the equal parts are being considered.

O

Odd number. Any member of the set of all natural (or whole) numbers not divisible by 2.

EXAMPLE: $\{1, 3, 5, 7, 9, 11, \ldots\}$

One-to-one correspondence. A system of matching or pairing each member of one set with exactly one member of another set so that no member of either set remains unmatched.

Operation. The action of applying a mathematic process, according to certain rules, to numbers or expressions and deriving an expression of solution from this.

Ordered pair of numbers. Two numbers considered in a definite order with one number designated as first, and the other number designated as second.

EXAMPLE: In coordinate geometry, a certain point could be designated as (1, 5). A more common use of ordered pairs of numbers is fractions, such as $\frac{2}{3}$.

Ordinal number. A number used to indicate a position of an object or element when the set is arranged in a definite order.

EXAMPLE: The fifth person in line.

P

Place-value (positional notation). A scheme of combining number symbols to represent numbers larger than the chosen base. In this scheme, each digit in the number represents the product of the number it names and the place-value assigned to its particular position.

Plane. A flat surface such as a floor, wall, or desk top, which may assume any position from the horizontal through the vertical.

Point. An abstract idea that cannot be defined or adequately described. A point is usually represented by a dot, but the point itself has no length, width, or depth, nor does it move, since it has a fixed location.

Prenumber idea. A concept in mathematics which involves the idea that any two sets can be compared without the use of numbers.

> EXAMPLE: When two sets are compared, one and only one of the following possibilities will be true:
> a. the first set is equal or equivalent to the second set;
> b. the first set is greater than the second;
> c. or the first set is less than the second.

Prime number.

> a. Prime numbers are considered to be the building blocks of numbers because other numbers (composite numbers) can be expressed as the product of prime numbers.
> b. A whole number greater than one that has only itself and one as factors.
> EXAMPLE: Set of prime numbers = $\{2, 3, 5, 7, 11, 13, 17, \ldots\}$

Prime factorization. The process of factoring a number until each factor is a prime number.

> EXAMPLE: $12 = (2 \times 2 \times 3)$

Product. The result obtained by multiplying two or more numbers together.

Proper subset. A subset that contains some, but not all of the members of the original set.

R

Ray. A line which begins at a point of origin and extends in one direction indefinitely.

> EXAMPLE: P ————————————————➤

Remainder set. Considered to be the set of all members remaining in the original set after a specific subset has been removed from the original set.

> EXAMPLE: $\{a, b, c, d, e\} \sim \{a, e\} = \{b, c, d$

Renaming (Numbers Have Many Names). A basic concept of mathematics that utilizes the idea that numbers can be named in more than one way.

EXAMPLE: The following all name the same number:

$$\frac{24}{4}, \ 3 \times 2, \ \text{six}, 5 + 1, \ \text{VI}, \ 10 - 4, \ 2 + 4,$$

$$\frac{18}{3}, \ldots$$

S

Set. Generally considered to be an undefined mathematical term that refers to a collection or grouping of things or objects. This grouping must be exact enough so that it can be determined whether or not something belongs to a particular set.

Solid figure. A geometric figure having the three dimensions of length, width, and depth.

EXAMPLES: a cube, cone, pyramid, and others.

Solution set (truth set). The set of all solutions such that each member of the set will make a given open mathematical sentence true.

EXAMPLE: Open sentence: Solution set:

$$2 + 1 < \square \qquad \{4, 5, 6, 7, 8, \ldots\}$$

Stated problem (story problem). A mathematical problem stated, either orally or written, in words rather than number symbols. These problems generally relate to practical situations in which application of mathematical concepts and algorisms are necessary to reach a solution.

Subset. A set which contains no members that are not also members of the original set.

Subtraction. A binary operation governed by certain laws or rules that can be thought of as:

a. a taking-apart or take-away process,

b. a comparison of two sets to determine how much more one set is than the other, or

c. the inverse of addition.

Sum (total). The result of applying the operation of addition to two or more numbers.

U

Union. A binary operation on sets that puts together or joins two sets to form a new superset so that each member of both original sets is represented in the new superset.

EXAMPLE: $\{a, b, c\} \cup \{1, 3, 5, 7\} = \{a, b, c, 1, 3, 5, 7\}$

Universal set The entire set, or class, of things under consideration:

EXAMPLE: the set of all horses in the world.

V

Venn diagram. A pictorial representation of sets using geometric figures. Usually a rectangle is used to represent the universal set, while circles are used to represent various subsets.

EXAMPLE:

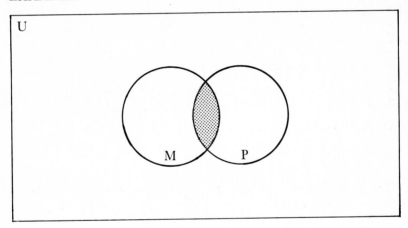

U = the set of all college students
M = the set of all math majors
P = the set of all students who like physics.

The shaded area represents those math majors who like physics.

SYMBOLS USED IN ELEMENTARY SCHOOL MATHEMATICS

1. 0, 1, 2, 3, 4, 5, 6, 7, 8, 9 : Hindu-Arabic numerals
2. + : plus or add
3. − : minus, negative, opposite
4. × : multiply
5. ÷ : divide
6. = : equal or equals, stands for the same thing
7. ≡ : equivalent or very similar
8. ≠ : is not equal, does not stand for the same thing
9. > : greater than
10. < : less than
11. ( ) : parentheses (used to indicate a pair or a product)
12. { } : brackets (used to indicate a set)
13. ∪ : union of sets
14. ∩ : intersection of sets
15. ∈ : is an element or member of a set
16. ∉ : is not an element or member of a set
17. ∿ : remainder set
18. A_n : the cardinal number of a set, the number of elements in a set
19. { } : the empty set or the null set (also sometimes written $\emptyset$)

504

20. ⊂ : is a subset of
21. ∴ : therefore
22. . . . : goes on and on into infinity
23. ∞ : infinity
24. // : is parallel to
25. ⊥ : is perpendicular to
26. ≅ : congruent, or exactly the same size and shape

INDEX